HOW TO USE THIS BOOK FOR SUCCESS

Reading for Meaning

Biologically Important Molecules and Cellular Organization of Living Things

TOPIC 2

Earth's living environment is made up of millions and millions of diverse organisms, a wide range that includes towering redwood trees, sleek antelope, tiny bacteria, mushrooms that grow in huge circles, microscopic organisms that turn the tides red, and the students in your class. These living organisms are both similar to and different from each other. They also differ from the nonliving parts of the environment. Although that difference may seem obvious, scientists have not been able to agree upon a simple definition of life.

2-1 The Characteristics of Life

VOCABULARY			
cell	growth	organ	reproduction
cell respiration	homeostasis	organelle	synthesis
classification	kingdom	organ system	taxonomy
eukaryotes	metabolism	prokaryotes	tissue

Most scientists agree that living things share certain characteristics that distinguish them from nonliving things.

- Living things are organized structures. All are made of one or more **cells**, which are the basic units of structure and function. They maintain their cellular organization throughout life.
- Living things use energy to maintain life and to grow and develop. These activities require that the cells carry out various chemical reactions. The combination of all the chemical reactions that occur in an organism is called **metabolism**.
- Living things maintain a fairly stable internal environment even when their external environment changes dramatically. The maintenance of this internal stability is known as **homeostasis**. To maintain homeostasis, organisms must respond and adapt to both their internal and external environments.
- Living things pass hereditary information to new organisms of the same species in the process of **reproduction**.

Only living things share the characteristics of life. Nonliving things have no functioning cells and no metabolic activity; they do not maintain homeostasis, nor do they reproduce.

Diversity Among Living Things

CLASSIFICATION Although living things share the characteristics of life, there are differences among the many kinds of organisms. Throughout history, people have tried to bring order to all the varieties of life on Earth by grou... organisms in logical ways. Organ... grouped, or classified, on the bas... common characteristics and rela... share. The science of classifying... organisms is called **taxonomy**. T... of organisms suggests relationsh... that may result from present for... oping from common ancestors. T... is based mainly on similarities o... it is supplemented by other evid... ships such as the fossil record, g... life cycles, embryo development,... similarities.

Before You Read
Each topic (chapter) is divided into sections. Before you read a section, scan its headings to help you focus on the main subject areas.

As You Read
At the beginning of each section is a list of key vocabulary words. These same words appear in boldface type when they are defined in the text. You may also use the Glossary at the end of this book to find the meaning of words that you are unsure of.

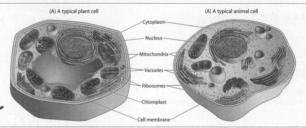
(A) A typical plant cell — (A) A typical animal cell
Cytoplasm / Nucleus / Mitochondria / Vacuoles / Ribosomes / Chloroplast / Cell membrane

Figure 2-6. Some cell organelles can be seen in these plant and animal cells.

Use Figures and Feature Boxes
As you read the text, you'll find helpful illustrations that make concepts more easily understood. Feature boxes such as *Memory Jogger*, *Digging Deeper*, and *Did You Know?* will also help you to better understand the required material.

information (as DNA in chromosomes). Many people think of the nucleus as the cell's control center because it directs the cell's activities.

MEMORY JOGGER

Because bacteria are prokaryotes, they have no nucleus—their genetic material simply floats in the cytoplasm as a large chromosome. Some bacteria also have smaller loops of DNA called plasmids.

Vacuoles The storage sacs within the cytoplasm are called **vacuoles**. They may contain either wastes or useful materials such as water or food. Food vacuoles are specialized to digest food; contractile vacuoles in some organisms pump excess water out of the cell.

The vacuoles in plant cells are usually much larger than the vacuoles in animal cells, as shown in Figure 2-6.

Endoplasmic Reticulum The E. R., as the **endoplasmic reticulum** is often called, is a network of membranes inside the cell. It plays a role in transport within a cell, and along with the **Golgi apparatus**, functions in the packaging of proteins for secretion from the cell.

Ribosomes The cell contains many tiny **ribosomes**, which are important to the process of making protein. Some ribosomes are attached to the endoplasmic reticulum. Others float in the cytoplasm. Ribosomes are not enclosed in a mem-

brane and they are found in both prokaryotic and eukaryotic cells.

Mitochondria **Mitochondria** are bean-shaped structures that contain special proteins, known as enzymes, which are used to extract energy from nutrients during aerobic respiration. Mitochondria are sometimes called the cell's powerhouses because they release most of the cell's energy and produce ATP.

Chloroplasts The green structures found in plants and some one-celled organisms are **chloroplasts**. They contain the green pigment chlorophyll and capture light energy, which is then used to produce food for the plant. Animal cells do not contain chloroplasts.

Cell Walls Unlike animals, plants and most bacteria and fungi have a cell wall outside the cell membrane. The walls of plant cells are made of cellulose. Cell walls provide some protection for plant cells, and because they can be quite rigid they also provide support. The walls of plant cells are attached to the walls of nearby cells, providing structural support for the plant. Since animal cells lack cell walls, animals often rely on bones or other structures for support.

 2-3 Review

1. Which structure is the boundary between a living cell and its environment? (A) cell membrane (B) cytoplasm (C) vacuole (D) ribosome

After You Read
Questions at the end of each section give you the opportunity to review key concepts. If you're unsure of an answer, go back and re-read the text related to the question.

v

Preparing for the Biology HSA Test

 2-2 Review

1. Living things are made mostly of these four main elements: (A) hydrogen, oxygen, nitrogen, and protein (B) water, protein, carbohydrate, and fat (C) carbon, hydrogen, oxygen, and nitrogen (D) glucose, salt, mineral, and base

2. H_2O is an example of (F) a molecule but not a compound (G) a compound but not a molecule (H) both a molecule and a compound (J) neither a molecule nor a compound

3. Matter made u... fat (B) elemen...

7. Fertilizers using radioactive nitrogen compounds are used in growing experimental plants. In which molecules would these compounds first be detected? (A) sugars (B) starches (C) lipids (D) proteins

8. A sample of soluble, organic molecules was analyzed and found to contain carbon, hydrogen, and oxygen. It is most likely that the molecules were (F) lipids (G) cellulose (H) protein (J) monosaccharides

9. Enzyme molecules are synthesized primarily from (A) amino acids (B) monosaccharides (C) fatty acids (D) phospholipids

Check Understanding at Every Step
You'll have many opportunities to assess your understanding with review questions at the end of each section.

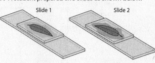 **Topic 2: Assess Your Understanding**

1. A few bacteria are placed in a nutrient solution. After several hours, thousands of bacteria are present. Which life activities are primarily responsible for this?
   (A) digestion and movement
   (B) digestion and reproduction
   (C) circulation and respiration
   (D) excretion and coordination

2. Mitochondria are organelles that
   (F) are necessary for the process of diffusion to take place
   (G) are found in the nucleus of some cells
   (H) initiate cell division in living cells
   (J) contain respiratory enzymes

3. In the diagram of root cells, three areas are indicated with the numbers 1, 2, and 3. In which direction would the net flow of water be the greatest as a result of diffusion?
   (A) 1 to 3
   (B) 1 to 2
   (C) 2 to 3
   (D) 3 to 2

   Key
   • = Water molecule

4. Which cellular structure is present in both eukaryotic cells and prokaryotic cells?

6. Most of the enzymes found in the mitochondria are involved in the reactions associated with
   (F) extracting energy from nutrients
   (G) storing energy in nutrients
   (H) DNA production
   (J) protein synthesis

7. A student prepared two slides as shown below.

   Slide 1   Slide 2

   Elodea leaf mounted in tap water
   Elodea leaf mounted in 6% salt solution

   The tap water used on Slide 1 contained 1 percent salt and 99 percent water, while the salt solution on Slide 2 contained 6 percent salt and 94 percent water. Elodea cells normally contain 1 percent salt. Ten minutes after the slides were prepared, a microscopic examination of cells on Slide 1 and Slide 2 would most likely show evidence that
   (A) water had moved out of the cells on Slide 2
   (B) salt had moved out of the cells of Slide 2
   (C) water had moved into the cells on Slide 2
   (D) salt had moved into the cells on Slide 1

8. The diagram below shows the change in position of ... each side of a membrane ...

Track Your Progress
Use the Correlation to *Maryland Core Learning Goals* as a checklist to record what you've studied.

Practice for Test-Taking Success
Assessment questions at the end of each topic and sample tests at the back of this book will help build your test-taking skills and your confidence.

Session 1

22 BCR A population of sea urchins in a kelp forest ecosystem is being overfished. A team of students believe that a decline in the number of sea urchins will affect the organisms in the kelp forest ecosystem. The kelp forest food web below shows the relationships among the organisms in the kelp forest ecosystem.

KELP FOREST FOOD WEB

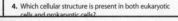

Northern Elephant Seals

Horn Sharks   Sea Otters

Sea Urchins   Kelp Crab

Kelp

The students believe that the kelp crab population will decrease if the sea urchin population decreases. Use the kelp forest food web to support or refute the students' conclusion. In your response, be sure to

• describe the roles of the kelp crab, sea otter, and sea urchin in the food web

• describe the relationships between the kelp crab, sea otter, and sea urchin

• explain how each organism in the food web would be affected by a change in the sea urchin population

Write your answer in your Answer Book.

Review Tips for Answering HSA Questions
Throughout your preparation, refer to the test-taking strategies in the Appendix at the back of this book. Techniques are provided for answering both types of HSA questions: Selected Response (multiple-choice questions) and Brief Constructed Response (essay questions).

Maryland HSA Goal 3: Concepts of Biology

 ## Core Content Overview

The following section outlines the Goal 3 key concepts you need to understand to be successful on the Maryland High School Assessment (HSA). Goal 3, Concepts of Biology, consists of six "Expectations"—things you should be able to do—listed below:

Expectation 3.1: Explain the correlation between the structure and function of biologically important molecules and their relationship to cell processes.

Expectation 3.2: Demonstrate an understanding that all organisms are composed of cells which can function independently or as part of multicellular organisms.

Expectation 3.3: Analyze how traits are inherited and passed on from one generation to another.

Expectation 3.4: Explain the mechanism of evolutionary change.

Expectation 3.5: Investigate the interdependence of diverse living organisms and their interactions with the components of the biosphere.

Expectation 3.6: Investigate a biological issue and develop an action plan. (Not tested on biology assessment.)

Each Expectation is further broken down into "Indicators of Learning." In the following pages, each "tested" indicator is listed for you. Bulleted lists for each Indicator provide the very basic ideas you must know to pass the HSA. Key terms appear in bold type.

After each bulleted list is a "Self Check" with one or more questions. Answers to these questions are provided at the end of this section so that you can check your understanding at any point.

Because many of the key concepts need more explanation for you to fully understand them, page numbers are provided where you can go to find additional information and more practice questions.

Indicator 3.1.1
Describe the unique characteristics of chemical substances and macromolecules utilized by living systems.

Water

- Water is an inorganic compound—one that does not contain the element carbon.

- Most chemical reactions in cells take place in water.

- Many chemical reactions in cells use water in the reaction itself.

- Water molecules have both positively and negatively charged regions, making them **polar**. This polarity affects how water interacts with other molecules.

- Water is denser as a liquid than as a solid (ice). This is why ice floats.

- The polarity of water helps make it a very good solvent. It is able to dissolve many other substances.

 Self Check

1. Write *T* beside the sentence below if it is true or *F* if it is false.

   Many of the chemical reactions in cells take place in carbon. ____

For more information on water see Topic 2, pages 2-4 and 2-5 in this book.

Carbohydrates

- A **carbohydrate** (kahr boh HY drayt) is a compound made of the elements carbon, hydrogen, and oxygen. Carbohydrates are organic molecules because they contain both carbon and hydrogen atoms.

- **Monosaccharide** molecules are the building blocks of carbohydrates. Small sugar molecules such as glucose are monosaccharides. They combine to form larger carbohydrate molecules such as starch and cellulose.

- All cells use carbohydrates for energy. When plants make food, they make sugar. Plants store extra sugar as starch.

Biology

PRENTICE HALL
MARYLAND HSA

John Bartsch

Mary P. Colvard

ORDER INFORMATION

Phone:
1-800-848-9500
Monday - Friday
8:00 AM to 6:00 PM EST

FAX:
1-877-260-2530
24 hours a day
7 days a week

Online:
Go online at PHSchool.com
24 hours a day
7 days a week

Mail:
Prentice Hall School
P.O. Box 2500
Lebannon, IN 46052-3009

PEARSON
Prentice Hall

Boston, Massachusetts
Upper Saddle River, New Jersey

Maryland Reviewers

PRENTICE HALL STAFF CREDITS

The people who made up the project team for this book—representing editorial, design services, marketing, and production services—are listed below.

Lois Ann Freier, Bret Kerr, Ellen Levinger, Patricia Schmid, Jerry Thorne

ISBN 0-13-203667-3
5 6 7 8 9 10   10 09 08

Maryland Biology Review

Table of Contents

- Carbohydrates are also the source of dietary fiber. **Cellulose** and other organic compounds that cannot be digested make up **dietary fiber**. Plant cell walls are made of cellulose.

- Carbohydrates are important structural components of cells. They are found in the cell wall and cell membrane.

 ## Self Check

2. Circle the letter of *each* sentence that is true about carbohydrates.

   (a) Carbohydrates have the element nitrogen.

   (b) Cells use carbohydrates for energy.

   (c) Carbohydrates make up some cell parts.

3. Circle a monosaccharide in the part of the starch molecule shown below.

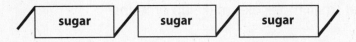

For more information on carbohydrates see Topic 2, page 2-5 in this book.

Lipids

- **Lipids** are organic molecules made up of carbon, hydrogen, and oxygen. Fats, oils, and waxes are examples of lipids.

- Cell membranes are made mostly of lipids.

- Cells store energy in lipid molecules for future use. Lipids have more energy per gram than carbohydrates do.

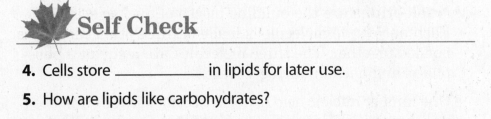 ## Self Check

4. Cells store _____ in lipids for later use.

5. How are lipids like carbohydrates?

   _____

   _____

For more information on lipids see Topic 2, pages 2-5 and 2-6 in this book.

Proteins

- **Proteins** are organic molecules. They contain carbon, hydrogen, oxygen, and nitrogen.

- Proteins are made up of many smaller compounds called amino acids. **Amino acids** are the building blocks of protein molecules. Cells combine amino acids in different ways to form thousands of proteins.

- Most cell structures are made of proteins.

- Proteins also have many functions in cells. Some proteins function as enzymes. **Enzymes** speed up the chemical reactions that take place in cells. Without enzymes, many chemical reactions would not take place.

 Self Check

6. What small molecules make up proteins?

_____

7. What do enzymes do?

_____

_____

For more information on proteins see Topic 2, page 2–6 in this book.

Nucleic acids

- **Nucleic acids** are long organic molecules that have the information that cells need to carry out all of their functions.

- **Nucleotides** are the building blocks of nucleic acids. Each nucleotide molecule is made of three other molecules bonded together. The three molecules are a sugar, a phosphate, and one of 5 nitrogen bases.

- One kind of nucleic acid is deoxyribonucleic (dee ahk see ry boh noo KLEE ik) acid—called **DNA** for short. DNA is a double helix. This means it looks like a spiral staircase.

- DNA stores genetic information and directs the cell's activities.

- DNA is located in the chromosomes of a cell. Chromosomes are in the nucleus of eukaryotic cells.

- DNA is able to make copies of itself in a process called **replication**. This makes it possible for DNA to be passed from parents to offspring.

- Ribonucleic (ry boh noo KLEE ik) acid, called **RNA**, is another type of nucleic acid. RNA is a single strand. It helps make proteins that the cell needs. RNA can be found in both the nucleus and the cytoplasm.

 **Self Check**

8. Fill in the table about nucleic acids.

Nucleic Acids		
Type	**Role in the Cell**	**Location in the Cell**
DNA	Carries information about living things	(a) _____
RNA	(b) _____ _____	cytoplasm and nucleus

9. Circle the letter of one function of nucleic acids.

(a) carry genetic information about the cell

(b) provide energy

(c) make up cell structures

For more information on nucleic acids see Topic 2, page 2–6 in this book.

Minerals

- **Minerals** are inorganic substances that organisms need in small amounts. Living things do not make them. They are present in the soil, and plants take them in through their roots.

- Minerals help the cell do many different jobs. They are important in many cellular processes. You obtain them by eating plants or animals that have eaten plants.

- Two minerals are calcium and iron. Calcium is important in bone formation. Iron is part of the hemoglobin molecule found in red blood cells.

 **Self Check**

10. What are minerals?

_____

_____

11. Circle the part of the plant in the diagram of the plant below that takes in minerals.

For more information on minerals see Topic 2, page 2-5 in this book.

Vitamins

- **Vitamins** are organic molecules. Like minerals, vitamins help the cell carry out many processes.

- Vitamins are needed in small amounts.

- The roles of three vitamins in human body are:

  ○ vitamin C – wound healing

  ○ vitamin K – blood clotting

  ○ vitamin D – bone growth

 **Self Check**

12. Circle the sentence that is true about vitamins.

    (a) Your body uses vitamins mainly for energy.

    (b) The body needs large amounts of vitamins.

    (c) Vitamins help the cell carry out many processes.

For more information on vitamins see Topic 2, pages 2-4 and 2-5 in this book.

13. (3.1.1 Review) Complete this concept map on organic compounds.

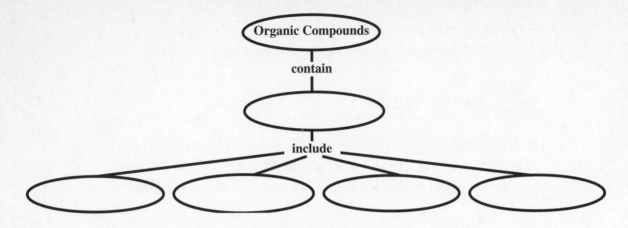

For additional questions related to Indicator 3.1.1, see:

- HSA 2004 Examination, questions 31, 35, and 47 on pages M–17, M–22 and M–28
- HSA 2005 Examination, questions 2 and 37 on pages M–33 and M–57

Indicator 3.1.2
Discuss factors involved in the regulation of chemical activity as part of a homeostatic mechanism.

Osmosis

- **Osmosis** (ahz MOE sis) is the diffusion of water across a cell membrane.

- The cell membrane lets only some substances pass through. Oxygen, food, waste products, and water are substances that can pass through the cell membrane.

- **Diffusion** is when substances move from an area of high concentration to an area of low concentration. It is like when people spread out from a crowded space to a less crowded space.

- Water moves out of a cell if the concentration of water inside of the cell is greater than the concentration of water outside the cell. Cells shrink when water moves out.

- Water moves into a cell if the concentration of water outside the cell is greater than the concentration of water inside the cell. Cells swell, or get larger, when water moves in.

• It is possible to predict which way water will flow across a membrane based on the cell's environment.

• Osmosis is an important process in living systems. Cells cannot function without the right amount of water.

 **Self Check**

14. The picture shows molecules of water spread inside and outside a cell. Circle the letter of the picture that shows how the molecules of water would look before osmosis has taken place.

a.

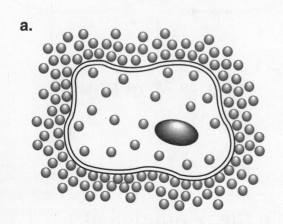

b.

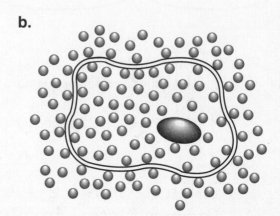

15. Read each word in the box. Then, in each sentence below, fill in the correct word or words.

shrinks	stays the same	swells

(a) When water moves into a cell, the cell _____.

(b) When water moves out of a cell, the cell _____.

For more information on water see Topic 2, pages 2–10 and 2–11 in this book.

Temperature

• All of the chemical reactions taking place in the cells of an organism are called its **metabolism**. Enzymes are needed in order for most of these chemical reactions to take place. When the rate of enzyme activity changes, the rate of metabolism changes.

• Because changes in temperature cause molecules to move faster or slower, an increase in temperature increases the rate of diffusion. A decrease in temperature slows the rate of diffusion.

- Enzymes work best at certain temperatures. Which temperature is best varies according to the enzyme. For example, human enzymes work best at human body temperature.

- If the temperature is too low, the rate of enzyme activity will decrease. As the temperature increases, the rate of enzyme activity increases—up to a point.

- At very high temperatures, enzymes lose their shape and no longer function.

- Changes in temperature determine a substance's state of matter. This has to do with how fast the atoms or molecules are moving. For example, at temperatures below 0°C, water is a solid. As the temperature increases from 0°C to 10°C, water molecules move faster and ice melts to become a liquid. As the temperature increases to above 100°C, the molecules move even faster and water becomes a gas.

Self Check

16. Write *T* beside the sentence below if it is true or *F* if it is false.

All enzymes work best at the same temperature. ___

17. Why does an increase in temperature increase the rate of diffusion?

_____

_____

For more information on temperature see Topic 3, page 3–8 in this book.

pH

- The **pH scale** is used to measure the strength of an acid or a base. The scale goes from 0–14. A solution with a pH of 7 is **neutral**. A solution with a pH of less than 7 is an **acid**. The lower the pH, the stronger the acid. A solution with a pH higher than 7 is a base. The higher the pH, the stronger the **base**.

- Most human body fluids have a pH of 7. Many human enzymes work best in a neutral environment. However, the enzymes in the human stomach require an acid pH.

- Organisms cannot survive in conditions that are too acidic or too basic. A healthy lake typically has a pH around 8. Lakes that receive a lot of acid rain or snow may have a pH of 4 or 5. This is too acidic for many organisms.

Expectation 3.1

18. What does pH measure?

_____

_____

19. Lye is a very strong base. Draw a circle around a group of three numbers on the pH scale below that could represent the pH of lye.

| 1 2 3 4 5 6 7 8 9 10 11 12 13 14 |

For more information on pH see Topic 3, pages 3–8 and 3–9 in this book.

Enzyme Regulation

• The rate of enzyme activity is affected by temperature. There is a specific temperature at which each enzyme works best. At temperatures higher or lower than the best one, the rate of reaction goes down.

• The rate of enzyme activity is also affected by pH. There is a specific pH at which each enzyme works best. If the pH changes or becomes more acidic or basic, the rate of enzyme activity decreases.

  ○ The rate of enzyme activity is affected by enzyme/substrate concentration. A **substrate** is the substance the enzyme acts upon.

  ○ Enzyme-controlled reactions depend on how many times molecules of the enzyme and substrate bump into each other.

  ○ When there is little enzyme present, adding more enzyme increases the rate of reaction—up to the point. When all the substrate molecules are in contact with enzyme molecules, adding more enzyme will not increase the rate of the reaction.

  ○ When there is little substrate present, adding more substrate increases the rate of reaction—up to a point. When all the enzyme molecules are in contact with substrate molecules, adding more substrate will not increase the rate of the reaction.

Self Check

20. What is a substrate?

_____

_____

21. List three factors that affect the rate of enzyme action.

(a)_____

(b)_____

(c)_____

For more information on enzyme regulation see Topic 2, pages 2-4 and 2-5 in this book.

For additional questions related to Indicator 3.1.2, see:
• HSA 2005 Examination, questions 6, 7, and 33 on pages M–36 and M–55.

Indicator 3.1.3
Compare the transfer and use of matter and energy in photosynthetic and non-photosynthetic organisms.

Water Cycle

• Water moves from Earth's surface to the air and back through the **water cycle.**

• **Evaporation** is when a liquid changes into a gas. In the water cycle, liquid water evaporates from bodies of water. Water also evaporates from the soil, plants, and animals. **Transpiration** is when water that is absorbed by plants evaporates from the leaves.

• Condensation is when a gas changes into a liquid. In the water cycle, water vapor condenses in the atmosphere to form water droplets. The water droplets then collect into clouds.

• In the water cycle, the droplets of water in the clouds fall back to Earth as precipitation. Precipitation includes rain, snow, and sleet. Some water runs off the land and into bodies of water. Some soaks down into the soil.

• Most living things take in and use liquid water in their life processes.

 **Self Check**

22. Complete the diagram of the water cycle by filling in the blanks.

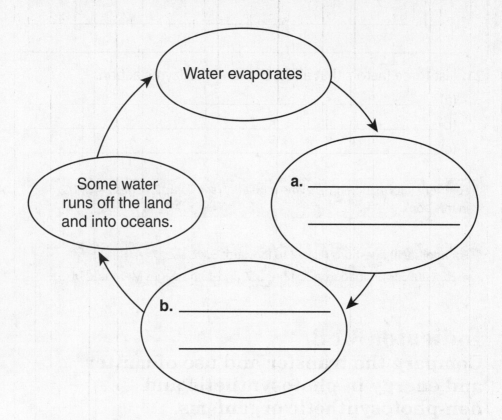

Water evaporates

Some water runs off the land and into oceans.

a. _____

_____

b. _____

_____

For more information on the water cycle see Topic 8, pages 8–2 and 8–3 in this book.

Carbon Cycle

- Living things need carbon and oxygen to live.

- In ecosystems, the carbon cycle is closely linked to the oxygen cycle.

- In the **carbon cycle**, producers take in carbon dioxide from the air to use in photosynthesis. Producers, consumers, and decomposers all release carbon dioxide back into the air as a waste product of respiration.

- In the oxygen cycle, many organisms take in oxygen from the air to carry out respiration. Producers release oxygen into the air as a waste product of photosynthesis.

Use the picture below to answer questions 23 and 24.

23. Circle the letter of what the tree releases into the air as a waste product of photosynthesis.

   (a) carbon dioxide

   (b) nitrogen

   (c) oxygen

24. Circle the letter of what the horse releases back into the air as a waste product of respiration.

   (a) carbon dioxide

   (b) nitrogen

   (c) oxygen

For more information on the carbon cycle see Topic 3, pages 3–4 and 3–5 in this book.

Nitrogen Cycle

- Air is about 78 percent nitrogen. Most organisms can use nitrogen only after it has been "fixed." Fixing nitrogen means combining it with other substances.

- Certain kinds of bacteria carry out nitrogen fixation. Once nitrogen fixation occurs, organisms can use nitrogen to make compounds in their cells.

- **Decomposers** break down dead organisms and animal wastes. This process adds nitrogen to the soil. Some of this nitrogen is in a form plants can use. Also, there are certain bacteria in the soil that break down nitrogen compounds and release nitrogen gas into the air.

- Humans have upset the nitrogen cycle by sometimes adding too much nitrogen fertilizer to the land. Much of the nitrogen fertilizer runs off into the lakes and rivers and causes the rapid growth of plants and algae.

 **Self Check**

25. Circle the letter of *each* sentence that is true about the nitrogen cycle.

   (a) Decomposers add nitrogen compounds to the soil.

   (b) There is almost no nitrogen gas in the atmosphere.

   (c) Most organisms can use nitrogen only after it has been "fixed."

For more information on the nitrogen cycle see Topic 7, page 7–11 in this book.

Photosynthesis

- During the process of photosynthesis, producers take in light energy. Green plant cells have special cell organelles called chloroplasts to absorb the energy in light.

- Producers use the captured energy to make food. To do this, plants also need water and carbon dioxide. Plants get water by absorbing it from the soil through their roots. Carbon dioxide gas enters the leaves through small openings in the leaves.

- Inside the chloroplasts, water and carbon dioxide go through a series of chemical reactions. The energy captured from light powers these reactions.

- One product of these chemical reactions is sugar. Plant cells use the energy from some of this sugar to carry out cell activities. Some of the sugar is changed into other molecules that make up plant structures. Any unused sugar is stored in the plant for future use.

- The other product of photosynthesis is oxygen. Oxygen goes out of the leaf through the same small openings that carbon dioxide entered the leaf.

- The word equation below summarizes the chemical changes that occur during photosynthesis:

$$\text{carbon dioxide} + \text{water} \longrightarrow \text{sugar} + \text{oxygen}$$

26. Fill in the concept map below about photosynthesis.

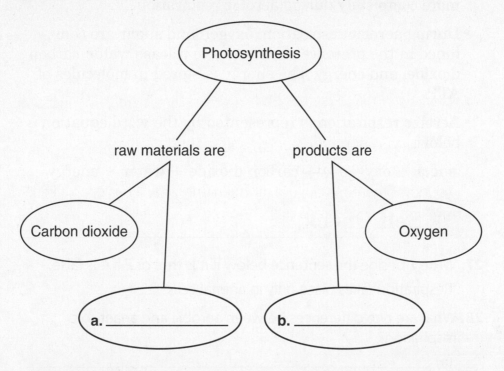

For more information on photosynthesis see Topic 3 and 4, pages 3–1 and 3–2 and 4–1 and 4–2 in this book.

Cellular Respiration

- **Respiration** is how cells get energy from sugar.

- Respiration takes place in all cells, including plant and animal cells. Respiration happens all the time because cells always need energy.

- The chemical reactions that release energy from sugar take place inside of cells.

- **Aerobic respiration** requires the presence of oxygen. Most of the chemical reactions associated with aerobic respiration take place inside organelles called **mitochondria**. These cell organelles are where enzymes necessary for the process are stored. Bacteria lack mitochondria. Even without mitochondria, many bacteria are able to carry out aerobic respiration.

- Many simple organisms—like some bacteria—cannot carry out aerobic respiration. They rely on anaerobic respiration for energy. **Anaerobic respiration** does not require the presence of oxygen. During exercise, human cells sometimes carry out anaerobic respiration.

- More energy is released from sugar molecules during aerobic respiration than during anaerobic respiration. This is because the sugar molecules are broken down more completely during aerobic respiration.

- During aerobic respiration, oxygen and sugar are combined in the presence of enzymes to release water, carbon dioxide, and energy. The energy is stored in molecules of ATP.

- Aerobic respiration is represented by the word equation below:

sugar + oxygen $\longrightarrow$ carbon dioxide + water + energy

 **Self Check**

27. Write *T* beside the sentence below if it is true or *F* if it is false.

Respiration takes place only in animal cells. ____

28. What are two differences between aerobic and anaerobic respiration?

(a) _____

(b) _____

29. Fill in the cycle diagram about photosynthesis and respiration.

Photosynthesis   **Respiration**

Plants produce oxygen.

Organisms use
a. _____.

Plants use
b. _____.

Organisms produce
carbon dioxide.

For more information on cellular respiration see Topic 3, pages 3–4 and 3–5 in this book.

Chemosynthesis

- Some bacteria carry out chemosynthesis. Unlike photosynthetic bacteria, they do not use light as a source of energy.

- During **chemosynthesis**, energy from the breakdown of inorganic compounds is used to make food.

 **Self Check**

30. Write *T* beside the sentence below if it is true or *F* if it is false.

During chemosynthesis, plants use energy from the breakdown of inorganic compounds to make food. ___

For more information on chemosynthesis see Topic 3, page 3–2 in this book.

ATP

- The energy released from food molecules during respiration is not used directly. It must first be transferred to energy carrier molecules.

- ATP is an energy carrier molecule. Energy that is ready for use is almost always stored in the bonds of ATP.

 **Self Check**

31. Complete the chart that shows movement of energy in a cell.

> Step 1: The energy in food is released through the process of _____.

> ↓

> Step 2: The released energy is stored in the energy carrier molecule _____.

> ↓

> Step 3: Energy is now available for cell processes.

For more information on ATP see Topic 3, pages 3–2 and 3–4 and 3–5 in this book.

For additional questions related to Indicator 3.1.3, see:

- HSA 2004 Examination, questions 9, 28, 40, 48, 49, and 50(BCR) on pages M–5, M–16, M–25, M–29, and M–30

- HSA 2005 Examination, questions 9, 31(BCR), 39, and 40 on pages M–38, M–53, M–58, and M–59

Indicator 3.2.1
Explain processes and the function of related structures found in unicellular and multicellular organisms.

Transport of Materials

- The cell is the basic building block of living things. Some organisms are composed of one cell. Other organisms, including you, are composed of trillions of cells.

- Each cell has many parts. The cell membrane forms the boundary between the cell and its environment. It is made up of lipids and proteins.

- The cell membrane controls what diffuses into and out of the cell in both unicellular and multicellular organisms.

- Both plants and animals have vascular tissues designed to conduct materials.

  ○ A tissue is a group of similar cells that do the same job.

  ○ In plants, vascular tissues conduct water and food throughout the plant.

  ○ In mammals, the cardiovascular system is made up of the heart, blood vessels, and blood. The heart pumps blood through the blood vessels. Blood carries oxygen, nutrients, and other needed materials to all the cells of the body.

- Circulatory systems help move materials from one part of an organism to another. Transport fluids that move through tubes (vessels) make up the vascular system.

Self Check

32. Circle the letter that describes the function of the cell membrane.

    (a) makes energy for the cell

    (b) controls what diffuses in and out of the cell

    (c) controls everything the cell does

33. The system that is made up of the heart, blood vessels, and blood is the _____ system.

For more information on the transport of materials see Topic 2, pages 2–10 and 2–11 in this book.

Waste Disposal

- Excretion is the removal of the waste products of metabolism. Wastes are produced when cells use nutrients.

- Many waste products are excreted directly through the cell membrane. Wastes move across the membrane from a region of high concentration in the cell to a region of low concentration outside the cell.

- The cell membrane controls what leaves the cell in both unicellular and multicellular organisms.

- Excretion maintains homeostasis by keeping an organism's internal environment stable and free from harmful levels of chemicals.

- Plants have no specialized organ systems for excretion. More complex animals do.

  - An organ is a body part that is made up of different kinds of tissues. Each organ does a certain job.

  - Excretory organs are designed to collect the wastes produced by cells and to remove the wastes from the body.

  - The circulatory system transports wastes to the excretory system.

    - Carbon dioxide, a waste product of respiration, diffuses into the blood from the cells. The blood carries carbon dioxide to the lungs, where it diffuses out of the blood and is excreted into the air.

    - Urea (yoo REE uh) is produced when cells break down proteins. The kidneys filter wastes, including urea, out of the blood. The watery wastes are called urine.

Self Check

34. Write *T* beside the sentence below if it is true or *F* if it is false.

    Excretory systems are designed to collect the wastes produced by cells and to remove the wastes from the body. ___

35. The _____ controls what leaves the cell in both unicellular and multicellular organisms.

For more information on waste disposal see Topic 4, pages 4–5 and 4–6 in this book.

Movement

- Many organisms have the ability to move from one place to another. Movement increases an organism's chances of survival by increasing its ability to

  - obtain food

  - find shelter

  - move away from harmful substances

  - escape predators

  - reproduce

- Many single-celled organisms such as bacteria and protozoans (proh tuh ZOH unz) have organelles specialized for movement.

  - Some bacteria and protozoans have a **flagellum** (fluh JEL um) attached to the outside of the cell membrane. The flagellum is a long, whiplike structure that helps a cell move.

  - Some protozoans move from one place to another and get food by forming **pseudopods** (SOO duh pahdz). Pseudopods are temporary bulges of the cell. They are formed when cytoplasm flows toward one direction and the rest of the organism follows.

  - Other protozoans have cilia (SIL ee uh). **Cilia** are hairlike structures that move with a wavelike motion. Cilia act like tiny oars to move the organism. Cilia may also be used to sweep food into the organism.

- Many animals have a skeleton that is made of bones. Bones, along with muscles, make it possible for these animals to move.

- Bones serve the following functions:

  - provide support and protection for body structures

  - serve as points of attachment for muscles

  - form levers to produce body movement

- Skeletal muscles are attached to bones. Because muscles can only contract (get shorter), skeletal muscles must work in pairs. For example, when the muscle in the front of your upper arm contracts, it pulls on the bones in your lower arm. This bends your elbow. To straighten your elbow, the muscle in the back of your upper arm contracts. This pulls on the bones in your lower arm.

Self Check

36. The pictures show two different protozoans. Circle the picture of the protozoan that has cilia.

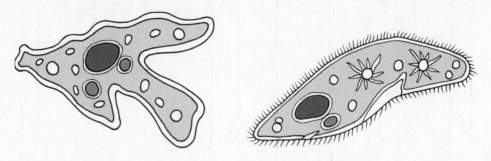

37. The drawing shows upper arm muscles. Which muscle, A or B, contracts to bend your elbow?

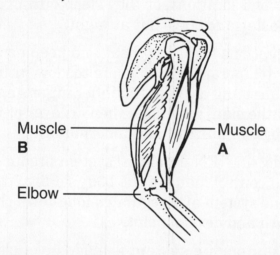

For more information on movement see Topic 4, pages 4–2 and 4–3 in this book.

Feedback

- **Homeostasis** (hoh mee oh STAY sis) is all of the ways an organism tends to keep itself in balance. It is the process by which an organism's internal environment is kept stable in spite of changes in the external environment.

- Examples of ways that organisms maintain homeostasis:
  - Water balance
    - The leaves of plants give off excess water through the process of transpiration.
    - Protozoans have specialized vacuoles that pump out excess water.
    - Some organisms remove excess water directly through their cell membranes.

Expectation 3.2

◆ Animals have excretory structures that regulate the amount of water present in their bodies.

○ pH

  ◆ Organisms may adjust the pH of different parts of the body to keep enzymes working at their best.

  ◆ Some digestive enzymes require an acid pH, while others require a neutral or basic pH.

○ Temperature

  ◆ The evaporation of water out of the leaves of plants tends to keep them cool on hot days.

  ◆ Many animals sweat on warm days. The evaporation of the sweat helps cool the body. Some animals seek out cooler locations, or they sleep during the hot part of the day and come out at night.

  ◆ Adaptations for saving heat and keeping an animal's body temperature from going too low include shivering, directing blood to the inner organs and away from the skin, growing a thicker layer of fat and/or fur for cool months, and hibernation.

○ The endocrine (EN duh krin) system produces chemicals that control many of the body's daily activities. The endocrine system also regulates long-term changes such as growth and development.

  ◆ The **endocrine system** is made up of glands that release hormones into the blood.

  ◆ **Hormones** are chemicals that control activities of the body. They turn on, turn off, speed up, or slow down body activities.

  ◆ The organs of the endocrine system release hormones when the brain sends them messages. Hormones affect only certain cells. The cells affected are called target cells.

  ◆ Through **feedback**, when the amount of a particular hormone in the blood reaches a certain level, the endocrine system detects it and sends signals that stop the release of that hormone.

  ◆ Here is another example of feedback: When the house is cold, the thermostat signals the furnace to make heat. Once the house is warm, the thermostat signals the furnace to stop making heat.

38. _____ are chemicals that control the activities of the body.

39. Circle the letter of the term that describes all the ways your body tends to keep itself in balance.

    (a) sweating

    (b) stress

    (c) homeostasis

For more information on feedback see Topic 4, pages 4–10 and 4–11 in this book.

Asexual Reproduction

- **Asexual reproduction** involves only one parent. The parent produces offspring that are identical to it. Here are some examples of asexual reproduction:

  ○ In **binary fission**, one cell divides to form two identical cells. The cells are the same size and carry the same genetic information. Bacteria and some protozoans reproduce by binary fission.

  ○ In unicellular organisms, **budding** is similar to binary fission except the cytoplasm divides unequally. The result is two cells with the same genetic information, but one cell is larger than the other. Yeast cells reproduce by budding.

  ○ In multicellular organisms, budding occurs as an outgrowth from the body of the parent. The outgrowth develops into a complete organism. Buds eventually separate from the parent. Hydras reproduce by budding.

  ○ **Vegetative propagation** occurs in plants. Complete new plants develop from parts of the parent plant, such as the root, stem, or leaf.

- All cells come from other cells by cell division. For living things to grow and repair, their cells must divide over and over again. In a cell containing a nucleus, the nucleus and cytoplasm divide by separate processes. Most cells divide by a process called **mitotic cell division** in which the nucleus divides through a series of events called **mitosis**.

  ○ In mitosis, the DNA shortens and thickens to form chromosomes. Each chromosome replicates. The result is that exact copies are made of all the chromosomes.

○ The chromosomes are next separated into two identical sets. In cells with a nucleus, a new nucleus forms around each set of chromosomes, creating two new nuclei.

○ At the end of mitosis, the cell usually divides to form two new cells that are genetically identical to each other and to the parent cell. The number of chromosomes remains the same.

 Self Check

40. When a cell makes an exact copy of its DNA, it is called _____.

41. Look at the two cells below. Circle the letter of the cell that is finishing mitotic cell division.

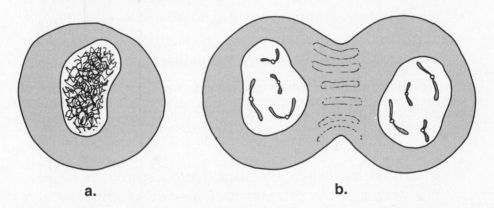

a. b.

For more information on asexual reproduction see Topic 4, pages 4–15 and 4–16 in this book.

Sexual Reproduction

• **Sexual reproduction** involves the production of eggs by the female and sperm by the male. The egg and the sperm join together during **fertilization**.

○ An **egg** is the sex cell produced by the female. A **sperm** is the sex cell produced by the male.

○ When an egg and sperm join, it is called **fertilization**. The cell that is formed is a fertilized egg, called a **zygote**.

• An **angiosperm** (AN jee uh spurm) is a plant that reproduces sexually. It produces flowers. Angiosperms also produce seeds protected by a fruit.

○ A flower is the structure in which seeds form.

○ Most flowers have male and female parts.

- ◆ The **stamens** (STAY munz) are the male parts. They produce the pollen. Pollen holds the sperm nuclei.

- ◆ The female part of a flower is the **pistil** (PIS tul). Egg nuclei form in the pistil.

- ○ The color, shape, and scent of flowers attract insects, birds, and bats. These animals pollinate flowers by moving pollen as they visit flowers to get food.

- ○ **Pollination** takes place when a pollen grain lands on the sticky top of the pistil.

- ○ After pollination, a sperm nucleus from a pollen grain joins with an egg nucleus inside the pistil. The fertilized egg, or zygote, develops into a young plant that will be inside of the seed.

- ○ As the seed develops, part of the pistil becomes the fruit. The fruit contains one or more seeds.

- ○ Fruits are a way that angiosperm seeds are scattered. Animals that eat fruits spread the seeds. Other fruits are scattered by wind or water.

- • Mammals are divided into groups that differ in how their young develop.

- ○ Most mammals are not born until they are fully developed. Humans, cats, and horses are examples.

  - ◆ After an egg is fertilized, it begins to divide right away. Once the fertilized egg begins to divide, it is called an **embryo** (EM bree oh). As more and more organs develop, the embryo becomes a fetus (FEE tus). In humans this occurs after about 9 weeks of development.

  - ◆ The fetus grows in its mother's uterus. Inside the uterus an organ called the **placenta** has many small blood vessels that allow oxygen and nutrients to diffuse from the mother's blood vessels to the baby's blood vessels. Wastes diffuse from the baby's blood to the mother's blood. The mother's blood and baby's blood do not mix.

Self Check

42. Read each word in the box. In each sentence below, fill in the correct word.

| pistil | petal | stamen |

(a) The structure in which seeds form in an angiosperm is a

_____.

(b) The structure where pollen grains form in an angiosperm is the _____.

43. The picture shows the parts of a flower. Label the pistil and the stamens.

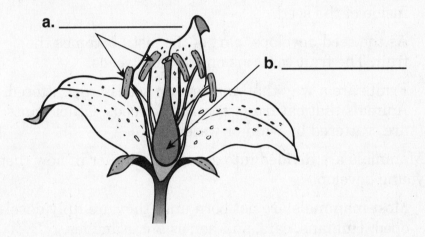

a. _____

b. _____

44. Which process does the diagram show? _____

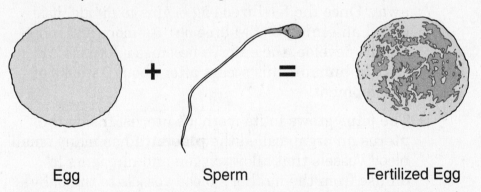

Egg   Sperm   Fertilized Egg

For more information on sexual reproduction see Topic 4, page 4–16 in this book.

Control of Structures

• A unicellular organism must perform the same tasks that a multicellular organism performs. For example, digesting food, moving, maintaining homeostasis, and growing are all done by single cells as well as by multicellular organisms.

- To help cells carry out life functions, they have tiny structures called organelles. An organelle is a structure that has a specific function within the cell.

  - The **nucleus** is the control center of the cell. It is protected by a membrane and contains the genetic information. It controls what the cell does and is involved in reproduction.

  - The **cell membrane** forms a boundary between a cell and its environment. It controls what goes in and out of the cell. Oxygen diffuses into a cell across the cell membrane. Wastes diffuse out of the cell across the cell membrane.

  - The **cell wall** is a stiff layer that protects and supports the cell. Plant cells have cell walls made of cellulose.

  - **Vacuoles** help to maintain water balance and are also where digestion may take place in some cells.

- To help humans carry out life functions, cells are organized into tissues, organs, and organ systems. These systems perform the same life processes that organelles perform in single cells.

  - The nervous system, including the brain and sensory organs, helps to regulate many human life processes. It detects changes in both the internal and external environment. The nervous system controls many human activities.

  - The endocrine system also controls many body functions by releasing hormones.

  - The respiratory and excretory systems are responsible for bringing oxygen into the human body and removing wastes. Oxygen diffuses across the surface of the lungs and enters the blood. Carbon dioxide diffuses from the blood, goes across the surface of the lungs, and leaves the body.

  - The human skeleton provides a stiff framework that protects and supports the organs.

  - The organs of the digestive system have three main functions. First, they break down food into molecules the body can use. Then, the molecules are absorbed into the blood and carried throughout the body. Finally, wastes are eliminated from the body.

 **Self Check**

45. Circle the letter of *each* sentence that is true about the nucleus.

   (a) The nucleus is the control center of the cell.

   (b) The nucleus holds the genetic information.

   (c) The nucleus captures the energy from sunlight

46. Fill in the blanks in the table about cell organelles and organ systems.

Jobs Done by Organelles and Organ Systems		
Organelle	**Organ System**	**Job**
cell membrane	respiratory system	brings in oxygen and removes carbon dioxide
a. _____	skeletal system	stiff framework that protects and supports
vacuoles	digestive system	b. _____

For more information on control of structures see Topic 2, pages 2–2, 2–8 and 2–9 in this book.

Capture and Release of Energy

- Nearly all living things obtain energy either directly or indirectly from light energy captured during the process of **photosynthesis** (foh toh SIN thuh sis).

  ○ During photosynthesis, plants and some other organisms use energy from the sun to convert carbon dioxide and water into oxygen and sugars.

  ○ Plant cells and some protozoans have special organelles called chloroplasts. **Chloroplasts** capture the energy in light and use it to make food.

- During respiration, cells break down simple food molecules such as sugar and release the energy these molecules contain.

  ○ Respiration constantly takes place in all cells because cells always need energy.

○ **Mitochondria** (my tuh KAHN dree uh) are the organelles where aerobic respiration takes place. Mitochondria are called the "powerhouses" of the cell because they release the energy stored in food molecules.

 **Self Check**

47. Read each word in the box. In each sentence below, fill in the correct word.

mitochondria	nucleus	chloroplast

(a) The organelle that captures the energy from sunlight is the _____.

(b) The organelle that releases the energy in food for use by the cell is the _____.

For more information on the capture and release of energy see Topic 3, pages 3–1 and 3–2 in this book.

Protein Synthesis

• During protein synthesis, the cell uses information from a gene on a chromosome to produce a specific protein.

• Protein synthesis takes places at the **ribosomes**. Ribosomes are organelles in the cytoplasm.

• Information coded in DNA serves as the instructions for building a protein.

 **Self Check**

48. Write *T* beside the sentence below if it is true or *F* if it is false.

Proteins are made in the nucleus in structures called ribosomes. ____

For more information on protein synthesis see Topic 3, pages 3–12 and 3–13 in this book.

For additional questions related to Indicator 3.2.1, see:

• HSA 2004 Examination, questions 5, 7, 20, 21(BCR), 24, 25, 26, and 27 on pages M–4, M–5, M–12, M–13, M–15, and M–16

• HSA 2005 Examination, questions 4, 15, 19, 20, 21, 23, 47, 48(BCR), and 49 on pages M–34, M–42, M–45, M–46, M–48, M–63, and M–64

Indicator 3.2.2

Understand that cells exist within a narrow range of environmental conditions and changes to that environment, either naturally occurring or induced, may cause changes in metabolic activity of the cell or organism.

Chemical Factors Affecting Metabolic Activity

- A change in the **pH** of the environment surrounding a cell affects the ability of the cell to carry out life processes.

  - Enzymes, including those that digest food, work best at a specific pH.

  - If the pH is changed, the rate of the chemical reaction the enzyme regulates is likely to decrease.

- **Water** is used for most of the chemical reactions taking place in a cell. Cells also require a watery environment so that materials can be transported.

- **Oxygen** is necessary for the process of aerobic respiration.

  - A change in the amount of oxygen present in a cell's environment directly influences its ability to release energy from food.

  - The type and number of organisms present in a lake or river is determined by the amount of oxygen dissolved in the water.

- **Carbon dioxide** is necessary for photosynthesis.

  - Without an adequate amount of carbon dioxide in the air or dissolved in water, photosynthetic organisms are not able to make enough food.

  - Too much carbon dioxide in a cell's environment may cause a change in the pH level, which could then interfere with other processes.

- The presence of different amounts of **toxic substances** in a cell's environment affects its metabolic activity. A toxin is a poison that produces disease conditions, damages tissue, or interferes with natural life processes.

  - Natural toxins are produced by the metabolic activities of certain living organisms. Nicotine is a natural toxin.

  - Synthetic toxins are made in the laboratory. Many of the chemicals used to kill insects (insecticides) and other pests (pesticides) are examples of synthetic toxins.

 **Self Check**

49. Look at the picture of the zebra eating grass.

   a. Describe one way the grass is affected by the carbon dioxide level in the environment.

   b. Describe one way the zebra's cells would be affected if the oxygen level in the environment decreased.

Physical Factors Affecting Metabolic Activity

- A change in the **temperature** of a cell's environment affects the ability of a cell to carry out life processes.

  ○ An increase or decrease of a few degrees can speed up or slow down the rate of metabolism.

  ○ Enzymes are affected by changes in temperature.

- **Light** is necessary for photosynthesis.

  ○ Not all photosynthetic organisms have the same light requirements. Some require many hours of bright light while others grow best in dim light.

  ○ A change in the amount of light in a cell's environment may directly affect its ability to perform photosynthesis.

  ○ Sunlight is also important in maintaining Earth's temperature.

- Exposure to different types of **radiation** may result in cancer. Normally, the body makes new cells at the same rate at which other cells die. In cancer, new cells are made too quickly. Cells keep dividing over and over again.

  ○ Cancer cells may form a lump of tissue called a tumor. A tumor can spread and kill healthy cells nearby. Tumor cells can also break away and travel in the blood. The cells may form new tumors in other parts of the body.

  ○ Some types of radiation include ultraviolet light (UV), x-rays, and cosmic rays.

  ○ Exposure to radiation may result in mutations. A **mutation** is a change in a gene or chromosome.

    ♦ A mutation may cause a cell to produce an incorrect protein during protein synthesis.

    ♦ Mutations are harmful if they reduce an organism's chance to survive and reproduce.

    ♦ Mutations are helpful if they help an organism survive and reproduce.

 Self Check

50. Write *T* beside the sentence below if it is true or *F* if it is false.

Mutations are always harmful. ____

51. Draw a line from each term to its meaning.

Term	Meaning
Tumor	type of radiation
Ultraviolet light	change in a gene
Mutation	lump of tissue formed by cancer cells

For more information on physical factors influencing metabolic activity see Topic 3, pages 3–8 and 3–9 in this book.

For additional questions related to Indicator 3.2.2, see:
- HSA 2004 Examination, questions 22 and 43 on pages M–14 and M–26
- HSA 2005 Examination, question 51 on page M–65

Indicator 3.3.1
Demonstrate that the sorting and recombination of genes during sexual reproduction has an effect on variation in offspring.

Meiosis

- Sexual reproduction involves **gametes**—the egg cells of females and sperm cells of males. These are produced by the division of special reproductive cells.

  ○ The original reproductive cell undergoes two divisions, resulting in four new cells. Cell division to produce gametes involves meiosis. **Meiosis** is a process that reduces the number of chromosomes in the nucleus by half.

  ○ For example, if the original reproductive cell has 46 chromosomes, each of the four gametes that are produced contains 23 chromosomes.

- Organisms that reproduce sexually show a greater amount of variation than organisms that reproduce asexually.

  ○ During meiosis, chromosome pairs replicate and pair up along the middle of the cell.

  ○ When chromosomes pairs line up, they sometimes tangle and swap parts as they separate into new cells. This is called **crossing over**.

  ○ Crossing over results in new gene combinations—which means more variety.

 **Self Check**

---

52. Write *T* beside the sentence below if it is true or *F* if it is false.

A sex cell produced by a female is a sperm. ___

53. Fill in the cycle diagram about meiosis.

Meiosis

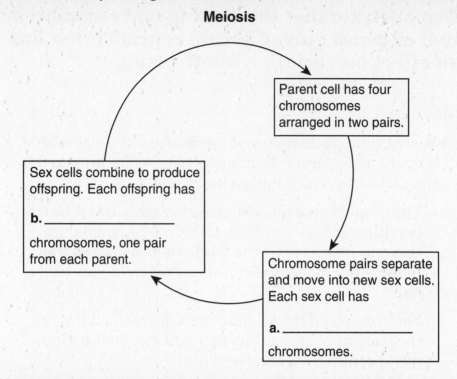

Parent cell has four chromosomes arranged in two pairs.

Sex cells combine to produce offspring. Each offspring has

b. _____

chromosomes, one pair from each parent.

Chromosome pairs separate and move into new sex cells. Each sex cell has

a. _____

chromosomes.

For more information on meiosis see Topic 4, page 4–17 in this book.

Fertilization

- When an egg and sperm join, it is called **fertilization**. The cell that is formed is a fertilized egg, called a **zygote**.

- The egg and sperm each contain half the normal number of chromosomes for the organism. After fertilization, the chromosome number is restored to the full number.

- For example, a human cell contains 46 chromosomes. Human sperm and egg cells each contain 23. When a sperm with 23 chromosomes fertilizes an egg with 23 chromosomes, the fertilized egg then has 46 chromosomes.

 **Self Check**

---

54. The picture shows two cells from the same living thing. One cell is a parent cell. One cell is a sex cell. Circle the letter of the sex cell.

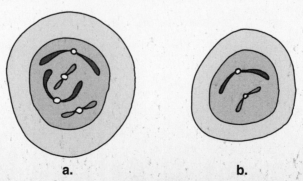

a.   b.

For more information on fertilization see Topic 4, page 4–16 in this book.

For additional questions related to Indicator 3.3.1, see:
- HSA 2004 Examination, questions 10 and 32 on pages M–6 and M–19
- HSA 2005 Examination, questions 12, 28, and 41 on pages M–40, M–50, and M–60

Indicator 3.3.2
Illustrate and explain how expressed traits are passed from parent to offspring.

Phenotypes

- An organism's phenotype (FEE noh typ) is its physical appearance, or visible traits. It is the expression of inherited characteristics.

- You can see that a puppy has black fur. Black fur is its phenotype.

 **Self Check**

55. Circle the letter of the correct answer. Which of the following is the best way to determine the phenotype of a mouse?

    (a) Do some chemical tests.

    (b) Look at it.

    (c) Examine its parents.

For more information on phenotypes see Topic 5, page 5–8 in this book.

Dominant and Recessive Traits

- Scientists call the factors that control traits genes. The different forms of a gene are called **alleles** (uh LEELZ). For example, the gene for stem height in peas has two alleles—one for tall stems and one for short stems.

- A **dominant** allele always shows up in an organism, even when the other allele is present. A **recessive** allele is hidden whenever the dominant allele is present.

- Geneticists use letters to represent alleles. A dominant allele has a capital letter. The allele for tall is *T*. A recessive allele has a lowercase letter. The allele for short is *t*.

 **Self Check**

56. Fill in the table about alleles and genes.

Alleles of Genes		
Type of Allele	**Description**	**Represented by**
Dominant	Always shows up when present	(a) _____ _____
Recessive	(b) _____ _____	Lowercase letter

For more information on dominant and recessive traits see Topic 5, page 5–8 in this book.

Sex-Linked Traits

- The sex chromosomes are one of the 23 pairs of human chromosomes.

- Sex chromosomes are the only chromosomes that do not always exactly match in size and number of genes. Females have two *X* chromosomes. Males have one *X* and one *Y* chromosome. The *Y* chromosome is much smaller than the *X* chromosome.

- Genes for some human traits are carried only on the *X* chromosome. These genes are called **sex-linked traits** because their alleles are passed from parents to offspring on the sex chromosome. One sex-linked trait is red-green colorblindness.

- Recessive sex-linked phenotypes are more often expressed in males because they have only one *X* chromosome. Therefore, they inherit only one gene for any sex-linked trait. Whatever gene they inherit is expressed.

 **Self Check**

57. Circle the letter of the correct answer. When a sperm cell with a Y chromosome fertilizes an egg cell, the fertilized egg will develop into an

(a) *XY* female

(b) *XY* male

(c) *XX* female

58. Write *T* beside the sentence below if it is true or *F* if it is false.

Males express recessive sex-linked phenotypes more often than females. ___

For more information on sex-linked traits see Topic 5, page 5–10 in this book.

Genotypes

- **Genotype** (JEN uh typ) is the genetic makeup, or total combination of alleles in an organism.

- The genotype for a particular trait is represented by one or more pairs of alleles. The genotype for a tall pea plant can be either *TT* or *Tt*.

- An organism that has two of the same alleles for a trait is homozygous (hoh moh ZY gus). A tall pea plant is homozygous when its genotype is *TT*. A short pea plant is always homozygous *tt* since it is showing the recessive trait.

- An organism with two different alleles for a trait is heterozygous (het ur oh ZY gus). A hybrid plant is heterozygous. A tall pea plant is heterozygous when it has the alleles *Tt*.

 **Self Check**

59. Draw a line from each term to its meaning.

Term	Meaning
Phenotype	(a) an organism with two different alleles for a trait
Genotype	(b) the way an organism looks
Heterozygous	(c) an organism with two of the same alleles for a trait
Homozygous	(d) an organism's genetic makeup

For more information on genotypes see Topic 5, page 5–8 in this book.

Punnett Square

- In a genetic cross, the likelihood that each parent will pass a particular allele on to its offspring is based on probability.

- A **Punnett square** is a chart that shows all the possible combinations of alleles that can occur in a genetic cross. Geneticists use Punnett squares to predict the results of a cross.

- The boxes in a Punnett square represent the possible combinations of alleles that offspring can inherit from their parents.

- You can use a Punnett square to find the probability that offspring will have certain combinations of alleles.

- In a cross between two hybrid tall pea plants (Tt), the Punnett square gives four possible combinations of alleles in the offspring. These are TT, Tt, Tt, and tt. This means that there is a 75% chance that the offspring will be tall and a 25% chance that the offspring will be short.

 **Self Check**

60. Fill in the Punnett square to show the possible allele combinations from a cross between two hybrid pea plants with round seeds (Rr).

	R	**r**
R	**RR**	a. _____
r	**Rr**	b. _____

61. In a cross between two hybrid pea plants with round seeds (Rr), what is the probability that a pea plant will have seeds that are wrinkled (rr)? Circle the letter of the correct answer.

(a) 3 in 4, or 75 percent

(b) 2 in 4, or 50 percent

(c) 1 in 4, or 25 percent

For more information on Punnett squares see Topic 5, page 5–9 in this book.

Pedigree

- One important tool geneticists use to trace the inheritance of traits is a pedigree.

- A **pedigree** is a chart or "family tree" that tracks the members of a family that have a certain trait.

- Geneticists use pedigrees to follow a trait though several generations of a family. This helps geneticists learn how a trait is inherited.

- In a pedigree, a circle stands for a female. A square stands for a man. A line connecting a square and a circle shows that the male and female are a mating pair. Children are connected to their parents by a line and a bracket.

- A shaded square or circle stands for a person who has the trait that is being studied. A half-shaded square or circle may be used to stand for a person who carries just one allele for the trait but does not show the trait. A person who carries one allele for the trait but does not show the trait is called a **carrier**. A circle or square that is not shaded stands for a person who does not have the trait.

 **Self Check**

62. The chart below follows hemophilia in a family. Hemophilia is a genetic disorder in which the blood does not clot normally. How many males have hemophilia? Circle the letter of the correct answer.

    (a) 1   (b) 2   (c) 3

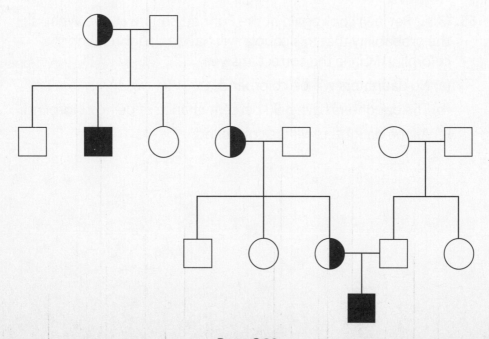

63. Look at the symbol below.

(a) Does this symbol stand for a male or a female? _____

(b) Does the symbol stand for a person who has the trait or one that is a carrier for the trait? _____

For more information on pedigrees see Topic 5, page 5–10 in this book.

64. (3.3.2 Review) The Punnett square below shows the possible genotypes of the children whose mother has one allele for color-blindness. Normal color vision (X^C) is dominant over colorblindness (X^c). The Y chromosome does not carry a gene for color vision. Circle the genotypes of the children that will be colorblind.

Father $X^C Y$

	X^C	Y
X^C	$X^C X^C$ Daughter	$X^C Y$ Son
X^c	$X^C X^c$ Daughter	$X^c Y$ Son

Mother $X^C X^c$

65. (3.3.2 Review) Look again at the Punnett square above. What is the probability that this couple will have a daughter who is colorblind? Circle the correct answer.

(a) No daughters will be colorblind.

(b) The daughters have a 50 percent chance of being colorblind.

(c) All the daughters will be colorblind.

For additional questions related to Indicator 3.3.2, see:
- HSA 2004 Examination, questions 8 and 36 on pages M–5 and M–22
- HSA 2005 Examination, questions 16, and 38(BCR) on pages M–43 and M–58

Indicator 3.3.3
Explain how a genetic trait is determined by the code in a DNA molecule.

Definition of a Gene

- Each gene is located at a specific place on a chromosome. A **gene** is a segment of DNA that codes for a protein or RNA.

- Body cells have pairs of chromosomes. Human body cells have 23 chromosome pairs, or a total of 46 chromosomes.

- Each chromosome in a pair has the same genes. The genes are lined up in the same order on both chromosomes of a pair.

- The alleles for some of the genes might be different. For example, one chromosome might have the A allele while the other chromosome has the a allele. In this case, the individual is heterozygous (Aa) for the trait.

 Self Check

---

66. Read each word in the box. In each sentence below, fill in the correct word.

alleles	chromosomes	genes

(a) Genes are located on _____.

(b) Each chromosome in a pair has the same _____.

67. Write *T* beside the sentence below if it is true or *F* if it is false.

In a chromosome pair, the alleles for the same genes might be different. ____

For more information on the definition of a gene see Topic 3, page 3–11 in this book.

The Sequence of Nitrogen Bases Directs Protein Formation

- Role of DNA

  ○ Chromosomes are made up mostly of DNA. DNA has four different nitrogen bases—adenine (A), guanine (G), thymine (T), and cytosine (C).

  ○ A gene is a section of DNA with a specific order of nitrogen bases.

  ○ A group of three nitrogen bases codes for a specific amino acid. The order of the three-base groups is a genetic code. This genetic code determines the order in which amino acids are joined to make a protein.

  ○ Cells make protein in a process called protein synthesis. Protein synthesis takes place at the ribosomes. The ribosomes are organelles in the cytoplasm.

  ○ The DNA in the chromosomes stays in the nucleus. RNA carries the DNA code into the cytoplasm.

  ○ RNA is like DNA, except RNA has only one strand instead of two. Like DNA, RNA has the nitrogen bases adenine (A), cytosine (C), and guanine (G). However, RNA has uracil (YOOR uh sil) (U) instead of thymine (T).

- mRNA

  ○ Protein synthesis begins when **messenger RNA** (mRNA) is made using the DNA code inside the nucleus. Messenger RNA molecules "read" the DNA code.

  ○ mRNA carries the code to the cytoplasm. In the cytoplasm, the mRNA attaches to a ribosome.

- tRNA

  ○ As the ribosome moves along the strand of mRNA, the ribosome holds the three-letter codes so that **transfer RNA** (tRNA) can match up with them.

  ○ Molecules of transfer RNA pick up molecules of amino acid. Each tRNA molecule carries a specific amino acid molecule to the ribosome and adds it to the growing protein.

◦ The amino acid chain grows until the ribosome comes to a three-letter code that acts as a stop sign. The ribosome releases the completed protein.

• rRNA

◦ Where ribosomal RNA is attached to the mRNA, a molecule of tRNA with the right code temporarily joins the mRNA. The amino acid brought into place by the tRNA joins the last amino acid in the growing chain and separates from the tRNA.

◦ The ribosome then moves along to the next three-letter code on the mRNA. A new tRNA joins the mRNA and the next amino acid molecule joins the growing protein chain.

 Self Check

68. Write *T* beside the sentence below if it is true or *F* if it is false.

Proteins are made in the cytoplasm in structures called ribosomes. ____

69. Fill in the table to show how DNA and RNA are alike and different.

Comparing Nucleic Acids			
Nucleic Acid	**Location**	**Number of Strands**	**Nitrogen Bases**
DNA	(a) _____	two	adenine, guanine, cytosine, thymine
mRNA	Moves from nucleus to cytoplasm	(b) _____	adenine, guanine, cytosine, (c) _____

70. The picture shows transfer RNA matching up to the three-letter code in messenger RNA. Circle the transfer RNA.

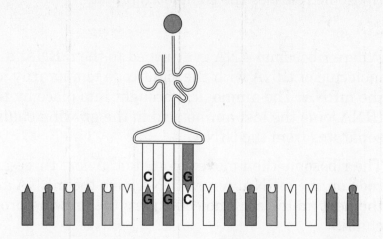

For more information on nitrogen bases and protein formation see Topic 2, pages 2-4 and 2-5 in this book.

Proteins Determine Traits

- Proteins, mainly enzymes, control the chemical reactions taking place in a cell. Therefore, proteins determine what traits an organism has.

- How well a cell functions depends mainly on the enzymes and other proteins it contains. How well a multicellular organism functions is determined by the individual cells that make it up.

- Since an organism's DNA is the source of the messages that tell the cell what proteins to make, DNA determines the individuality of the organism.

 **Self Check**

71. Write *T* beside the sentence below if it is true or *F* if it is false.

Enzymes are proteins that control many of the chemical reactions taking place in a cell. ___

For more information on proteins determining traits see Topic 3, pages 3–11 through 3–13 in this book.

For additional questions related to Indicator 3.3.3, see:
- HSA 2004 Examination, questions 4, 38(BCR), and 46 on pages M–4, M–23, and M–28
- HSA 2005 Examination, questions 27, 45, and 46 on pages M–50 and M–63

Indicator 3.3.4
Interpret how the effects of DNA alteration can be beneficial or harmful to the individual, society, and/or the environment.

Mutations

- Mutations can cause a cell to produce an incorrect protein during protein synthesis. As a result, an organism's trait, or phenotype, may be different from what it normally would have been.

- A mutation is any change in a gene or chromosome.

  - Sometimes mutations happen when DNA is copied or when RNA is made. The wrong base might be added, an extra base might be added, or a base might be removed. These mutations can cause the cell to make the wrong protein. The wrong protein can change the organism's phenotype or traits.

  - Sometimes, during meiosis, chromosomes tangle and fail to separate. This results in egg cells or sperm cells that have too many or too few chromosomes. This may result in an organism with too many or too few chromosomes.

  - Mutations are a source of variation within a species. Some variations may be beneficial. For example, a mutation might produce a new protein that helps an organism survive in a different environment or in a changing environment.

 Self Check

72. Circle the letter of what may happen when chromosomes do not separate correctly during meiosis.

    (a) An extra base is added to DNA.

    (b) The wrong base is added to DNA.

    (c) A cell might have too many chromosomes.

73. Explain how a mutation can be beneficial.

    _____

    _____

For more information on mutations see Topic 5, pages 5–13 and 5–14 in this book.

Chromosome Number

- Some human genetic disorders are caused by changes in chromosome number. In Down syndrome, a person has one extra copy of chromosome 21. Their body cells contain 47 chromosomes instead of the normal 46. People with Down syndrome may have some mental retardation, as well as heart problems.

  - A **karyotype** is a picture of all the chromosomes in a cell. A karyotype shows whether a person has the correct number of chromosomes.

  - Genetic counselors use karyotypes to determine if an individual has a chromosome mutation.

- Sometimes errors during meiosis result in plants that have a whole extra set of chromosomes. These plants are often larger and stronger than plants without the mutation.

 Self Check

74. Give an example of a beneficial chromosome number mutation.

_____

For more information on chromosome number see Topic 5, page 5–14 in this book.

Genetic Engineering

- In genetic engineering, genes from one organism are put into the DNA of another organism. **Gene splicing** is a technique used by researchers to create bacteria that can make human proteins such as insulin. The human insulin gene is put into bacterial cells. The cells make insulin. The scientists collect the insulin and use it to treat diabetes.

- **Recombinant DNA** is DNA produced by combining DNA from two different sources. Bacterial DNA that contains the human insulin gene is an example of recombinant DNA.

- Cloning is one method for developing organisms with desirable traits.

  ○ A clone is an organism that has exactly the same genes as the organism from which it was produced.

  ○ Some plants are very easy to clone. Just cut a stem from the plant and put the stem in soil. The stem will grow into a new plant. The new plant is genetically identical to the plant the stem was taken from.

  ○ Scientists have cloned some animals. Cloning animals is more difficult than cloning plants. The nucleus of an animal's body cell is used to produce an animal clone.

 ## Self Check

---

75. Which is an example of a clone? Circle the letter of the correct answer.

(a) corn grown from seeds

(b) a plant grown from the stem of a cut plant

(c) kittens that look different from the mother

76. Scientists transfer genes from one organism into the DNA of another organism in _____.

For more information on genetic engineering see Topic 5, pages 5–14 and 5–15 in this book.

For additional questions related to Indicator 3.3.4, see:

- HSA 2004 Examination, questions 29 and 51 on pages M–17 and M–30
- HSA 2005 Examination, question 26 on page M–49

Indicator 3.4.1
Explain how new traits may result from new combinations of existing genes or from mutations of genes in reproductive cells within a population.

Natural Selection

- In natural selection, individuals that are better adapted to their environment are more likely to survive and reproduce.

- Factors that affect natural selection are overproduction, competition, and variation.

- Most species produce far more offspring than can possibly survive. Overproduction makes it likely that some offspring will survive.

- Food and other resources are limited. Members must compete with each other for these resources. Some members of the species may not get enough to eat, so they do not survive.

 **Self Check**

77. Look at the picture of the turtle eggs below. Circle the letter of the factor affecting natural selection that the picture shows.

    (a) competition

    (b) overproduction

    (c) variation

For more information on natural selection see Topic 6, page 6–4 in this book.

Adaptations and Variations

- Any difference between individuals of the same species is called a **variation**. An **adaptation** is any kind of inherited trait that improves the chances of survival and reproduction of an organism.

- Some variations make individuals better adapted to their environment. Individuals that are better adapted are more likely to produce more offspring. Their offspring may inherit these helpful traits. After many generations, more members of the species will have the helpful variations.

- Variations in characteristics are caused by mutations, the shuffling of alleles during meiosis, and the new combinations of alleles that result from sexual reproduction.

- Over time, species gradually change. This is due to the natural selection of more favorable traits and the elimination of individuals with less favorable traits. This gradual change is called **evolution**.

 Self Check

78. Draw a line from each factor that affects natural selection to its meaning.

Factor	Meaning
Competition	(a) difference between individuals of the same species
Overproduction	(b) caused by limited food and other resources
Variation	(c) produce more offspring than can survive

79. What is an adaptation? Circle the letter of the correct answer.

(a) a difference between two animals

(b) a trait that helps an organism survive and reproduce

(c) a way for plants and animals to get to an island

For more information on adaptations and variation see Topic 6, pages 6–5 and 6–6 in this book.

For additional questions related to Indicator 3.4.1, see:

• HSA 2004 Examination, questions 11, 12, and 14 on pages M–6 and M–8

• HSA 2005 Examination, questions 11 and 32 on pages M–40 and M–53

Indicator 3.4.2
Estimate degrees of relatedness among organisms or species.

Classification

- Biologists use classification to organize living things into groups so that the organisms are easier to study. **Classification** is grouping things based on their similarities.

- The scientific study of classification is taxonomy (tak SAHN uh mee). Taxonomy is useful because once a living thing is classified, a biologist knows a lot about it. For example, if a crow is classified as a bird, you already know that a crow has feathers and lays eggs.

- Organisms are classified based on their cell type, their ability to make food, and the number of cells in their bodies.

  ○ One way to classify organisms is by whether their cells contain a nucleus.

    ♦ **Prokaryotes** (proh KA re ohtz) are living things whose cells do not contain a nucleus. A nucleus is a dense area in a cell that holds genetic material. Bacteria are prokaryotes.

    ♦ **Eukaryotes** (yoo ka ree ohtz) are living things with cells that have a nucleus. Protozoans, fungi, plants, and animals are eukaryotes.

  ○ Organisms are grouped by characteristics they have in common.

  ○ The lowest level of classification is the species. The characteristics of a species are very specific. Only one kind of organism is in the species level.

80. Look at the picture of the unicellular organism below. Is this organism eukaryotic or prokaryotic? Explain why.

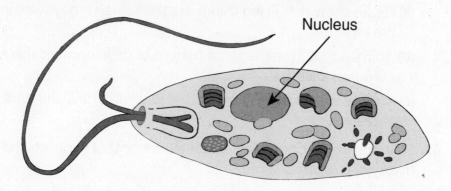

Nucleus

_____

_____

For more information on classification see Topic 2, pages 2–1 and 2–2 in this book.

Anatomical Similarities

- **Fossils** show that living things from the past were very different from the living things of today. A fossil is the preserved remains or traces of an organism that lived in the past.

- Some scientists study what organisms look like when they are just beginning to develop. For example, the early stages of development of all animals with backbones all look similar. Patterns of early development can show that animals are related. These animals share a common ancestor that evolved over time into different species.

- How bones are arranged in the body also gives clues to evolution. Many animals with backbones have body structures that do different things, but the bones are arranged the same way. These are called **homologous structures**. These structures show that animals have evolved from a common ancestor.

 **Self Check**

81. Circle the letter of *each* sentence that is true about evidence for evolution.

   (a) Fossils show that living things are the same as they were in the past.

   (b) Animals that have the same pattern of development share a common ancestor.

   (c) Animals with body structures that look alike have different ancestors.

82. Fill in the graphic organizer about evidence that supports the theory of evolution.

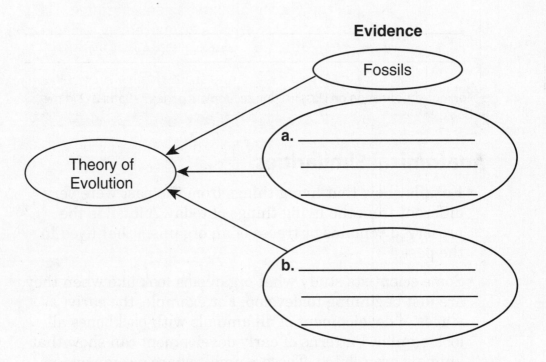

For more information on anatomical similarities see Topic 6, pages 6–8 and 6–9 in this book.

Similarities of DNA Base and Amino Acid Sequences

- Scientists have combined the evidence from DNA, protein structure, fossils, early development, and body structure to determine the evolutionary relationships among species.

- DNA and proteins give clues to how different organisms are related. The more alike the DNA and protein sequences are, the more closely related the species are.

  ○ Gel electrophoresis allows scientists to compare DNA fragments from different organisms.

    ◆ A mixture of DNA or protein fragments is placed at one end of a porous gel. An electric current is turned on. When the power is on, the DNA or protein fragments move toward the other end of the gel.

    ◆ This separates the fragments by size. Smaller fragments move through the gel faster than the larger fragments.

    ◆ Once the fragments have been separated, the power is turned off. Scientists study the pattern of bands made by the fragments of DNA or protein.

    ◆ The patterns of bands from different organisms can be compared. The more similar the patterns, the more closely related the organisms are.

  ○ Once scientists have a good idea about how species are related, they draw branching tree diagrams to show these relationships.

 **Self Check**

---

83. Read each word in the box. In each sentence below, fill in the correct word or words.

branching tree	proteins	species

(a) Scientists compare DNA and proteins to find out how _____ are related.

(b) Scientists show the relationships among species using a diagram called a _____.

84. The branching tree shows how scientists think raccoons, lesser pandas, giant pandas, and bears are related. Are bears more closely related to raccoons or to giant pandas?

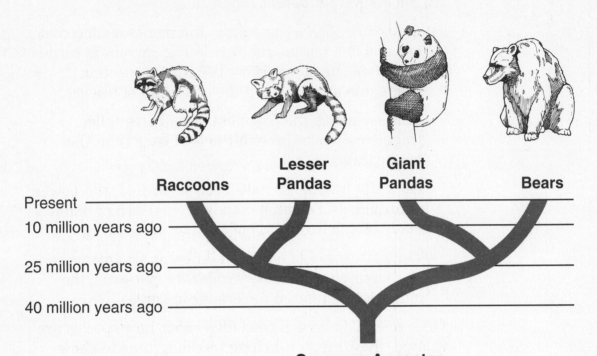

Present
10 million years ago
25 million years ago
40 million years ago

Raccoons   **Lesser Pandas**   **Giant Pandas**   **Bears**

Common Ancestor

For more information on similarities of sequences in DNA and proteins see Topic 3, pages 3–12 and 3–13 in this book.

For additional questions related to Indicator 3.4.2, see:

• HSA 2004 Examination, questions 17(BCR), 19, and 37 on pages M–10, M–12, and M–22

• HSA 2005 Examination, questions 17(BCR), 35, 42, and 53 on pages M–44, M–56, M–62, and M–66

Indicator 3.5.1
Analyze the relationships between biotic diversity and abiotic factors in environments and the resulting influence on ecosystems.

Abiotic and Biotic Factors

- An organism interacts with living and nonliving parts of its habitat. A habitat is the place where an organism lives.

  - Each organism affects all of the other organisms in its habitat. All the other organisms also affect it.

  - The living parts of the habitat are called **biotic** (by AHT ik) **factors**. Biotic factors are animals, plants, and other living things.

- Each organism affects all the nonliving parts of its habitat. The nonliving parts also affect it. The nonliving parts of the habitat are called **abiotic factors**. Abiotic factors include space, soil, water, air, light, and temperature.

- **Ecology** is the study of how living things affect one another. Ecology also is a study of how living things affect the environment and how the environment affects living things.

  - The smallest level of organization is a single organism. It belongs to a **population** that includes other members of its species that live in an area.

  - All the different populations in an area make up a **community**. All of the living organisms that live in a forest are a community.

  - An **ecosystem** is the community of organisms in an area and the nonliving parts of the area. It includes the biotic and abiotic factors in an area.

Expectation 3.5

85. Complete the concept map about abiotic factors by filling in the blanks in the circles.

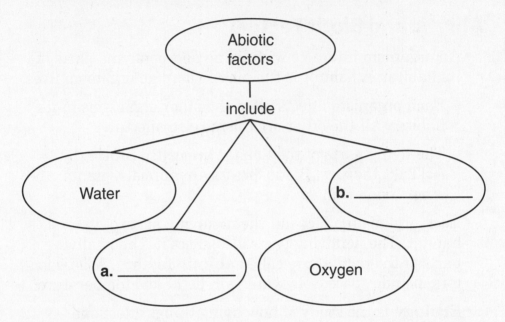

86. Complete the diagram below. The diagram shows the levels of organization in an ecosystem. The diagram begins on the left with the smallest level of organization.

| Organism | (a) _____ | (b) _____ | Ecosystem |

For more information on abiotic and biotic factors see Topic 7, page 7–1 in this book.

Relationships

- Competition

  - **Competition** is a struggle between organisms to stay alive.

  - For example, birds that live in the same part of a tree compete with one another for nest locations, food, water, and other resources.

- Predator – prey

  - Predation is when one organism kills another for food. For example, a hawk catches and eats a mouse.

  - The organism that kills another is called a predator. A hawk is a predator.

- An organism that is killed and eaten is called the prey. A mouse is the hawk's prey.

- Predators have adaptations to help them kill prey. For example, a cheetah can run fast to catch prey.

• A close relationship between members of two species is called **symbiosis** (sim bee OH sis). At least one species is helped by the relationship.

- Symbiosis is called **parasitism** (PA ruh sit iz um) when one species is harmed. The organism that is helped is the **parasite**. The organism that is harmed is the **host**. A flea is a parasite on a dog, which is the host.

• Symbiosis is called **mutualism** (MYOO choo uh liz um) when both species help each other. An example of mutualism is a bee and a flower.

• Symbiosis is called **commensalism** (kuh MEN suh liz um) when one species is helped and the other species is neither helped nor harmed. An example of commensalisms is a bird building its nest in a tree.

 Self Check

87. The picture below shows a python eating a mouse. Label the predator and the prey on this picture.

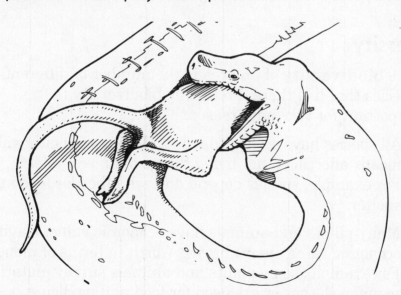

88. Draw a line from each term to its meaning

Term	Meaning
Commensalism	(a) a relationship in which one species is helped and the other is harmed
Mutualism	(b) relationship in which one species is helped and the other is not harmed
Parasitism	(c) relationship in which both species help each other

For more information on relationships see Topic 7, pages 7–2 through 7–6 in this book.

For additional questions related to Indicator 3.5.1, see:
- HSA 2004 Examination, questions 1, and 2 on pages M–3
- HSA 2005 Examination, questions 22(BCR), 24, 36, 50, and 52 on pages M–47, M–48, M–56, and M–65

Indicator 3.5.2
Analyze the interrelationships and interdependencies among different organisms and explain how these relationships contribute to the stability of the ecosystem.

Diversity

- The **biodiversity** of an area is the number of different species that live there. Protecting biodiversity is important for two main reasons:

  - All species have ecological value. Having ecological value means affecting other living things in an ecosystem. For example, species depend on each other for food and shelter.

  - Many plants and animals have economic value. Having economic value means having worth in terms of money. For example, some plants and animals supply materials to make clothes or are used for food and medicine. Tourists often visit places to view the biodiversity there.

- Biodiversity varies from place to place.
  - It can depend on its size. A larger area usually has greater biodiversity than a smaller area.
  - It can depend on its climate. Tropical rain forests, for example, have great biodiversity.
- The organisms in a healthy population have a diversity of traits.
  - Each organism has some genes that others in the same species do not have. The total number of genes found in a species is called its gene pool.
  - A species with a lot of different alleles in its gene pool has a diversity of traits—many different traits. Having gene pool diversity makes it more likely that a species will be able to adapt to changes in the environment.

 **Self Check**

89. Circle the letter of *each* sentence that is true about factors affecting biodiversity.

    (a) Climate does not affect an area's biodiversity.

    (b) Tropical rainforests and coral reefs have great biodiversity.

    (c) A larger area usually has a greater biodiversity than a small area.

90. Circle the letter of the sentence that explains why having gene pool diversity is good for a species.

    (a) The species can more easily adapt to changes in the environment.

    (b) The species is less likely to adapt to changes in the environment.

    (c) The species will never adapt to changes in the environment.

For more information on diversity see Topic 7, pages 7–14 and 7–15 in this book.

Succession

- The series of changes that occur in a community over time is called **succession**.
- **Primary succession** is the start of succession. It occurs where almost nothing exists to grow on. There is no soil or organisms at the beginning of primary succession. An example would be when a volcano forms a new island.

○ Pioneer organisms are the first to populate an area.

○ Pioneer organisms change the environment so that other organisms are able to live in the same area. These other organisms eventually replace the pioneer organisms.

○ Each new population changes the environment. This allows other populations to grow and replace the earlier ones.

○ Eventually a community develops that does not change. The populations are in balance with one another. This stable community will remain until some major event, such as a fire or flood, changes it.

• Secondary succession occurs when an ecosystem has been changed in some way by a catastrophic event. An ecosystem is already in place at the beginning of secondary succession. An example would be the changes that take place in an ecosystem after a forest fire.

 Self Check

Use the pictures to answer questions 91 and 92.

91. This series of pictures is an illustration of _____.

92. Circle the letter of the sentence that best describes the ecosystem in picture 3.

   (a) The forest will remain unchanged unless there is a major change in the environment.

   (b) The deer and rabbits will destroy the trees and it will become a field.

   (c) It will change from a pond to a forest and back each spring and summer.

For more information on succession see Topic 7, page 7–16 in this book.

Expectation 3.5

Trophic Levels

- Energy enters most ecosystems as sunlight. Each organism in an ecosystem plays a part in the movement of energy.

- Each of the organisms in an ecosystem fills one of these energy roles: producer, consumer, or decomposer.

  ◦ An organism that can make its own food is called a **producer**.

  ◦ An organism that gets its energy by eating other organisms is called a **consumer**. **Herbivores** are consumers that eat only plants. **Carnivores** are consumers that eat only animals. **Omnivores** are consumers that eat both plants and animals. **Scavengers** eat plant and animal remains.

  ◦ An organism that gets energy by breaking down organic matter such as wastes and dead things is a **decomposer**. Fungi and bacteria are decomposers.

- The movement of energy through an ecosystem can be shown in diagrams called food chains and food webs.

  ◦ A **food chain** shows a series of organisms that eat other organisms.

    • The first organism in a food chain is always a producer.

    • The organism that eats the producer is a first-level consumer. It is an herbivore.

    • The organism that eats a first-level consumer is called a second-level consumer. It is a carnivore.

  ◦ A **food web** is made up of the many food chains present in an ecosystem. The food chains overlap and connect with one another.

- Each step in a food chain or food web is called a **trophic** level.

  ◦ Producers make up the first trophic level.

  ◦ Consumers make up the second, third, and higher trophic levels.

- Each consumer depends on the trophic level below it for energy.

 **Self Check**

93. Energy enters most ecosystems as _____.

94. A diagram made up of many food chains is called a(an) _____.

95. Draw a line from each term to its meaning.

Term	Meaning
Decomposer	(a) an organism that makes its own food
Producer	(b) an organism that gets energy by eating other organisms
Consumer	(c) an organism that gets energy from wastes and dead organisms

96. The picture below shows a food chain. In this food chain, there is a producer, a first-level consumer, and a second-level consumer. Circle the organism that is the first-level consumer.

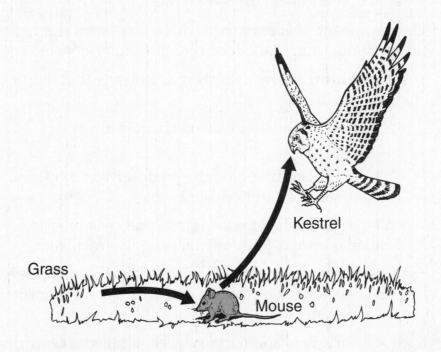

For more information on trophic levels see Topic 7, pages 7–6 and 7–7 in this book.

Ecological Niches

- The role of organism within an ecosystem is its **niche**. It can also be thought of as the way an organism "makes its living."

- A niche includes the types of food an organism eats. It also includes how an organism gets its food and when it reproduces.

 ## Self Check

97. The way an organism "makes its living" is called its _____.

For more information on ecological niches see Topic 7, pages 7–5 and 7–6 in this book.

Pyramid

- In an **energy pyramid**, the most energy is available at the producer level of the pyramid. As you move up the pyramid, each level has less energy available than the level below.

  - An energy pyramid is a diagram in the shape of a pyramid. It shows how much energy moves from one feeding level to another, from the bottom level to the top level.

  - The first level in an energy pyramid represents the first trophic level and has the most energy.

  - Each level of an energy pyramid has less energy than the level below it. Only about 10 percent of the energy in one level is transferred to the next higher level.

  - Most of the energy that is not transferred to the next level is lost as heat.

- In a **biomass pyramid**, the greatest mass is in the producer level of the pyramid. As you move up the pyramid, each level has less mass than the level below it.

  - The amount of biomass that can be supported at each level depends on the amount of energy available at that level.

  - The total mass of living organisms (biomass) at each level is much less than the mass at lower levels.

 **Self Check**

98. Circle the letter of *each* sentence that is true about energy pyramids.

(a) Energy moves from the bottom level to the top level.

(b) The first level has the most energy.

(c) Each level has more energy than the level below it.

99. What does a biomass pyramid show?

_____

_____

For more information on pyramids see Topic 7, pages 7–10 and 7–11 in this book.

For additional questions related to Indicator 3.5.2, see:

- HSA 2004 Examination, questions 6(BCR), 15, 30, and 45 on pages M–9, M–17, and M–27
- HSA 2005 Examination, questions 29, 30, 34, and 43 on pages M–53, M–56, and M–62

Indicator 3.5.3
Investigate how natural and man-made changes in environmental conditions will affect individual organisms and the dynamics of populations.

Depletion of Food

- The amount of available food and water can limit the size of a population. All organisms need food and water to live. Food and water are limiting factors.

  ○ A limiting factor keeps a population from getting larger.

  ○ The largest population of a species that an area can support is called the area's carrying capacity.

- Humans need a stable food supply. Agriculture has helped provide this stable supply.

  ○ Agricultural scientists have developed new crops that produce a lot of food.

- Many new crops are grown using a practice called monoculture. In monoculture, large fields are planted with a single crop year after year. This requires the use of fertilizers and pesticides.

 **Self Check**

100. Read each word in the box. In each sentence below, fill in the correct words.

carrying capacity	limiting factor	food

(a) A _____ keeps a population from increasing in size.

(b) The largest population an area can support is called the area's _____.

For more information on depletion of food see Topic 7, pages 7–2 and 7–3 in this book.

Destruction of Habitats

- Habitat destruction occurs when people take over natural habitats for their own use.

- When forests and other habitats are destroyed, there are trade-offs. Humans must assess the risks and the benefits of habitat destruction.

- Decisions about the environment involve comparing the needs of the environment with the needs of people.

  ○ A forest is home for many living things.

  ○ Trees and other plants in the forest are necessary for a healthy environment. They produce oxygen that organisms need for aerobic respiration. Tree roots hold the soil in place.

  ○ Cutting down a forest may hurt the environment, but the lumber may help people who build houses.

 **Self Check**

101. Write *T* beside the sentence below if it is true or *F* if it is false.

Trees and other plants produce oxygen that all organisms need. ____

102. State a trade-off that must be considered when someone suggests that a forest habitat be destroyed so that homes can be built.

_____

_____

For more information on destruction of habitats see Topic 8, pages 8–6 and 8–7 in this book.

Disease

- A disease is any change, other than an injury, that interferes with the normal functioning of a living thing.

  ○ Some diseases are caused by pathogens. Pathogens include bacteria, fungi, viruses, and other organisms.

  ○ Some materials in the environment cause diseases. These include cigarette smoke, pesticides, and other chemicals.

- Disease may spread naturally and can also spread as a result of human activities.

  ○ Some bacteria have become resistant to antibiotics. This is partly a result of overuse of antibiotics by humans.

  ○ Some insects that spread disease have become resistant to pesticides. This is partly due to overuse of pesticides by humans.

  ○ Chemicals that cause disease may enter the environment as a result of human activities.

  ○ Diseases can spread and kill off may members of a species. This will most likely upset the stability of an ecosystem.

 **Self Check**

103. Circle the letter of *each* sentence that is true about disease.

  (a) A disease is a change, other than an injury, that interferes with homeostasis.

  (b) Chemicals in the environment may cause disease.

  (c) Antibiotics will always cure a disease caused by bacteria.

For more information on disease see Topic 4, pages 4–12 and 4–13 in this book.

Natural Disasters

- A **natural disaster** is not directly caused by human activity. Volcanic eruptions, earthquakes, landslides, tornadoes, and hurricanes are a few hazards that may cause natural disasters.

- The effects of natural disasters may be made worse when they occur in association with human activity. For example, when humans dam a river and an earthquake causes the dam to break, a natural disaster occurs.

- Natural disasters result in economic and human losses. Natural habitats are destroyed, which can upset ecosystem stability.

 ## Self Check

104. Write *T* beside the passage below if it is true or *F* if it is false.

A mudslide is a natural hazard. The destruction of homes as a result of the mudslide is a natural disaster. ___

For more information on water see Topic 8, page 8–2 in this book.

Pollution

- **Pollution** is a harmful change in the chemical makeup of water, soil, or air. Substances that cause pollution are called pollutants. These may be natural or a result of human activity.

- Pollution damages living things and their habitats. Pollution may result in some species becoming endangered or extinct.

- **Air pollution** damages habitats and harms the organisms that live in them.

  - Burning fossil fuels is one source of air pollutants. This process puts excess sulfur, nitrogen, and carbon dioxide into the air.

    - Acid rain is a form of air pollution caused by the burning of fossil fuels. Acid rain lowers the pH of lakes and ponds.

    - The pH of the water may become too acidic for many organisms to survive.

  - Global warming is the result of higher levels of carbon dioxide and some other gases entering the atmosphere.

    - Most of these gases result from burning fuel for transportation and industry.

    - The result is that Earth's average temperature is rising.

○ Ozone depletion is another result of air pollution. Chemicals released into the air have caused Earth's ozone layer to get thinner.

♦ The ozone layer screens out much of the ultraviolet radiation reaching Earth from the sun.

♦ Ultraviolet radiation may kill cells and cause mutations.

♦ A thinner ozone layer allows more ultraviolet radiation to reach Earth.

• **Water pollution** is the result of wastes entering rivers, lakes, and oceans.

○ Water pollutants include:

♦ Sewage and chemicals from homes and factories

♦ Animal wastes and chemicals from farms

○ Water pollutants change abiotic conditions.

♦ Plants may take up pollutants. The chemicals build up in the organisms that eat the plants. The concentration of chemicals increases at each level in the food chain.

♦ Pollutants may also affect the amount of oxygen dissolved in the water. One example is hot water released from power plants. Hot water decreases dissolved oxygen in surrounding waters. If the level of dissolved oxygen is too low, organisms will die.

 Self Check

105. Circle the letter of each sentence that is true about pollution.

(a) Acid rain is a result of burning fossil fuels.

(b) Ozone depletion is responsible for an increase in Earth's temperature.

(c) Pollution may result in some species becoming endangered or extinct.

106. The contamination of Earth's land, air, and water is called

_____.

For more information on pollution see Topic 8, pages 8–2 and 8–10 through 8–12 in this book.

Population Increase and Urbanization

- The human population has been growing faster and faster since the 1600s.

- As a population grows, there is an increased demand for natural resources. This has resulted in the destruction of many habitats.

- As the human population grows, there is increased pollution.

- As the human population grows, there is increased urbanization. **Urbanization** is the increase in the number of people living in cities and towns. It also refers to the size and number of cities and towns. Urbanization leads to the destruction of natural habitats.

 Self Check

107. Circle the letter of each sentence that is true about population growth.

   (a) The human population has been growing faster and faster since 1600.

   (b) Population growth decreases the demands for natural resources.

   (c) Population growth has resulted in the destruction of many habitats.

For more information on population increase and urbanization see Topic 8, pages 8–4 and 8–5 in this book.

For additional questions related to Indicator 3.5.3, see

- HSA 2004 Examination, questions 16, 35, and 44 on pages M–10, M–22, M–27

- HSA 2005 Examination, question 44 on page M–62

Indicator 3.5.4
Illustrate how all organisms are part of and depend on two major global food webs that are positively or negatively influenced by human activity and technology.

Oceanic Food Web

- An oceanic food web is one based primarily on organisms that live in the ocean. These food webs serve as a major source of food for humans and other organisms. Oceanic producers are the source of much of Earth's oxygen.

- Humans have harmed oceanic food webs through activities such as:
  - Overharvesting of fish and other organisms
  - Dumping of wastes
  - Contamination with chemical fertilizers and pesticides

- Human attempts to preserve oceanic food webs include:
  - Regulations limiting the number of fish and other organisms that can be harvested
  - Laws to prevent the dumping of wastes

 **Self Check**

108. Write *T* beside the sentence below if it is true or *F* if it is false.

The ocean is so large that dumping wastes into it will not make any difference. ____

For more information on the food web see Topic 7, page 7–7 in this book.

Terrestrial Food Web

- A terrestrial food web is one based primarily on land.
  - There are connections among oceanic and terrestrial food webs. For example, humans, who live on land, eat fish from the ocean.
  - Producers in terrestrial food webs also produce a lot of oxygen.

- Humans have harmed terrestrial food webs through activities such as:

  ◦ Overharvesting of animals

  ◦ Contamination of the land with chemical fertilizers and pesticides

  ◦ Contamination of the land with sewage and garbage

  ◦ Destruction of terrestrial habitats

- Human attempts to preserve terrestrial food webs include:

  ◦ Hunting and fishing regulations

  ◦ Laws and regulations about pollution and how land can be used

  ◦ Setting aside natural areas as parks and wetlands

- Education is leading to increased awareness of the importance of preserving both oceanic and terrestrial food webs. These food webs supply the living organisms of Earth with food and oxygen.

 **Self Check**

109. Why is it important to know about terrestrial food webs?

_____

_____

_____

For more information on the terrestrial food web see Topic 7, page 7–7 in this book.

Answer Key

1. F
2. (b) and (c)
3. A rectangle that contains the word **"sugar"** should be circled.
4. energy
5. Both contain carbon, hydrogen, and oxygen. Both store energy.
6. amino acids
7. Enzymes speed up chemical reactions that take place in cells.
8. (a) chromosomes (or nucleus)
   (b) helps make protein"
9. (a)
10. Minerals are inorganic substances organisms need in small amounts.
11. The plant's roots should be circled.
12. (c)
13. Organic compounds contain **Carbon** and include **Proteins** and **Carbohydrates** and **Lipids** and **Nucleic Acids**.
14. Cell (a) should be circled.
15. (a) swells
    (b) shrinks
16. F
17. The molecules move faster at higher temperatures.
18. pH measures the strength of an acid or a base.
19. Any group of three numbers higher than 9 is correct. For example, 10, 11, and 12 could be circled. (12, 13, and 14 would also be correct if circled)
20. A substrate is the substance an enzyme acts upon.
21. **Temperature**, **pH**, and **enzyme/substrate concentration** are three factors that affect the rate of enzyme action.
22. (a) water condenses to form droplets
    (b) water falls to Earth as precipitation
23. (c)
24. (a)
25. (a) and (c)
26. a. water
    b. sugar
27. F
28. (a) Aerobic respiration requires oxygen; anaerobic does not.
    (b) Aerobic respiration releases more energy than anaerobic respiration releases.
29. a. oxygen
    b. carbon dioxide
30. T
31. Step 1: respiration
    Step 2: ATP
32. (b)
33. cardiovascular (or circulatory, or transport)

34. T
35. cell membrane
36. The organism on the right should be circled.
37. "Muscle **A**" should be circled.
38. Hormones
39. (c)
40. replication (or mitosis)
41. "b." should be circled.
42. (a) pistil
    (b) stamen
43. a. stamens
    b. pistil
44. fertilization
45. (a) and (b)
46. a. cell wall
    b. break down food (or water balance)
47. (a) chloroplast
    (b) mitochondria
48. F
49. a. With less carbon dioxide, the grass would produce less food.
    b. With less oxygen, the zebra's cells could not release as much energy from food.
50. F
51. Tumor—lump of tissue formed by cancer cells
    Ultraviolet light—type of radiation
    Mutation—change in a gene
52. "b." should be circled.
53. F
54. a. half the normal number of
    b. the full number of
55. (b)
56. (a) a capital letter
    (b) is hidden when a dominant allele is present
57. (b)
58. T
59. Phenotype—(b)
    Genotype—(d)
    Heterozygous—(a)
    Homozygous—(c)
60. a. Rr
    b. rr
61. (c)
62. (a) male
    (b) carrier
63. (b)
64. Only the X^cY Son in the lower right box should be circled.
65. (a)
66. (a) chromosomes
    (b) genes
67. T
68. T

69. (a) nucleus
    (b) one
    (c) uracil
70. The structure that has a shaded circle at the top and has CCG at the bottom should be circled.
71. T
72. (c)
73. A mutation might produce a new protein that helps an organism survive in a different environment.
74. Plants with extra chromosomes are often larger and stronger than plants without the mutation.
75. (b)
76. gene splicing
77. (b)
78. Competition—(b)
    Overproduction—(c)
    Variation—(a)
79. (b)
80. This organism is eukaryotic because it has a nucleus.
81. (b)
82. a. (or b.) similar patterns of development
    b. (or a.) homologous structures
83. (a) species
    (b) branching tree
84. Bears are more closely related to giant pandas.
85. The answers to a. and b. can be any two of the following: **soil**, **light**, **temperature**, **air**, or **space**.
86. (a) population
    (b) community

87. The snake is the predator and the mouse is the prey.
88. Commensalism—(b)
    Mutualism—(c)
    Parasitism—(a)
89. (b) and (c)
90. (a)
91. succession
92. (a)
93. light
94. food web
95. Decomposer—(c)
    Producer—(a)
    Consumer—(b)
96. The **mouse** is the first-level consumer and should be circled,
97. niche
98. (a) and (b)
99. It shows that the greatest mass is in the producer level and that each level has less mass than the level below it.
100. (a) limiting factor
     (b) carrying capacity
101. T
102. People get homes but many organisms are destroyed.
103. (a) and (b)
104. T
105. (a) and (c)
106. pollution
107. (a) and (c)
108. F
109. Terrestrial food webs supply organisms with food and oxygen.

Answer Key

Inquiry Skills and Processes

Science is both a body of knowledge and a way of knowing things. In the scientific process, human thinking is applied to discovering and explaining how the world works. Science originates when people ask questions.

At one time, "scientific" knowledge was just a collection of opinions and unrelated ideas that attempted to explain observations. For example, one hotly debated topic was whether Earth was flat or round. Those believing that Earth was flat pointed to the fact that some ships never returned home. (See Figure 1-1.) They offered this observation as **evidence**—support for the idea that something is true. They believed that these ships had been destroyed when they sailed over Earth's edge.

Those who believed that Earth was round also had evidence. They had observed boats approaching land and noticed that the tops of the sails became visible before the hull of the boat.

1.1 Science and Inquiry

VOCABULARY			
assumption	dependent variable	independent variable	research plan
bias	evidence	inference	
control group	experiment	observation	
controlled experiment	hypothesis	opinion	

Another formerly common idea was that living organisms could come from nonliving things. Some people believed that when conditions were just right, frogs formed from the mud, water, and gases at the bottom of a pond. People also thought that if you left some grain and a dirty shirt in a wooden box, mice would develop after a period of time.

Many people were certain that reproduction was not necessary for life to form. This idea, too, was discussed and debated.

Today, scientists do more than debate whether a new opinion or idea seems to make sense. They develop explanations using observations as evidence. New information is combined with what

Figure 1-1. Ships at sea: At one time a flat Earth seemed to make sense.

people already know. Learning about the historical development of scientific concepts and about the individuals who have contributed to scientific knowledge helps us understand the thinking that has taken place. At first, it might seem silly to believe that Earth is flat, but based on observations made at the time and the tools available at the time, it's not surprising that many people believed in a flat Earth. The emergence of life from pond mud once seemed equally reasonable.

The Scientific Process

Scientific investigation involves

- observing
- questioning
- experimenting
- collecting and organizing data
- finding evidence and drawing conclusions
- repeating the experiment several times
- having the work verified by others

Questioning is at the heart of science. Progress in science depends on people who not only observe and wonder how the world works but who also take the time to come up with questions. These are not just any questions, but those that can be tested and answered.

Observations and Inferences

OBSERVATIONS **Observations** are made using any of the senses. Tools such as thermometers, balances, and microscopes help us extend our senses.

As more and better tools are developed, the ability of scientists to observe the natural world increases and so does our understanding of it. For example, the invention of the microscope increased our ability to observe the structure of living organisms beyond what could be seen with the naked eye. (See Figure 1-2.) This development led to the realization that all living things are composed of cells. Later, the electron microscope allowed the visualization of even greater detail, which led to further scientific advances.

INFERENCES Conclusions based on observations are **inferences**. Inferences may be very subtle. An inference can also be thought of as an idea or conclusion based on the results of an experiment or observation. For example, you may infer that a slug that remains motionless for several hours is dead—but you are not sure.

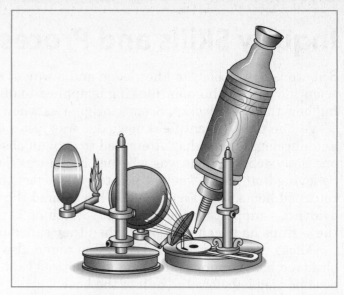

Figure 1-2. The microscope: With the invention of the microscope, scientists could finally observe microorganisms.

Assumptions A good experiment keeps assumptions to a minimum. An **assumption** is the belief that something is true. Assumptions also may be very subtle, and at first you may be unaware you are making them. For example, when doing a seed germination experiment, you might assume that all 100 seeds planted will germinate when watered and kept under favorable conditions. The idea that 100% of the seeds will grow is an assumption. An assumption that could be made during a slug feeding experiment is that slugs will eat every day if provided with desirable food—but it is possible that they will not.

Opinions Ideas people have that may or may not have any basis in fact are **opinions**. Opinions are often **biased,** or influenced by an assumption that may or may not be correct. Although everyone has opinions, a good way to avoid bias is to leave opinions out of data collection and analysis.

Bias can also come from data. Data are sometimes slanted—intentionally or unintentionally. For example, data from an experiment investigating the effectiveness of losing weight by using a new exercise machine might be suspected of being biased if it was funded by the manufacturer, rather than by an independent group of scientists from a university.

THE SCIENTIFIC VIEW Understanding the scientific view of the world is essential to personal, societal, and ethical decision making. To think scientifically, you must critically analyze events, explanations, and ideas. You should use these skills, as well as ideas from other disciplines, to develop your understanding of natural events. You should also be able to create visual models and mathematical formulations to represent your thinking.

Keep in mind that asking questions to develop an explanation is a continuing and creative process. Sometimes conflicting explanations arise from the same body of evidence. For example, plants seem to grow better when talked to daily. Some may try to explain this by crediting the effect of voice or words. Others may point out that simply breathing carbon dioxide on the plant may help it grow. Science is a search for the truth. Scientific thinking can keep you from being misled and making poor judgments.

Inquiry Skills

Everyone needs to understand certain concepts about science and inquiry. Scientific literacy involves applying critical thinking skills to everyday life, particularly to claims related to health, technology, and advertising.

For example, imagine you are watching a television commercial with your family. The advertiser claims its company has developed a cream that makes hair grow when applied to the scalp. According to the commercial, people with thin hair or no hair have both used the cream with success. Before rushing out to buy this product, you should think about the advertiser's claims and begin to question some of what you heard. Next, think about how you can get answers to your questions. Then you should evaluate whether the information is to be believed. What follows is a way to approach the problem.

QUESTIONING Inquiry involves asking questions and locating, interpreting, and processing information from a variety of sources. You may begin by thinking about the following questions.

- How many people were tested?
- What is in the product?
- How long do you have to use it to get results?
- Does it have any side effects?

Next, you ask your friends, and no one knows anything about the product. You also find that your state's consumer product information agency has no information about the company or the hair growth product. Then, you may go to the Internet and find that the company has a Web page that claims 50% of the people using the product grew a full head of hair after 10 applications.

Now ask yourself: Are you ready to use the product based on the information you have found? Do you know enough about the product to make an informed decision? You might want to find answers to more questions.

- How many people actually took part in the study? In other words, 50% of how many people grew hair?

- What caused the participants to have thinning hair or to be bald? Did they have a medical condition that needed attention?

- How long has the company been in business?

- Why hasn't the consumer information agency heard of them and their product?

- Was the cream tested scientifically with careful experimental techniques and design?

Keep in mind that careful scientific inquiry involves doing research to find answers to questions and explanations of natural phenomena. Much of the research in the hair product example was done by finding information without actually doing a laboratory investigation.

MAKING JUDGMENTS Inquiry involves making judgments about the reliability of the source and relevance of information. Scientific explanations are accepted when they are consistent with experimental and observational evidence.

When evaluating evidence and making decisions about how useful your information is, keep the following in mind.

- All scientific explanations are tentative. They can be changed or updated as new evidence emerges. What seems to be true today may be disproved tomorrow.

- Each new bit of evidence can create more questions than it answers. This leads to an increasingly better understanding of how things work.

- Good scientific explanations can be used to make accurate predictions about natural phenomena.

- Beyond the use of reasoning and consensus, scientific inquiry involves the testing of proposed explanations using conventional techniques and procedures. In other words, logic is not enough. Questions should be answered using a good experimental design and thoughtful interpretation.

For example, suppose you read in a magazine about a newly developed HIV vaccine that is said to be effective on monkeys. You should ask.

- Are these results preliminary and tentative, or are they the final results of extensive studies?

- How was the testing done? How many animals were used? How long did they stay healthy?

- Is HIV in monkeys the same as HIV in humans? Is this the solution to the HIV epidemic in humans or just an early step?

DEVELOPING A RESEARCH PLAN The development of a research plan is an important step in the scientific process. A **research plan** involves finding background information, developing a hypothesis, and devising an experimental process for testing a hypothesis.

Most research plans begin with a thorough library search. This search may include the use of electronic information retrieval (the Internet and library databases), a review of the literature (scientific journals), and feedback from the investigator's peers. (See Figure 1-3.) This background work is done so that the researcher has a thorough

Figure 1-3. Research: A review of the literature must be done before the investigation can be designed. Useful resources include primary science journals, professional Web sites, and library databases.

understanding of the major concepts being investigated and any similar investigations.

MAKING HYPOTHESES Inquiry involves developing and presenting proposals, including formal hypotheses, to test explanations. A good **hypothesis** attempts to explain what has been observed in a way that can be tested. It is a tentative answer to a question. Experiments cannot prove a hypothesis; they can only either support the hypothesis or fail to support it.

Most hypotheses would make sense if the words "I think that" were added to the beginning of the statement. Try adding "I think that" to the beginning of each hypothesis in Table 1-1.

Table 1-1. Examples of Hypothesis Statements
This hormone will make plants grow faster.
The presence of this chemical in our drinking water does not harm us.
If this hormone is applied to plant leaves, then the plant will grow faster.
If this chemical is safe, then it will not harm us when it is added to our drinking water.

A good hypothesis can also help determine how an experiment is conducted and how data are interpreted. Testing a hypothesis is valuable even when the hypothesis is not supported by experimental results, since new information is gained in the process of testing any hypothesis.

Designing an Experiment

Once the background work has been done and the hypothesis developed, the actual experiment must be designed. An **experiment** is a series of tests that are done to support or refute (disprove) a hypothesis.

Let's say you suspect that applying a plant growth hormone, IAA, to plant leaves will increase the growth rate of the plant. Your hypothesis might read as follows: *If IAA is applied to the leaves of plants, then the plants will grow more rapidly than those that do not have IAA applied to their leaves.* Once you have written your hypothesis, you must make decisions about variables and experimental techniques.

THE DEPENDENT VARIABLE What is it that you will measure? In the above experiment, you will measure the effect of IAA on plants. What you will measure is called the **dependent variable,** since it depends on what you do to the plants. Since you asked about how the plants will grow, you will need to measure how large the plants are at the beginning as well as at regular intervals until the conclusion of the experiment. Since the plants will be responding to the treatment you apply, the dependent variable is sometimes called the "responding variable." You will also have to decide how to make the measurements. Will you measure only the height of the stem, or will you also measure the size of the leaves? What units will you use?

INDEPENDENT VARIABLES Factors that might influence the dependent variable are independent variables. An **independent variable** is a variable the investigator manipulates—this is why it is sometimes called the "manipulated variable." If you are investigating the effect of IAA being applied to the leaves, you must decide on the concentration of IAA. How often will it be applied to the leaves, and how will you apply it? You may even decide to test several concentrations of IAA. In this example, the frequency of applications and the concentration of IAA are independent variables.

CONTROLLING VARIABLES How will you control the independent variables that might affect your interpretation of the results? You should start with plants that are of the same kind and are about the same age and size. All of the plants should be healthy, grown in the same kind of soil, and provided with the same amount of water and light. If you neglect to control all independent variables, one or more of them may affect plant growth, and you may reach a false conclusion concerning IAA.

A **controlled experiment** is one in which the possible variables have been carefully considered and regulated so the results are due only to the independent variable you are testing. It consists of one or more experimental groups and a control group. The control group is used as a basis for comparison—it allows you to compare the experimental group results with the control group results to determine whether the treatment made a difference.

Each experimental group is treated differently from the control group in only one way. The **control group** in this example is the one that is *not* treated with IAA. However, the plants in the control group will have distilled water applied to their leaves in place of IAA. It is important to apply something to the leaves of the control group or

they would be treated differently in two ways from the experimental group. The plants will be the same type, size, and age as those in the experimental group. They will be grown in the same soil, with the same amount of light and water. (See Figure 1-4.)

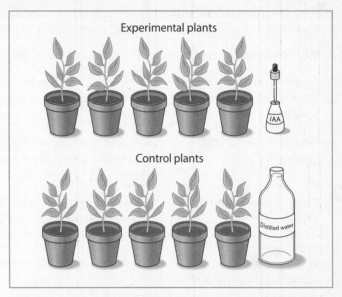

Figure 1-4. Experimental controls: The control group in this experiment is treated with distilled water instead of IAA.

Keep in mind that there should only be one variable being tested at one time. You can test different concentrations of IAA, or you can test the frequency of applying IAA, but you cannot test both on the same plants at the same time. You also cannot test both the impact of fertilizer *and* the impact of IAA on the same plants at the same time.

DEVELOPING EXPERIMENTAL TECHNIQUES Selecting, acquiring, and building apparatus, as well as considering safety precautions and planning how to avoid bias, are important parts of this stage in the development of the research plan. For example, in the IAA study, you need to decide how many plants to use. Would one plant for each concentration of IAA be enough? Should you use 100 plants for each concentration?

Think about these possibilities. With only a few plants, genetic differences could cause variations in growth. Could one of the plants have been infected with a fungus while still an embryo? Would using multiple plants help to cancel out this type of problem? Is one trial enough, or would five or six trials be better? Large sample sizes with repeated trials provide much more accurate information, and there is less probability of error due to chance. Large sample sizes and multiple trials are more likely to produce valid results.

When designing an experiment, ask yourself the questions in Table 1-2. Remember that you should first formulate the question you want to answer or the problem you want to solve. Then review the literature to learn about the topic you are investigating.

Table 1-2. Experimental Design Guide

Question	Explanation
What is your hypothesis?	The hypothesis should suggest a possible answer to the question you are investigating.
What is your dependent variable?	What should change and what is it that you will measure in the experiment? Make a data table to record the data as they are collected.
What is your independent variable?	What factors will you manipulate to test your hypothesis? How will you record their effect on the dependent variable? Will there be several groups with more than one treatment, such as several pH values, colors of light, or temperatures?
How will you control the experiment?	Are you only changing one factor at a time to see its effect? What other possible factors may vary that could also affect the results and make your experiment inconclusive?
What steps will you take to conduct this experiment?	Make a list of procedures and materials needed to conduct the experiment.

1.1 Review

1. The graph represents the results of an investigation of the growth of three identical bacterial cultures incubated at different temperatures.

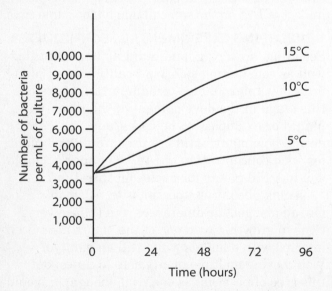

Which inference can be made from the graph? (A) Temperature is unrelated to the reproductive rate of bacteria. (B) Bacteria cannot grow at a temperature of 5°C. (C) Life activities in bacteria slow down at high temperatures. (D) Refrigeration will most likely slow the reproduction of these bacteria.

2. When heavy rains occur while apple orchards are in bloom, the apple crop the following fall is much smaller than normal. This information can best be described as (F) an inference (G) a hypothesis (H) a prediction (J) an observation

3. Scientists breed mice to be as genetically alike as possible to use in experiments.

   • What is the advantage of using mice that are genetically similar?

   • Why would cloned mice be even better?

4. Which of the steps listed below would be first in a scientific investigation? (F) Perform the experiment. (G) Analyze the experimental data. (H) Formulate a hypothesis. (J) Define the problem to be investigated.

5. Diagrams, tables, and graphs are used by scientists mainly to (A) design a research plan for an experiment (B) test a hypothesis (C) organize data (D) predict the independent variable

6. In an investigation to determine the effects of environmental pH on the germination of dandelion seeds, 25 dandelion seeds were added to each of five petri dishes. Each dish contained a solution that differed from the others only in its pH, as shown below. All other environmental conditions were the same. The dishes were covered and observed for 10 days. The data table the student designed is shown below.

The Effect of pH on Seed Germination

Petri Dish	pH of Solution	Number of Seeds Germinated
1	9	
2	8	
3	7	
4	6	
5	5	

Identify the independent variable in this investigation.

7. A student wants to shorten the ripening time for tomatoes. He predicts that the more water the seedlings receive, the faster the tomatoes will ripen. To test this prediction, he grows 20 tomato plants in a garden in full sunlight that has dry soil and 20 in a garden in a shadier location where there is greater moisture content in the soil. He then records the time it takes for fruit to develop and ripen on the plants in each garden location.

Evaluate the design of this experiment and do the following.

- Provide a likely hypothesis for this experiment.

- Identify the independent and dependent variables.

- Describe one error the student made with the design of this experiment.

8. In attempting to demonstrate the effectiveness of a new vaccine, a scientist performed these experimental procedures.

- One hundred genetically similar rats were divided into two groups of 50 rats each (group A and group B).

- Each rat in group A was given an injection of the vaccine in a glucose-and-water solution.

- Each rat in group B was given an injection of the glucose-and-water solution containing no vaccine.

- After several weeks, all rats in both groups were exposed to the disease for which the vaccine was developed.

Evaluate this experiment and do the following.

- Explain why it was important to have more than 2 or 3 rats in each group.

- Explain why the rats in group B were given any injection at all.

- Describe the data that would show the vaccine was *not* effective.

9. A new drug for the treatment of asthma is tested on 100 people. The people are evenly divided into two groups. One group is given the drug, and the other group is given a glucose pill.

The group that is given the glucose pill serves as the (A) control group (B) limiting factor (C) experimental group (D) indicator group

10. As part of a laboratory experiment, a thin slice of peeled raw potato weighing 10 grams is placed in an oven at 80°C. After 5 hours, the potato sample is removed from the oven and weighed again.

The purpose of this experiment might be to
(F) test for the presence of starch in living tissues
(G) isolate cells in various stages of cell division
(H) determine the water content of potato tissue
(J) study the rate of photosynthesis in potatoes

11. What is the function of a control group in an experiment?

12. A scientist performed an experiment using the steps below. Write the directions that belong in box X.

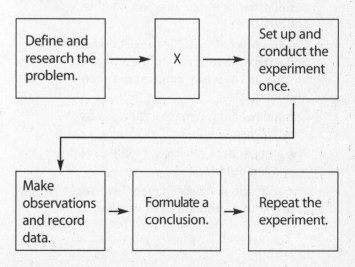

1.2 Organizing and Using Data

In science, **data** generally refers to the results of trials, or tests, completed during experiments. Scientific inquiry involves the ability to use various methods of recording, representing, and organizing data.

Data can be organized into diagrams, tables, charts, graphs, equations, and matrices. Scientists must then be able to interpret the organized data and make inferences, predictions, and conclusions based on those data.

Data Tables

A data table is an important initial stage in making sense of the information you collect while doing an experiment. (See Figure 1-5.) When constructing a table to record your data, keep the following checklist in mind.

Figure 1-5. Data collection: Making measurements and carefully recording data are important parts of doing an experiment.

Data Table Checklist

√ The table has a title that relates the independent variable to the dependent variable. For example: The Effect of Fertilizer Concentration (the independent variable) on Plant Growth (the dependent variable).

√ Column headings include the dependent and independent variables. They may also include trial or set-up numbers or other information.

√ Column headings need to indicate units of measurement.

√ The independent variable is typically recorded in increasing order.

√ The dependent variable is recorded to correspond with the independent variable.

Graphs

Frequently, the next step is to construct a graph that allows you to see trends or patterns in your data. Almost every day you interpret graphs. Television, newspapers, and other media often use graphs to illustrate ideas. Advertisers use graphs to convince us to use their products. They know that a carefully constructed graph can help us understand a large amount of information. Examining columns of numbers in a data table is time consuming and sometimes difficult. Looking at a graph allows us to form opinions and to make comparisons quickly. (See Figure 1-6.)

Changes in Average Life Expectancy from 1910–1970

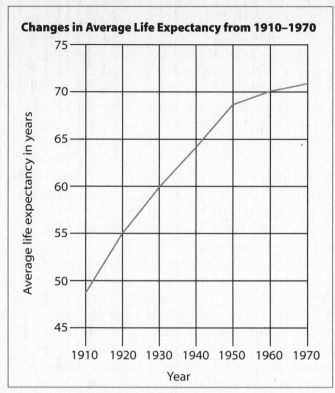

Figure 1-6. **Interpretation of graphs:** Graphs like this one help make trends and patterns clear.

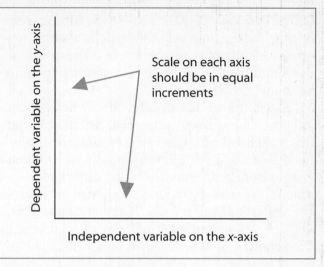

Figure 1-7. **Rules for a line graph**

There are four basic types of graphs

- line graph
- bar graph
- histogram
- circle graph

A scientist must decide which type of graph will be the most effective for presenting data so that the conclusion will be clear. Different rules are used in drawing each type of graph. However, there are a few rules common to all line and bar graphs.

Rule 1: The dependent variable is plotted on the vertical, or y-axis. Remember that the dependent variable is what you find out as a result of doing the experiment. It is what you measure during the experiment.

Rule 2: The independent variable is plotted on the horizontal, or x-axis. This is the factor you varied to find its effect on the dependent variable.

Rule 3: The spacing between the numbers on both axes must be in equal increments. Figure 1-7 shows how to apply the three rules to a line graph. Use the Graph Construction Checklist when constructing a graph.

Graph Construction Checklist

√ Title your graph so that the reader knows what it is illustrating. You can often use the same title you used on the data table.

√ Place the dependent variable on the vertical axis.

√ Label the vertical axis, including units of measure.

√ Make sure that the scale on the vertical axis is appropriate and is spaced at even intervals.

√ Place the independent variable on the horizontal axis.

√ Label the horizontal axis, including units of measure.

√ Make sure the scale on the horizontal axis is appropriate and spaced at even intervals.

√ Plot points accurately.

√ Connect the data points and do not go beyond any points. (You know only what you measured; anything beyond that is speculation.)

√ Include a legend that indicates the meaning of each line if there is more than one. It serves as a key to the lines or bars on the graph.

Analyzing Results

A careful examination of the experimental results involves the ability to look at relationships between the hypothesis and the actual result.

DRAWING VALID CONCLUSIONS After carefully considering how well the hypothesis and the actual results of the experiment correspond, a decision about the outcome—a **conclusion**—can be made.

A scientist needs to determine whether the hypothesis has been supported. Scientists often use statistical analysis to determine the likelihood that their results were produced by chance. Errors in measurement, genetic differences among the test organisms, or chance may affect the validity of the results. If the data analysis does reveal a significant pattern or relationship, the scientist next tries to explain what the results mean.

A **model** can often be used to explain the results of an experiment. A model is a way of explaining or demonstrating what is happening and of predicting what will occur in new situations. For example, a model explains how DNA carries the genetic code and how traits are passed from one generation to the next. (See Figure 1-8.) As more is learned about the structure and function of DNA, parts of the model are confirmed or changed.

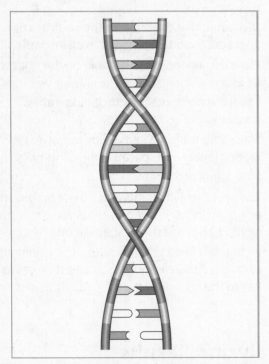

Figure 1-8. **A model of DNA:** It shows a structure that scientists can use to account for how DNA functions.

REPORTING RESULTS One assumption of science is that other individuals could arrive at the same explanation if they had access to similar evidence. Experiments that cannot be repeated exactly with the same results have little worth. Research must be shared in such a clear manner that other scientists can repeat the investigation and get the same results. When reporting the results of an experiment, a scientist must pay close attention to detail. The experimental results may be used by hundreds of other scientists to repeat the experiment. Thus, each step of the experiment must be described accurately.

If you wanted to repeat an experiment done by a friend, would you be able to do it if your friend told you to heat a mixture "for a little while"? Or if you had to add some soap powder to the mixture, would it be acceptable for your friend to tell you to "add two pinches"? If you expect to obtain the same results, your friend must provide precise instructions, such as to heat the mixture at a temperature of 75°C for 5 minutes, and then add 2 grams of a specific kind of soap powder.

Scientific inquiry also requires the ability to develop a written report for public scrutiny. Scientists report their findings in scientific journals or during presentations at professional meetings. The report describes the hypothesis (including a literature review of previous studies), the experiment performed, its data and the scientist's conclusion, and suggestions for further study.

Based on the results of the experiment and public discussion and review, inquiry may also require the scientist to revise the explanation and think about additional research.

A **peer review**, in which several scientists examine the details of an experiment, is an important part of the scientific process. Scientists are expected to question explanations proposed by other scientists. Peers analyze the experimental procedures, examine the evidence, identify faulty reasoning, point out statements that go beyond the evidence, and suggest alternative explanations for the same observations. Peer review is one of the systems of checks and balances in science. (See Figure 1-9.)

Figure 1-9. Peer review: Scientists examine one another's work to ensure that the results are correct.

All scientific explanations are subject to change as more is learned. Scientists know and accept this as a part of the way they work. With new information, they must be willing to change their thinking and, therefore, their explanations.

Evidence is a collection of facts offered to support the idea that something is true. Scientists accept evidence when it is supported by many facts. Until they have a large collection of supportive evidence, scientists must remain neutral.

Sometimes claims are made that are not supported by actual evidence. Scientific claims should be questioned if

- the data are based on samples that are very small, biased, or inadequately controlled
- the conclusions are based on the faulty, incomplete, or misleading use of numbers

For example, experiments must be designed so that genetic differences, chance, and inaccuracies in measurement cannot be responsible for the results. Wherever appropriate, a statistical analysis of the results should be done. This could be something as simple as finding the average, calculating the percentage of difference, or determining the frequency. Claims should also be questioned if

- fact and opinion are intermingled
- adequate evidence is not cited
- conclusions do not follow logically from the evidence given

Development of Theories

In science, a **theory** is a well-tested explanation that unifies a wide range of observations. A theory enables researchers to make accurate predictions when new situations arise. Well-accepted scientific theories are supported by many different scientific investigations, often involving contributions of individuals from different disciplines. In developing a theory, scientists carry out many investigations, which may vary in complexity, scale, and focus.

Research within different scientific disciplines can bring to light multiple views of the natural world. For example, the Gene-Chromosome Theory began as a hypothesis. Over many years, the idea that genes are arranged along chromosomes at specific locations was supported by many scientists working on different experiments focused on the inheritance of traits. Evidence from these investigations mounted and the hypothesis became so well supported that eventually scientists considered it a theory.

The scientific meaning of the word *theory* is very different from the way it is used in everyday conversation. People often use the word *theory* in a very different sense—to imply that the idea is not supported by evidence. In everyday use, a theory is just an idea and nothing more.

Even with all the strong support scientific theories have, they are still not considered to be an absolute truth. As scientists develop new research tools, perform new experiments, and learn more about a given situation, the strengths and weaknesses of the theory are analyzed and reviewed. This process may lead to the theory being revised or even replaced by a more useful explanation. New evidence determines which ideas are supported and used by scientists and which are replaced.

1.2 Review

1. A student conducted an original, well-designed experiment, carefully following proper scientific procedure. For the conclusions to become generally accepted, the experiment must (A) contain several experimental variables (B) support the original hypothesis (C) be repeated to verify the reliability of the data (D) be conducted by a scientist

2. A student tossed a coin five times and observed results of four tails and one head. He concluded that when a coin is tossed, there is an 80% chance of getting a tail and a 20% chance of getting a head.

The conclusion would be more valid if (F) a greater number of tosses had been used (G) the weight of the coin had been taken into consideration (H) only two tosses of the coin had been used (J) the surface the coin landed on had been taken into consideration

3. A scientist obtained 24 frogs and separated them into two equal groups. Group A was placed in an environment in which the temperature was a constant 35°F. Group B was placed in a similar environment, except the temperature was a constant 65°F.

Equal amounts of food were given to each group at the start of the experiment and again every 24 hours. Immediately before each daily feeding, the excess food from the prior feeding was removed and measured. This allowed the scientist to determine the daily amount of food each group of frogs consumed. Each day, the heart rate and breathing rate of the frogs were checked. At the end of the experiment, the following bar graphs were prepared:

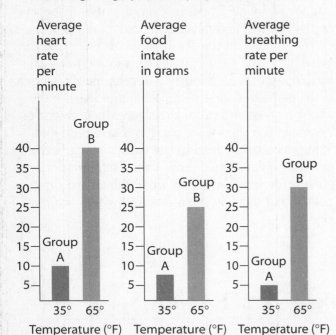

Average heart rate per minute   Average food intake in grams   Average breathing rate per minute

Temperature (°F)   Temperature (°F)   Temperature (°F)

Review the procedure and data from the experiment. Provide an analysis of the experiment. Be sure to include the following

- the variables the scientist controlled

- an appropriate hypothesis for this experiment

- the independent variable in this experiment

- a conclusion that could be drawn from the data in the tables

Base your answers to questions 4 through 6 on the information below and on your knowledge of biology.

A student was working on an investigation to measure the relative activity of an enzyme at various pH values. He collected the following data: pH 2, enzyme activity 10; pH 8, enzyme activity 50; pH 12, enzyme activity 10; pH 4, enzyme activity 20; pH 6, enzyme activity 40; pH 10, enzyme activity 40.

4. Organize the data above by filling in the data table provided. Follow these directions when completing your data table.

- Provide an appropriate title for the data table. Fill in the first box in each column with an appropriate heading.

- Arrange the data so that pH values are in increasing order.

Title:	

5. Construct a graph using the information in the data table, the following directions, and the grid provided.

- Provide an appropriate title for the graph.

- Make and label an appropriate scale on each axis.

- Plot and connect the points.

- Surround each data point with a small circle.

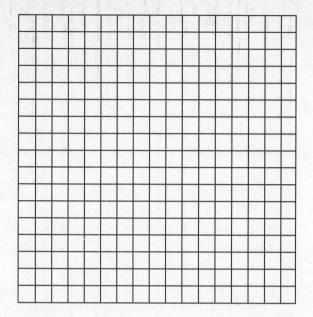

6. According to the data, this enzyme would probably work best at what pH values? (F) 7 and 8 (G) 2 and 12 (H) 6 and 7 (J) 4 and 10

7. To investigate the effect of a substance on plant growth, two bean plants of the same species were grown under identical conditions with Substance X added to the soil of one of the plants.

   At the end of 2 weeks, the plant grown with Substance X was 12.5 centimeters tall, and the plant grown without Substance X was 12.2 centimeters tall. The researcher concluded that the presence of Substance X causes plants to grow taller.

   Explain why this conclusion may not be valid.

8. A student prepared the following list of steps for performing a laboratory investigation. She omitted one important step for completing the investigation. Identify the procedure that is missing in the chart.

Steps to Follow in an Experiment

1 Define a problem.
2 Develop a hypothesis.
3 Select suitable lab materials and perform a controlled experiment to test the hypothesis.
4 Collect, organize, and graph the experimental data.
5 ??????

9. In experiments designed to test new drugs on human patients, doctors usually give one group the new drug while the other group is given a sugar pill, or placebo, instead.

   Explain why it is important to give the placebo to the second group rather than giving those patients no pill at all.

10. An experiment was designed to see what effects ibuprofen would have on laboratory mice. Large numbers of male mice and an equal number of female mice were used in this investigation. The male mice were placed in an area with food and water. The female mice were placed in a separate area of the same size. The female mice were given additional food and water. The males were each given 100 milligrams of ibuprofen each day, mixed with their food, and the females were each given 50 milligrams of ibuprofen each day, mixed with their food.

    Identify two errors in the design of this experiment.

11. A scientist conducted an experiment in which he fed rats large amounts of the amino acid cysteine. He observed that this amino acid protected rat chromosomes from damage by toxic chemicals. The scientist then claimed that cysteine, added to the diet of all animals, would protect the animals' chromosomes from damage.

    State whether or not this is a valid claim. Support your answer.

1. A scientist determines the number of Calories in one ounce each of protein, carbohydrate, and fat. The results are shown in the table below.

Calorie Content of Substances

Compound Tested	Number of Calories Produced
Protein	147
Fat	271
Carbohydrate	152

Which statement represents a valid conclusion based on the data?

(A) An ounce of fat contains about twice as many Calories as an ounce of protein.

(B) Protein is a better energy food than carbohy-drate.

(C) Carbohydrates, fats, and proteins all yield approx-mately the same number of Calories per unit of weight.

(D) Proteins and carbohydrates provide the most Calories per ounce.

2. Which laboratory procedure would be best for demonstrating the effect of light intensity on the production of chlorophyll in pea plants?

(F) using 10 plants of different species, each grown in the same intensity of light

(G) using 10 plants of different species, each grown in a different intensity of light

(H) using 10 plants of the same species, each grown in the same intensity of light

(J) using 10 plants of the same species, each grown in a different intensity of light

3. In an early trial of the Salk vaccine for polio, 1,830,000 school children participated. This original trial was an attempt to determine whether the Salk vaccine was effective in preventing polio. Of the 1,830,000 children involved, only 440,000 received the vaccine. The remainder were not given the vaccine because they

(A) had a natural immunity

(B) already had polio

(C) served as controls

(D) were allergic to the vaccine

4. A scientific study showed that the depth at which some microscopic plants were found in a lake varied from day to day. On clear days, the plants were found as far as 6 meters below the surface of the water, but on cloudy days they were only 1 meter below the surface. Which hypothesis would these observations support?

(F) Light intensity affects the growth of microscopic plants.

(G) Wind currents affect the growth of microscopic plants.

(H) Nitrogen concentration affects the growth of microscopic plants.

(J) Precipitation affects the growth of microscopic plants.

Use the statements from the Steps of Development list below to match with each statement in Numbers 5 through 8. The steps are in no particular order and may be used more than once or not at all.

Steps of Development

A. Test the hypothesis with an experiment.

B. State the results.

C. Draw a conclusion from the results.

D. Form a hypothesis.

5. Beans will grow faster if you fertilize them at regular intervals than if you only fertilize the ground once before you plant them.

6. If I add more catalyst to the reaction, the reaction will speed up.

7. A scientist took saliva from his dog's mouth and mixed it with a solution of starch and warm water. He took the same amount of saliva from his own mouth and mixed it with the contents of a second tube of starch and warm water. One hour later, the contents of both tubes were checked for the pres-ence of sugar.

8. In an experiment, caterpillars consumed 8 grams of lettuce leaves and 0.4 grams of tomato leaves.

9. A scientist is planning to carry out an experiment on the effect of heat on the function of a certain enzyme. Which would NOT be an appropriate first step?

(A) doing research in the library

(B) having discussions with other scientists

(C) completing a data table of expected results

(D) using what is already known about the enzyme

10. The analysis of data gathered during a particular experiment is necessary in order to

(F) formulate a hypothesis for that experiment

(G) develop a research plan for that experiment

(H) design a control for that experiment

(J) draw valid conclusions from that experiment

11. Which statement best describes the term *theory* as used in the Gene-Chromosome Theory?

(A) A theory is never revised as new scientific evidence is presented.

(B) A theory is an assumption made by scientists and implies a lack of certainty.

(C) A theory refers to a scientific explanation that is strongly supported by a variety of experimental data.

(D) A theory is a hypothesis that has been supported by one experiment performed by two or more scientists.

12. A student hypothesized that lettuce seeds would not germinate (sprout) unless they were exposed to darkness. The student planted 10 lettuce seeds under a layer of soil and scattered 10 lettuce seeds on top of the soil. The data collected are shown in the table below.

The Effect of Light on Seed Germination

Seed Treatment	Number of Seeds Germinated
Planted under soil	9
Scattered on top of soil	8

One way to prove the validity of these results would be to

(F) conclude that darkness is necessary for lettuce seed germination

(G) conclude that light is necessary for lettuce seed germination

(H) revise they hypothesis

(J) repeat the experiment

13. A student observes that an organism is green. A valid conclusion that can be drawn from this observation is that

(A) the organism must be a plant

(B) the organism cannot be single celled

(C) the organism must be an animal

(D) not enough information is given to determine whether the organism is a plant or an animal

14. Why do scientists consider any hypothesis valuable?

(F) A hypothesis requires no further investigation.

(G) A hypothesis may lead to further investigation even if it is not supported by the experiment.

(H) A hypothesis requires no further investigation if it is supported by the experiment.

(J) A hypothesis can be used to explain a conclusion even if it is not supported by the experiment.

15. The current knowledge concerning cells is the result of investigations and observations of many scientists. The work of these scientists forms a well-accepted body of knowledge about cells. This body of knowledge is an example of a

(A) hypothesis

(B) controlled experiment

(C) theory

(D) research plan

16. An experimental design included references from prior experiments, materials, equipment, and step-by-step procedures. What else should be included before the experiment can be started?

(F) a set of data

(G) a conclusion based on data

(H) safety precautions to be used

(J) an inference based on results

17. A biology student wanted to investigate the effects of fish oil fertilizer on the growth of plants. A month ago, she planted 10 bean plants. Five of the plants were fertilized once a week with 1 mL of the fertilizer mixed in 10 mL of water. The other five plants were given 11 mL of water each week in place of the fertilizer. All other conditions were kept exactly the same for both groups of plants. The information the biology student collected during the experiment appears in Tables 1 and 2.

Table 1: Height Increase in Centimeters – Fertilizer Added

Plant	Height (cm) on Day 1	Growth (cm)				Total Growth (cm)	Average Growth per Week (cm)
		Week 1	Week 2	Week 3	Week 4		
A	15.0	2.6	1.4	3.0	2.5	9.5	2.4
B	10.0	1.1	1.5	2.0	2.5	7.1	1.8
C	17.0	3.0	2.0	1.9	1.9	8.8	2.2
D	12.0	2.1	2.2	1.8	2.3	8.4	2.1
E	16.0	2.3	2.0	1.7	2.4	8.4	2.1
Totals	–	11.1	9.1	10.4	11.6	42.2	10.6

Table 2: Height Increase in Centimeters – No Fertilizer Added

Plant	Height (cm) on Day 1	Growth (cm)				Total Growth (cm)	Average Growth per Week (cm)
		Week 1	Week 2	Week 3	Week 4		
F	16.0	2.0	1.0	2.0	1.2	6.2	1.6
G	11.0	1.0	1.1	1.0	1.5	4.6	1.2
H	18.0	2.0	1.2	1.1	1.3	5.6	1.4
I	11.0	1.1	1.4	1.2	1.3	5.0	1.2
J	17.0	1.3	1.0	1.4	1.4	5.1	1.3
Totals	–	7.4	5.7	6.7	6.7	26.5	6.7

The student wrote the following hypothesis before designing the experiment: "Adding fish oil fertilizer to the soil will affect the growth of bean plants."

Analyze the hypothesis, procedure, and data from her experiment. In your response, be sure to answer the following:

- Do the results of her experiment support her hypothesis? Use data from the two tables to support your answer.

- Why should the student compare average plant height gain instead of comparing individual plants?

- Why was the extra water used in place of the fertilizer in the *No Fertilizer Group* of the experiment?

18. A student places five geranium plants of equal size in five environmental chambers. Growing conditions were the same for each plant except that each chamber was illuminated by a different color of light of the same intensity. She measures the plants at the end of 20 days.

Describe how she could improve her experiment. In your response, be sure to include

- a possible hypothesis for this experiment
- a control that could be used in this experiment
- modifications you would make in the design of this experiment to make the results more reliable

19. A student performed an experiment involving two strains of microorganisms, strain A and strain B, cultured at various temperatures for 24 hours. The results of this experiment are shown in the following data table.

Microorganism Growth and Temperature

Temperature	Microorganism Growth (Number of Colonies)	
(°C)	Strain A	Strain B
25	10	11
28	10	7
31	11	3
34	12	0

Based on the description and results of this experiment, do the following.

- State an assumption that was made in the design of the experiment.
- State an inference that can be made about the effect of heat on these two strains of bacteria. Use data from the table to support your answer.
- Describe what additional steps are needed in order to form a valid conclusion about the effect of heat on these two strains of bacteria.

20. On a television talk show, a guest claims that people who exercise vigorously for 15 minutes or more every day are able to solve math problems more rapidly than people who do no vigorous exercise as part of their daily routine.

Describe a controlled experiment that could be conducted to test this claim.

- State the purpose of the experiment.
- State why the sample used should be large.
- Describe how the experimental group will be treated and how the control group will be treated.
- State the specific data to be collected during the experiment.
- State one way to determine whether the results support the claim.

21. Plants respond to their environment in many different ways. Design a controlled experiment to test the effect of one environmental factor (such as light, acidity of precipitation, etc.) on some aspect of plant growth.

- State the hypothesis.
- List the steps of the procedure.
- Identify the control set-up for the experiment.
- Include a data table with appropriate column headings.
- Identify the independent variable in the experiment.

22. A magazine advertisement claims that a certain brand of cough drop reduces coughing for 8 hours. Describe an investigation that could be used to determine whether this claim is valid. In your answer include a description of

- the treatment to be given to the experimental group
- the treatment to be given to the control group
- the data to be collected
- when the data should be collected
- one observation that would lead to the conclusion that the claim is valid

23. A biology student observes the behavior of earthworms in soil. The student suggested that air in the soil promotes root development of plants. The student then set up the following experiment, using an air pump, jars, and two bean plants with their stems cut off at ground level.

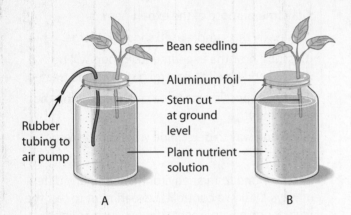

Analyze the set-up of the experiment to help the student improve his results. In your response, be sure to include

- the independent variable
- the hypothesis being tested in this experiment
- what the student could do in this experiment to improve the validity of the his conclusions

24. A drug company tested a new medication before putting it on the commercial market. Pills without medication were given to 500 test subjects in group A, and pills with medication were given to 500 subjects in group B. In this experiment, the individuals in group A served as the

(F) host group

(G) dependent variable

(H) control

(J) hypothesis

25. To find the percentage of organic matter in soil from several different locations, a student collected the samples, weighed them immediately, roasted them for several minutes in the flame of a Bunsen burner to burn off organic matter, and weighed them again.

The student concluded that the difference between the first and second weights represented the weight of the organic matter in the soil.

Which is the most serious mistake that the student made in this experiment?

(A) taking large samples

(B) failing to dry the samples before first weighing them

(C) weighing the samples before roasting them

(D) assuming that roasting could remove the organic matter

26. Researchers performing a well-designed experiment should base their conclusions on

(F) the hypothesis of the experiment

(G) data from repeated trials of the experiment

(H) a small sample size to insure a reliable outcome of the experiment

(J) results predicted before performing the experiment

27. Tomato plants in a garden are not growing well. The gardener hypothesizes that the soil is too acidic. To test this hypothesis accurately, the gardener could

(A) plant seeds of a different kind of plant

(B) move the tomato plants to an area with less sunlight

(C) change the pH of the soil

(D) reduce the amount of water available to the plant

Biologically Important Molecules and Cellular Organization of Living Things

Earth's living environment is made up of millions and millions of diverse organisms, a wide range that includes towering redwood trees, sleek antelope, tiny bacteria, mushrooms that grow in huge circles, microscopic organisms that turn the tides red, and the students in your class. These living organisms are both similar to and different from each other. They also differ from the nonliving parts of the environment. Although that difference may seem obvious, scientists have not been able to agree upon a simple definition of life.

2.1 The Characteristics of Life

VOCABULARY			
cell	growth	organ	reproduction
cell respiration	homeostasis	organelle	synthesis
classification	kingdom	organ system	taxonomy
eukaryotes	metabolism	prokaryotes	tissue

Most scientists agree that living things share certain characteristics that distinguish them from nonliving things.

- Living things are organized structures. All are made of one or more **cells**, which are the basic units of structure and function. They maintain their cellular organization throughout life.

- Living things use energy to maintain life and to grow and develop. These activities require that the cells carry out various chemical reactions. The combination of all the chemical reactions that occur in an organism is called **metabolism**.

- Living things maintain a fairly stable internal environment even when their external environment changes dramatically. The maintenance of this internal stability is known as **homeostasis**. To maintain homeostasis, organisms must respond and adapt to both their internal and external environments.

- Living things pass hereditary information to new organisms of the same species in the process of **reproduction**.

Only living things share the characteristics of life. Nonliving things have no functioning cells and no metabolic activity; they do not maintain homeostasis, nor do they reproduce.

Diversity Among Living Things

CLASSIFICATION Although living things share the characteristics of life, there are differences among the many kinds of organisms. Throughout history, people have tried to bring order to all the varieties of life on Earth by grouping living organisms in logical ways. Organisms are grouped, or classified, on the basis of certain common characteristics and relationships they share. The science of classifying and naming organisms is called **taxonomy**.

The **classification** of organisms suggests relationships among them that may result from present forms of life developing from common ancestors. This classification is based mainly on similarities of structure, but it is supplemented by other evidence of relationships, such as the fossil record, genetic makeup, life cycles, embryo development, and chemical similarities.

CLASSIFICATION SYSTEMS Several classification systems have been popular at different times. Because of a new and more extensive understanding of evolutionary relationships, current classification systems are undergoing change. Currently, biologists classify organisms into five or six **kingdoms**—large groups of related organisms.

PROKARYOTES AND EUKARYOTES Regardless of the formal system used, there are some basic divisions that should be understood. All living organisms are grouped as either prokaryotes or eukaryotes. **Prokaryotes** have cells with an outer membrane but without distinct internal organelles that are enclosed by a membrane—such as a nucleus. Bacteria are prokaryotes. The nuclear material of bacteria "floats" in the cell cytoplasm in the form of a chromosome rather than being enclosed in a nuclear membrane. **Eukaryotes** have cells containing many different membrane-bound organelles. All living organisms that are not bacteria are eukaryotic—from amoebas to humans.

DID YOU KNOW?

Many scientists do not classify viruses with living things. The reason is that viruses are not cellular. Instead, they consist of a protein coat enclosing genetic material (DNA or RNA). As a result, viruses do not independently carry out all life processes.

Similarities Among Living Things

Although living things have many differences, they are also alike in important ways. The first similarity is that they share the characteristics of life. They are made of cells, they reproduce, they maintain homeostasis, and they carry out metabolic activities. They also share similar life processes, organization, and chemical composition.

LIFE PROCESSES Living things are similar in that they rely on a variety of specific processes to maintain life. However, organisms differ in the way they carry out these processes. Some of these life processes include:

- obtaining nutrients from the environment and breaking them down for transport

- transporting materials throughout the organism

- breaking certain nutrients into smaller units to release the chemical energy stored in them through the process of **cell respiration**

- combining some simple substances into complex substances through the process of **synthesis**

- increasing the size or number of cells through the process of **growth**

- removing waste products from the organism through the process of excretion

- responding to internal and external stimuli

ORGANIZATION The shared organization of specialized structures that work together to accomplish a specific task is another similarity of living things. In other words, organisms share a similar "building plan." The basic structural and functional unit of living things is the cell. Simple organisms may consist of just one cell; complex organisms may consist of billions of cells. Most cells contain specialized structures called **organelles**, which have specific functions.

This organization of cells into increasingly specialized structures is typical of much of the complex life on Earth. Complex organisms have several advantages over simpler organisms. For example, many complex organisms can explore their environment or gain energy in ways that simpler organisms cannot.

In multicellular organisms, specialized cells may be organized into **tissues** to expand how they function. For example, a single muscle cell would not be strong enough to move any organism—not even one as light as a hummingbird. Grouped with other muscle cells, however, muscle tissue can move an elephant.

Different kinds of tissues may be combined to form an **organ** that performs one or more life processes; several organs may work together as an **organ system**. For example, the heart is an organ with the function of pumping blood. The organ may be a simple "arch" like the heart of the earthworm, or it may be a complex four-chambered structure like the heart of a monkey. In either case, the organ's function is to pump blood. Each heart is part of an organ system that transports materials throughout the body. This organization is illustrated in Table 2-1.

Table 2-1. The Structural Organization of Organisms

Cells	of a particular kind ⟹ work together in a	**Tissue**
Tissues	of various types ⟹ work together in an	**Organ**
Organs	of various types ⟹ work together in an	**Organ System**
Organ Systems	of various types ⟹ work together in an	**Organism**

2.1 Review

1. Some large, insoluble food molecules are reduced to small, soluble food molecules by the process of (A) digestion (B) excretion (C) response (D) growth

2. One characteristic of all living organisms is that they (F) make food (G) live on land (H) maintain homeostasis (J) move from place to place

3. A biologist would most likely study all of the chemical activities of an organism to obtain information about the organism's (A) number of mutations (B) reproductive cycle (C) development (D) metabolism

4. The science of naming and classifying organisms is called (F) taxonomy (G) ecology (H) synthesis (J) homeostasis

5. Which of the following statements about cells is *not* true? (A) One or more cells make up all living organisms. (B) Cells carry on the basic life functions of living organisms. (C) Cells contain structures that carry on life functions. (D) Most cells cannot reproduce.

6. Cells are to tissues as organs are to (F) organ systems (G) cells (H) genes (J) organelles

7. The ability of an organism to maintain internal stability is known as (A) metabolism (B) homeostasis (C) circulation (D) excretion

8. Which sequence is listed in order from simplest to most complex?
(F) tissue → cell → organ system → organ
(G) cell → tissue → organ → organ system
(H) cell → tissue → organism → organ
(J) organism → tissue → organ → organ system

9. The life activity known as synthesis is chiefly characterized by the (A) distribution of essential compounds throughout the organism (B) production of complex molecules from simple molecules (C) elimination of waste products from the organism (D) regulation of external stimuli

10. A modern classification system should reflect (F) the types of habitats in which organisms live (G) evolutionary relationships (H) color and size relationships (J) the eating habits of organisms

11. Suppose someone brings you a specimen that they claim is a living organism. Explain how you could use a microscope to help determine whether the specimen is a living or nonliving thing.

12. State two ways in which a single-celled organism, such as an amoeba, and a human body cell are alike.

13. State two ways in which living and nonliving things differ.

14. The chart contains a number of characteristics for three different organisms. The characteristics can be used in classifying these organisms.

Characteristic	Organism A	Organism B	Organism C
Number of cells	unicellular	multicellular	unicellular
Type of nutrition	autotrophic	autotrophic	heterotrophic
Nuclear membrane	absent	present	absent
DNA	present	present	present

Which two organisms would be expected to have the most similar genetic material? Support your answer using information from the chart.

2.2 Chemical Compounds in Living Organisms

VOCABULARY

amino acids	dietary fiber	minerals	protein
atoms	digestion	molecule	RNA
carbohydrates	DNA	monosaccharides	solute
cellulose	inorganic	nucleic acid	solvent
compounds	ionic bonding	nucleotide	vitamin
covalent bonding	ions	organic	
density	lipid	polarity	

The chemicals and structures in all living things are made from four main elements—carbon (chemical symbol C), hydrogen (H), oxygen (O), and nitrogen (N)—as well as many other elements, such as phosphorus, sulfur, calcium, iron, iodine, and potassium, in smaller amounts. Each element is made up of particles called **atoms**. The atoms of a given element are alike. They are different from the atoms of other elements.

Molecules are chemical combinations of two or more atoms. **Compounds** are molecules that are made up of two or more elements. Atoms combine to form molecules either by transferring electrons from one atom to another or by sharing electrons. When electrons are transferred, the atoms acquire a charge and become **ions**. The attraction between oppositely charged ions is called **ionic bonding**. When electrons are shared, the process is called **covalent bonding** and molecules are formed.

The composition of a compound can be shown by a formula. For example, the formula for a simple sugar (a monosaccharide) can be written as $C_6H_{12}O_6$. A structural formula (see Figure 2-1) shows the numbers and types of atoms in a sugar molecule in more detail, including how the atoms in the molecule are joined by covalent bonds.

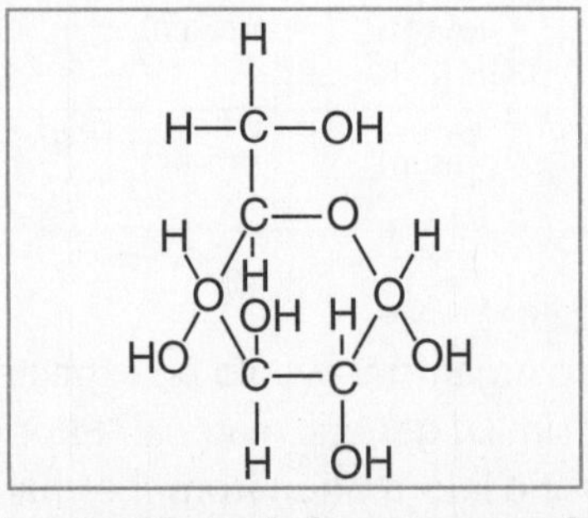

Figure 2-1. **Structural formula for a monosaccharide (a simple sugar)**

Inorganic Molecules

Inorganic molecules do *not* contain *both* carbon and hydrogen, but can contain any other combination of elements. **Inorganic** molecules include salts and minerals, most acids and bases, oxygen (O_2), carbon dioxide (CO_2), and water (H_2O). They do not provide energy but are important for many different life functions.

WATER Of all of the materials in living cells, water is the most abundant. In some cells, the cytoplasm is more than 90% water. Water is essential for the life functions of cells primarily because it is the substance in which many other chemicals dissolve. Most chemical reactions occur only in water solutions. This is in part because of the polar nature of the water molecule: one part of the water molecule has a slight positive charge while another part has a slight negative charge.

In a solution, one substance dissolves into another. Salt water, for example, is a solution of salt and water. The salt, which dissolves in the water, is a **solute**. The water, the substance into which the salt dissolves, is the **solvent**. The **polarity** of water makes it an excellent solvent for many substances. Grape juice is a solution of sugar and minerals (the solutes) dissolved in water (the solvent).

Another important property of water is that it is most dense when in the liquid state at a temperature of 4.0°C. Matter on Earth usually exists in three forms or phases: solid, liquid, and gas. The density changes with changes in phase. Most substances increase in **density** (mass per unit of volume) as they change from gas to liquid to solid. They have the highest density as a solid because the atoms are closest together in this phase. Because of its polar nature, this is not true of water—solid water (ice) expands as it freezes and floats on liquid water. In most cases, the solid form sinks in the liquid.

The fact that water expands upon freezing may cause cells to burst if they are frozen. Organisms in cold environments have many adaptations to prevent this, including reducing the water content of cells or making a kind of antifreeze.

Water also tends to moderate Earth's climate. It takes 1 calorie to raise the temperature of 1 gram of water 1 degree Celsius. It takes about 0.2 calories to raise the temperature of 1 gram of one kind of common rock 1 degree Celsius. Water has the greatest resistance to temperature change of all naturally occurring substances. This is why large bodies of water have a major moderating effect on climate and weather.

MINERALS **Minerals** are inorganic substances essential for cellular processes. They are used to make many different body structures and are important for maintaining homeostasis. They help maintain osmotic balance and are essential in enzyme function. Common minerals required by plants and animals include those in Table 2-2.

Table 2-2. Major Minerals Required by Living Things	
Mineral	**Importance**
Phosphorus	Part of ATP; nucleic acids (DNA and RNA); phospholipids (in the cell membrane) and some enzymes
Calcium	Part of bones; needed for enzyme and cell membrane function
Sulfur	Part of some proteins
Iodine	Involved in synthesis of thyroid hormone
Iron	Needed to make hemoglobin molecules in red blood cells, which carry oxygen in the blood
Potassium	Needed for active transport; helps maintain osmotic balance; important in the functioning of guard cells and stomates in plants

Organic Molecules

Organic molecules contain *both* carbon and hydrogen and include all of the major molecules of life. They are often very complex in structure. The major kinds of organic molecules found in living things are carbohydrates, lipids, proteins, and nucleic acids. Vitamins are another important group of organic molecules.

CARBOHYDRATES **Carbohydrates** are composed of carbon, hydrogen, and oxygen. Most carbohydrates are made up of units of simple sugars called **monosaccharides**. Many simple sugars bonded together into long chains form complex polysaccharide molecules such as cellulose. Figure 2-2 shows a diagram of part of a cellulose molecule.

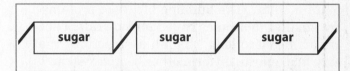

Figure 2-2. **Segment of cellulose molecule showing 3 monosaccharide units**

In living things, sugars are sources of energy. Surplus sugars that are not immediately needed are stored in the form of starches. Sugars are soluble in water and easily transported from one location to another in plants (in vascular tissue) and animals (in the circulatory system). Starches are not as soluble in water and are not transported. They must first be broken down into simpler molecules. Carbohydrates are also used to make cell structures, such as the **cellulose** in cell walls. Cellulose serves as **dietary fiber**, helping the human digestive system transport food materials as they are broken down.

LIPIDS Like carbohydrates, **lipids** are made of carbon, hydrogen, and oxygen. Unlike many carbohydrates, they are not soluble in water. Lipids include fats, which are solid at room temperature, and oils, which are liquid. Lipids are used in living things as sources of stored energy. Some, such as phospholipids, also serve as components of cell organelles. Phospholipids are phosphate-containing lipid molecules that make up part of the structure of cell membranes.

A typical lipid molecule is made by combining three fatty acid molecules and one molecule of glycerol. (See Figure 2-3.)

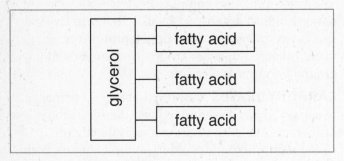

Figure 2-3. Lipid molecule

PROTEINS **Proteins** contain the elements carbon, hydrogen, oxygen, and nitrogen. Many also contain sulfur. The building blocks of proteins are smaller molecules called **amino acids**. These are arranged in long, chain-like structures that may fold, spiral, or form other complex structures. (See Figure 2-4.) The shape of protein molecules is often related to their ability to function. Heat can disrupt these shapes and therefore affect how the protein functions. Living cells synthesize thousands of proteins. Examples are enzymes, some hormones (such as insulin), and hemoglobin, the protein that carries oxygen in the blood of humans and many other animals. Some proteins form part of cell structures such as cell membranes.

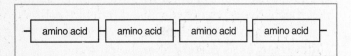

Figure 2-4. Segment of a protein molecule showing part of the amino acid chain

NUCLEIC ACIDS **Nucleic acids** (DNA and RNA) are very large molecules consisting of long chains of building blocks called nucleotides. **Nucleotides** are made from three smaller units: a sugar, a phosphate, and a nitrogen base. There are two main kinds of nucleic acids—DNA and RNA. **DNA** consists of two strands that are twisted to form a double helix (see Figure 2-5), while **RNA** molecules are single stranded and are smaller than DNA molecules.

DNA carries the important hereditary information (instructions for making proteins), while RNA plays a vital role in the actual production of proteins for use in the cell. DNA and RNA are discussed further in Topic 3.

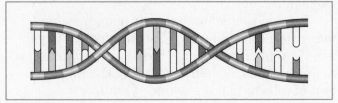

Figure 2-5. Part of a DNA molecule showing the double helix made of nucleotide subunits

VITAMINS **Vitamins** are organic molecules with very important roles in the human body. Three of the most critical vitamins are: Vitamin C, which helps in the healing of wounds; Vitamin D, which is important for the proper growth of bones; and Vitamin K, which is essential for blood to clot properly.

Interactions of Molecules and Cells

Both organic and inorganic substances are present in cells and are involved in the chemical reactions that maintain life. Some organic molecules, including proteins and starches, are too large and complex to enter the cell. Large molecules must first be broken down into simpler molecules in the process known as **digestion**. The digestion of proteins results in amino acids, while the digestion of starches results in simple sugars. Digestion is important because only small molecules, such as amino acids and simple sugars, can diffuse into or out of blood vessels or cells.

When some nutrients from food enter a cell, they become the building blocks of compounds necessary for life. This process, called synthesis, is like manufacturing. Simple molecules, such as amino acids and sugars, are assembled or reassembled into more complex molecules. In this way, proteins, starches, DNA, and other substances necessary for life are made available.

Not all nutrients are used as building blocks. Some nutrients that enter a cell are broken down even further to release the energy stored in their chemical bonds. This is the process of cell respiration. All of these processes will be reviewed in more detail in later topics.

2.2 Review

1. Living things are made mostly of these four main elements: (A) hydrogen, oxygen, nitrogen, and protein (B) water, protein, carbohydrate, and fat (C) carbon, hydrogen, oxygen, and nitrogen (D) glucose, salt, mineral, and base

2. H_2O is an example of (F) a molecule but not a compound (G) a compound but not a molecule (H) both a molecule and a compound (J) neither a molecule nor a compound

3. Matter made up of only one kind of atom is a(n) (A) fat (B) element (C) compound (D) nucleus

4. Which pair of substances can be classified as inorganic? (F) nucleic acids and minerals (G) proteins and water (H) nucleic acids and proteins (J) water and minerals

5. The most abundant compound in cytoplasm is (A) water (B) lipids (C) protein (D) carbohydrates

6. What are the most common building blocks of lipids? (F) glycerol and amino acids (G) glycerol and fatty acids (H) monosaccharides and amino acids (J) monosaccharides and fatty acids

7. Fertilizers using radioactive nitrogen compounds are used in growing experimental plants. In which molecules would these compounds first be detected? (A) sugars (B) starches (C) lipids (D) proteins

8. A sample of soluble, organic molecules was analyzed and found to contain carbon, hydrogen, and oxygen. It is most likely that the molecules were (F) lipids (G) cellulose (H) protein (J) monosaccharides

9. Enzyme molecules are synthesized primarily from (A) amino acids (B) monosaccharides (C) fatty acids (D) phospholipids

10. In plants, simple sugars are least likely to be (F) linked together to form proteins (G) broken down into carbon dioxide and water (H) used as an energy source (J) stored in the form of starch molecules

11. The results of an experiment to determine the chemical composition of the cytoplasm of organism X are shown in the data table below.

Substance	Percent by Mass in the Cytoplasm
Water	77
Proteins	15
Lipids	5
Carbohydrates	2
Minerals	1

What percentage of the cytoplasm is composed of organic material? (A) 15 (B) 20 (C) 22 (D) 92

12. Which molecule is correctly paired with an end product of its digestion? (F) nucleic acid — glycerol (G) carbohydrate — fatty acid (H) lipid — nucleotide (J) protein — amino acid

13. Water is known to be an excellent solvent for many materials. Which characteristic makes water such a good solvent? (A) It is a polar molecule. (B) It is more dense as a liquid than as a solid. (C) It is an inorganic molecule. (D) It makes up more than 90% of the cytoplasm of many cells.

14. Identify two different ways that nutrients that enter cells may be used.

15. When scientists search for life on other planets, they test for the presence of water. Explain why water is necessary for life as we know it on Earth.

16. Seeds from plants may serve as an important food source for humans. The seeds contain carbohydrates such as starch and cellulose. Discuss the importance of carbohydrates in the human diet.

   • Identify the building blocks of carbohydrates.

   • Describe how the building blocks of carbohydrates are used in the body.

   • Explain why starches must be digested before they can be used by cells.

   • Describe the role of cellulose in the human diet.

2.3 Cells: The Basic Structure of Life

Many organisms are made of only one cell, but all organisms—no matter how simple or complex—are made of cells. Each cell contains a jellylike substance surrounded by a thin membrane. Most cells also contain organelles that perform specific tasks for the cell. Despite their seemingly simple structure, cells carry out the processes of life and function together in a coordinated manner.

Inside the Cell

The jellylike substance inside the cell is known as the **cytoplasm**. The cytoplasm contains specialized structures, transports materials through the cell, and is the site of many chemical reactions associated with cell metabolism.

ORGANELLES Organelles are distinct structures suspended in the cytoplasm. Organelles vary enormously in size, shape, and function. They interact to transport materials, extract energy from nutrients, build proteins, dispose of waste, and store information. Figure 2.6 shows several organelles in plant and animal cells.

Nucleus The **nucleus** is a large structure that controls cell metabolism and stores genetic information (as DNA in chromosomes). Many people think of the nucleus as the cell's control center because it directs the cell's activities.

MEMORY JOGGER

Because bacteria are prokaryotes, they have no nucleus—their genetic material simply floats in the cytoplasm as a large chromosome. Some bacteria also have smaller loops of DNA called plasmids.

Vacuoles The storage sacs within the cytoplasm are called **vacuoles**. They may contain either wastes or useful materials such as water or food. Food vacuoles are specialized to digest food; contractile vacuoles in some organisms pump excess water out of the cell.

Vacuoles in plant cells are usually much larger than the vacuoles in animal cells, as shown in Figure 2-6.

Endoplasmic Reticulum The E.R., as the **endoplasmic reticulum** is often called, is a network of membranes inside the cell. It plays a role in transport within a cell, and along with the

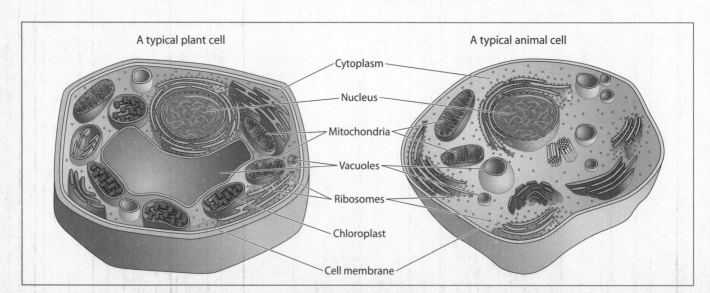

A typical plant cell   A typical animal cell

Cytoplasm
Nucleus
Mitochondria
Vacuoles
Ribosomes
Chloroplast
Cell membrane

Figure 2-6. Some cell organelles can be seen in these plant and animal cells.

Golgi apparatus, functions in the packaging of proteins for secretion from the cell.

Ribosomes The cell contains many tiny **ribosomes**, which are important to the process of making protein. Some ribosomes are attached to the endoplasmic reticulum. Others float in the cytoplasm. Ribosomes are not enclosed in a membrane and they are found in both prokaryotic and eukaryotic cells.

Mitochondria **Mitochondria** are bean-shaped structures that contain special proteins, known as enzymes, which are used to extract energy from nutrients during aerobic respiration. Mitochondria are sometimes called the cell's powerhouses because they release most of the cell's energy and produce ATP.

Chloroplasts The green structures found in plants and some one-celled organisms are **chloroplasts**. They contain the green pigment chlorophyll and capture light energy, which is then used to produce food for the plant. Animal cells do not contain chloroplasts.

Cell Walls Unlike animals, plants and most bacteria and fungi have a cell wall outside the cell membrane. The walls of plant cells are made of cellulose. Cell walls provide some protection for plant cells, and because they can be quite rigid they also provide support. The walls of plant cells are attached to the walls of nearby cells, providing structural support for the plant. Since animal cells lack cell walls, animals often rely on bones or other structures for support.

2.3 Review

1. The genetic material of an animal cell is found in the (A) nucleus (B) cytoplasm (C) ribosomes (D) vacuole

2. The cell nucleus functions (F) in obtaining energy for the cell (G) in the storage of digestive enzymes (H) as the center of control for cell metabolism and reproduction (J) in the transport of materials throughout the cell

3. Current evidence indicates that ribosomes are most closely associated with (A) contraction of the cytoplasm (B) production of DNA (C) synthesis of protein (D) regulation of mitosis

4. The structures labeled 1, 2, 3, and 4 in the following diagram represent (F) organelles (G) organs (H) nuclei (J) mitochondria

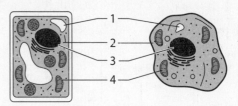

5. Mitochondria are organelles in which (A) digestive enzymes are broken down (B) secretory products are packaged and stored (C) the energy needed by the cell is released from nutrients (D) protein manufacture occurs

6. Transport of materials within a cell is most closely associated which organelle? (F) cell membrane (G) cell wall (H) ribosome (J) endoplasmic reticulum

7. Which is the most accurate statement concerning protein synthesis in cells? (A) Proteins are synthesized in the mitochondria of all living cells. (B) Proteins are synthesized by the ribosomes in all living cells. (C) Proteins are synthesized by the ribosomes in plant cells only. (D) Proteins are synthesized by nuclei in animal cells only.

8. A student could tell the difference between onion skin cells and human cheek cells because the onion skin cells have a (F) cell membrane (G) nucleus (H) cytoplasm (J) cell wall

9. Describe what would most likely happen if the ribosomes in a cell were not functioning.

10. A scientist wanted to know whether the cells of a particular single-celled green algae could survive without any mitochondria. The scientist removed all of the mitochondria from hundreds of these cells. All of the cells died. Explain the most likely reason the green algae could not survive without mitochondria.

11. The energy demands of a green plant are met through the activity of two specific organelles.

   • Identify the two organelles that plants use to meet their energy demands.

   • For each organelle, explain its role in meeting the energy demands of the plant.

   • Describe how activities of the cell membrane are directly related to the functioning of the two organelles you identified above.

2.4 Activities of the Cell Membrane

The **cell membrane** is a thin structure that surrounds the cell. It is made mainly of phospholipids (a type of fat), with some proteins embedded throughout, as shown in Figure 2-7. Some of the functions of the cell membrane are to

- separate cell contents from the environment
- control material transport in and out of the cell
- recognize and respond to chemical signals

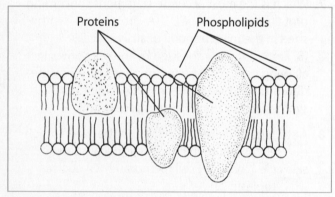

Figure 2-7. The cell membrane: composed mainly of proteins and phospholipid molecules

Maintaining Separation

Cells are organized internally. Without the cell membrane cells would not be distinct units and this organization would be lost.

Controlling Transport

If the cell is to survive, the membrane cannot totally separate the cell from its environment. Some materials, such as water, oxygen, and nutrients, must be able to enter the cell. Other materials, such as waste products, must be able to pass out of the cell.

Cell membranes are **semipermeable**, meaning that certain molecules may pass through, while other molecules cannot. Size is a key factor in this permeability. Smaller molecules can often pass more easily than larger ones. Other factors, including electrical charge, may also be important. The polarity of the phospholipids in the cell membrane is a key factor in the membrane's ability to attract water and in determining which molecules may easily enter or leave the cell. Molecules may enter or leave a cell by diffusion, osmosis, or active transport.

DIFFUSION Molecules are constantly in motion because of heat in the environment. Even if it is extremely cold, there is still enough heat to keep molecules moving. As they move, they bump into one another, then bounce away like bumper cars at an amusement park. In time, the molecules will have bumped and bounced until they are evenly distributed. The result is that the concentration of molecules in any container remains approximately the same everywhere in the container.

When the concentration of certain molecules is greater in one area of a container than they are in another area of the container, the molecules will spread into areas where their concentration is lower. This movement of molecules from areas of high concentration to areas of low concentration is called **diffusion**. Because diffusion results from the normal movement of molecules, it requires no input of energy by cells. It is like sledding downhill.

Increasing the temperature may speed up the rate of diffusion, since additional heat makes molecules move around more quickly. This is one reason that sugar dissolves faster in hot tea than in iced tea.

OSMOSIS Many molecules diffuse into and out of cells. One of the most important molecules is water. The diffusion of water through a membrane is called **osmosis**. Figure 2-8 shows this process.

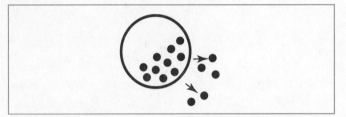

Figure 2-8. Diffusion/osmosis: These molecules are moving from an area where they are more concentrated to an area where they are less concentrated (diffusion). If the molecules that are shown here represent water, the process is called osmosis.

Osmosis is important to the maintenance of homeostasis. For example, plant cells maintain a stable balance of water and dissolved minerals. This is typically about 98% water and 2% dissolved materials. When salt is spread on roads and walkways, that balance changes. The runoff water from these salted roads may reach concentrations of 5% salt—which means only 95% water. Damage can occur when water in the plant cells diffuses from the higher (98%) concentration in the cell to the lower (95%) concentration outside the cell. Under these conditions, the loss of water places serious stress on the plant. In some cases the plant may die.

Gain of water by cells may also be harmful—animal cells may swell and burst as a result of taking in too much water. Bursting is less likely in plant cells since they have cell walls to resist the increased osmotic pressure.

ACTIVE TRANSPORT Moving a molecule from an area of low concentration to an area of high concentration is like pulling a sled uphill. It requires energy. Cells must use energy from ATP to transport molecules from areas of low concentration through the cell membrane to areas of high concentration. The process is called **active transport**. See Figure 2-9. The contractile vacuoles of some freshwater organisms actively transport water from an area of lower concentration in the organism to an area of higher water concentration outside the organism.

Many desert plants use active transport to bring water—which is at low concentrations in

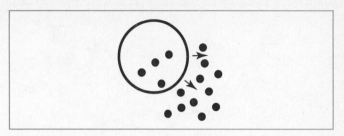

Figure 2-9. Active transport: These molecules are moving from an area of low concentration to an area of high concentration. They are being "pumped" out of the cell.

the soil—into root cells where the water concentration is higher. Some pond organisms use active transport to "collect" calcium or other essential minerals that are often present in very low concentrations in the pond water. Actions such as these are part of the maintenance of homeostasis in organisms.

Recognizing Signals

Certain protein molecules in the cell membrane can receive chemical messages from other cells. These molecules are called **receptor molecules**.

When cells are part of a larger organism, receptor molecules play an important role in the interactions between cells. As shown in Figures 2-10 and 2-11, chemicals produced in the endocrine glands—**hormones**—and chemicals produced by nerve cells are primarily responsible for communication between cells. If nerve or hormone signals are blocked, cellular communication is interrupted, and the organism's homeostasis may be affected.

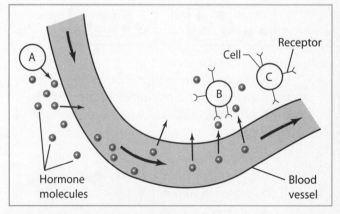

Figure 2-10. Receptor molecules: Specific receptor molecules on the membranes of some cells detect hormones that stimulate the cell to respond. In this case, only Cell B (not Cell C) will respond to the hormone from Cell A. Note the shape of the receptors on cells B and C.

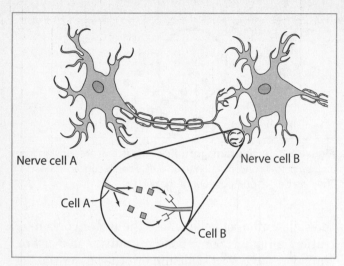

Figure 2-11. Receptor molecules: Nerve cells secrete chemicals that signal adjacent nerve, muscle, or gland cells. These secretions are detected by specific receptor molecules on the cell membranes.

2.4 Review

1. Which of the following would be *least* affected by defective receptor proteins on a cell membrane? (A) homeostasis (B) muscle activity (C) nerve signals (D) diffusion

2. A student prepared a normal wet mount slide of an *Elodea* leaf and observed it with a compound microscope. He then made the drawing labeled Slide 1. His second drawing, Slide 2, shows his observations of the same cell after it was mounted in a 5% salt solution.

The results are most fully explained by (F) loss of water from the cell (G) entrance of water into the cell (H) shrinkage of the cell wall (J) entrance of salt into the cell

3. In both plant and animal cells, the cell membrane (A) produces enzymes (B) controls reproduction (C) is composed of sugars (D) regulates diffusion

4. Which process accomplishes the movement of gases illustrated by the arrows in the diagram? (F) excretion (G) diffusion (H) carbohydrate synthesis (J) chemical digestion

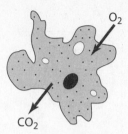

5. A student using a compound light microscope to study plant cells observed that most of the cells resembled the one shown in the following diagram.

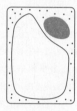

Which diagram best illustrates how the plant cell will appear after being placed in a solution that has a lower water concentration than the cell?

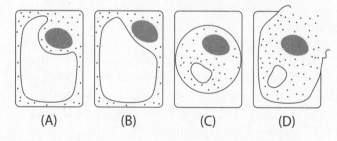

6. A paramecium (a single-celled organism) lives in a pond where the relative concentration of water is greater than the concentration of water in its cytoplasm. As a result, water molecules constantly move from the pond into the paramecium.

   The best long-term solution to the problem of maintaining a stable internal environment is for the paramecium to (F) change the water into carbon dioxide and excrete it (G) store water molecules (H) incorporate water molecules into its structure (J) actively transport water molecules out of its cell

7. A biologist diluted a blood sample with distilled water. While observing the sample with a microscope, she noted that the red blood cells had burst. This bursting is most likely the result of which process? (A) staining (B) osmosis (C) digestion (D) active transport

8. Amino acids tend to move from a blood capillary into the adjacent cell because (F) this is the only direction in which they can move (G) the brain directs the movement into cells (H) the cell needs the amino acids to make protein (J) the concentration of amino acids is lower in the cell

9. An animal cell is placed in distilled water and then transferred to a 5% salt solution. As a result of this procedure, the cell would be likely to (A) get larger (B) get larger, then smaller (C) get smaller (D) get smaller, then larger

10. Cytoplasm in a plant cell will shrink if the cell is (F) placed in a concentrated salt solution (G) kept warm and moist and in medium light (H) placed in distilled water (J) exposed to a different concentration of nitrogen gas

11. The following diagram represents a cell in water. Formulas of molecules that can move freely across the membrane are shown. Some molecules are located inside the cell and others are in the water outside the cell.

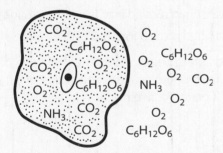

Based on the distribution of molecules, what would most likely happen to these molecules after a few hours? (A) The concentration of $C_6H_{12}O_6$ will increase inside the cell. (B) The concentration of CO_2 will increase outside the cell. (C) The concentration of NH_3 will increase inside the cell. (D) The concentration of O_2 will increase outside the cell.

12. A cell containing 98% water in its cytoplasm is placed in a 2% salt solution. It should (F) lose water (G) gain water (H) neither lose nor gain water (J) gain salt because of the high rate of diffusion

13. A high concentration of calcium salts is normally found within the cytoplasm of a certain protozoan, while the surrounding environment contains a lower concentration of the calcium salts.

    The higher concentration in the protozoan is most probably the result of (A) diffusion (B) osmosis (C) active transport (D) cellular dehydration

14. In the following diagram, nerve cell A is communicating with nerve cell B. Write the name of the structures present on the membranes of nerve cell B that enable it to detect a message from nerve cell A.

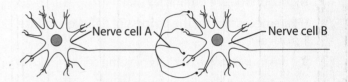

15. Molecules A and B are both organic molecules found in many cells. When tested, it is found that molecule A cannot pass through a cell membrane, but molecule B easily passes through.

    State one way the two molecules could differ, which would account for the difference in their ability to pass through the cell membrane.

16. One of your classmates tells you that diffusion and active transport can both occur in a dead cell. Explain whether your classmate is correct in his thinking. Use an example to support your answer.

17. A scientist placed some skin cells from a pond animal and some skin cells from a land animal in a salt solution with a concentration of 0.85% salt. The scientist examined the cells with a microscope and observed that the pond animal's cells had swollen and burst and that the land animal's cells had shrunk. Based on what you know about diffusion, explain these results.

18. People sometimes use large quantities of salt to preserve food. The salt kills bacteria that would otherwise cause the food to spoil. Based on what you know about diffusion, explain how the salt acts as a preservative.

19. Cell communication involves a cell detecting and responding to signals from other cells. Describe the role of receptor molecules in the communication process and include

    • the location of receptors

    • how a chemical message is transferred from one part of a multicellular organism to another

Topic 2: Assess Your Understanding

1. A few bacteria are placed in a nutrient solution. After several hours, thousands of bacteria are present. Which life activities are primarily responsible for this?

   (A) digestion and movement

   (B) digestion and reproduction

   (C) circulation and respiration

   (D) excretion and coordination

2. Mitochondria are organelles that

   (F) are necessary for the process of diffusion to take place

   (G) are found in the nucleus of some cells

   (H) initiate cell division in living cells

   (J) contain enzymes for cellular respiration

3. In the diagram of root cells, three areas are indicated with the numbers 1, 2, and 3. In which direction would the net flow of water be the greatest as a result of diffusion?

   (A) 1 to 3

   (B) 1 to 2

   (C) 2 to 3

   (D) 3 to 2

   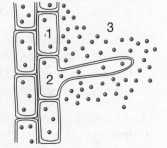

   Key
   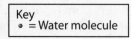
   • = Water molecule

4. Which cellular structure is present in both eukaryotic cells and prokaryotic cells?

   (F) nuclear membrane

   (G) mitochondrion

   (H) cell membrane

   (J) chloroplast

5. The transfer of specific molecules through cell membranes is an important factor in the process of

   (A) cytoplasmic flow

   (B) mitotic division

   (C) homeostasis

   (D) nuclear transfer

6. Most of the enzymes found in the mitochondria are involved in the reactions associated with

   (F) extracting energy from nutrients

   (G) storing energy in nutrients

   (H) DNA production

   (J) protein synthesis

7. A student prepared two slides as shown below.

   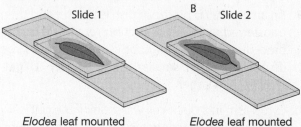

   Elodea leaf mounted   *Elodea* leaf mounted
   in tap water   in 6% salt solution

   The tap water on Slide 1 contained 1% salt and 99% water, while the salt solution on Slide 2 had 6% salt and 94% water. *Elodea* cells normally contain 1% salt. Ten minutes after the slides were prepared, a microscopic examination of cells on Slide 1 and Slide 2 would most likely show evidence that

   (A) water had moved out of the cells on Slide 2

   (B) salt had moved out of the cells of Slide 2

   (C) water had moved into the cells on Slide 1

   (D) salt had moved into the cells on Slide 1

8. The diagram below shows the change in position of two kinds of molecules on each side of a membrane over a period of five hours.

   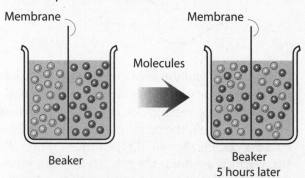

   Which process explains the change in the positions of molecules after five hours?

   (F) respiration

   (G) photosynthesis

   (H) diffusion

   (J) excretion

9. The ability to avoid danger is possible because of the life process of

(A) excretion

(B) reproduction

(C) nutrition

(D) movement

10. In the diagram of the amoeba (a single-celled organism), the arrows show the direction of movement of various substances.

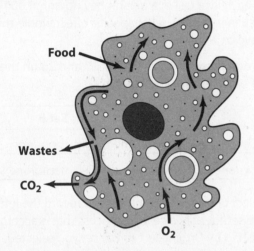

Which of the cell's life activities are represented by the arrows?

(F) digestion, reproduction, and respiration

(G) excretion, transport, and respiration

(H) immunity, digestion, and movement

(J) digestion, coordination, and reproduction

11. All cells are able to continue living because of their ability to

(A) produce food

(B) excrete wastes

(C) produce offspring

(D) secrete hormones

12. Some people believe that large doses of vitamin C can speed up the healing of surgical wounds. Describe an experiment to test this hypothesis. Your answer must include

- the difference between the experimental group of subjects and the control group
- two conditions that must be kept constant in both groups
- data that should be collected
- an example of experimental results that would support this hypothesis

Base your answers to questions 13 through 15 on your knowledge of biology and on the information in the following graph.

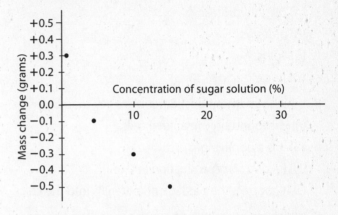

13. Four pieces of apple were cut so that all were the same mass and shape. The pieces were placed in four different concentrations of sugar water. After 24 hours, the pieces were removed and their masses determined. The above graph indicates the change in the mass of each piece.

What was the change in mass of the apple piece in the 10 percent sugar solution?

(A) a decrease of 0.45 grams

(B) an increase of 0.30 grams

(C) a decrease of 0.30 grams

(D) an increase of 0.1 0 grams

14. At approximately what sugar concentration should pieces neither lose nor gain mass?

(F) 6%

(G) 10%

(H) 3%

(J) 20%

15. The four points on the graph represent

(A) assumptions

(B) data

(C) hypotheses

(D) conclusions

16. Most of the reactions by which energy from sugars is released for use by the cell takes place within the

(F) vacuoles

(G) nuclei

(H) ribosomes

(J) mitochondria

17. A rotten egg may give off a foul-smelling gas containing sulfur. Which decomposing chemical compounds in the egg are the most likely source of this odor?

(A) carbohydrates

(B) proteins

(C) lipids

(D) nucleic acids

18. Which statement best describes a cell membrane?

(F) It is found only in animal cells.

(G) It is a nonliving structure.

(H) It controls reproduction in a cell.

(J) It controls the passage of materials into the cell.

19. Which structure is the boundary between a living cell and its environment?

(A) cell membrane

(B) cytoplasm

(C) vacuole

(D) ribosome

20. The diagram shows a particle of food being taken into a cell from the outside environment. Structure 1 stores the material until it is eventually digested.

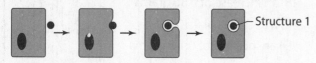

Structure 1 is most probably a

(F) mitochondrion

(G) ribosome

(H) vacuole

(J) nucleus

21. Which cell organelles are most closely associated with energy changes in a plant?

(A) mitochondria and chromosomes

(B) chloroplasts and mitochondria

(C) chromosomes and nucleus

(D) chloroplasts and nucleus

22. The cell organelles that are the sites of aerobic cellular respiration in both plant and animal cells are

(F) mitochondria

(G) chloroplasts

(H) nuclei

(J) vacuoles

Use the technical passage below to answer questions 23 and 24.

Receptor molecules play an important role in cell communication. Human cells have insulin receptors that are needed for the movement of glucose out of the blood.

23. State one way the shape of the insulin receptor is related to its role in cell communication.

24. A typical human liver cell can have over 90,000 insulin receptors. If a genetic error occurred, resulting in each liver cell in a person having only 1,000 insulin receptors, what specific effect would this have on the liver cells?

Base your answers to questions 25 and 26 on the two sets of organelles in the chart.

	Set A	Set B
Organelle 1	Ribosome	Mitochondrion
Organelle 2	Nucleus	Cell membrane

25. Select one set of organelles and record the letter of the set. Identify a cellular process that is accomplished by Organelle 1 in the set you selected.

26. Explain how Organelle 2 *in the set you selected* interacts with Organelle 1 to carry out the cellular process you identified in question 25.

Read the following passage, and then answer questions 27 through 30.

The heart of an older person or of someone recovering from a heart attack may become severely weakened or damaged. This sometimes leads to a serious condition called congestive heart failure in which the heart muscle is too weak to pump enough blood throughout the body. As a result, the heart may become exhausted. Sometimes it completely stops.

In a recent study, 2,647 patients were given a type of drug called a beta-blocker which lowered their risk of death by 34 percent over 15 months (compared to patients who did not take the drugs). Another study reached a similar conclusion.

Although beta-blockers have long been used for treating heart attacks, doctors thought they were too dangerous for patients with congestive heart failure. Their reason was that beta-blockers counteract the body's response to adrenaline, a hormone that stimulates the heart to beat faster by attaching to receptors on heart muscle cells. Since beta-blockers also attach to these adrenaline receptors, they keep the adrenaline molecules from making contact. This leads to a slowing of the heart, which would appear to cause a problem for a person whose heart is not pumping blood effectively anyway.

The opposite turns out to be the case. When the heart of a person with congestive heart failure is not pumping enough blood, the body responds by releasing more adrenaline to stimulate the heart. As a result, the heart is overstimulated and works even harder—which in turn makes it more likely to fail. Since beta-blockers interrupt this destructive cycle, the heart stabilizes.

Doctors hope that once more studies are done, proper use of beta-blockers may eventually save many thousands of lives.

27. Describe how adrenaline is involved in the cell-to-cell communication of a person with congestive heart failure.

28. On the diagram of the heart muscle shown below, use the numbers 1, 2, and 3 to label the heart receptors and the two kinds of molecules shown. Use information from the passage to determine where the correct labels should go.

1—beta-blocker molecule

2—adrenaline molecule

3—heart cell receptor

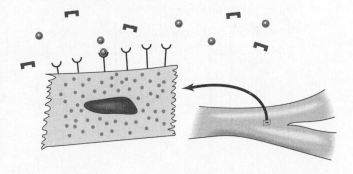

29. Explain how you could tell which objects represent the adrenaline and which represent the beta-blocker in question 28.

30. Many drugs have side effects that make them dangerous to some people. For this reason, individuals who take prescription drugs must watch for any unexpected changes in their health.

Based on the information provided in the passage and on your knowledge of biology, describe one possible side effect that might result when people *without* congestive heart failure use beta-blockers.

31. Which two systems are most directly involved in providing molecules needed for the synthesis of fats in cells of a mammal?

(A) digestive and circulatory

(B) excretory and digestive

(C) immune and muscular

(D) reproductive and circulatory

Use the information below to answer questions 32 and 33.

In a class, each student made three models of the small intestine using three artificial membrane tubes as shown below:

Tube Number	Tube Contents
1	equal amounts of water, starch, protein, and vitamin C, plus starch-digesting enzyme
2	equal amounts of water, starch, protein, and vitamin C, plus protein-digesting enzyme
3	equal amounts of water, starch, protein, and vitamin C, with **no** enzyme added

The ends of the membrane tubes were sealed and the tubes were soaked for 24 hours in beakers of pure water.

The beakers were numbered 1, 2, and 3, corresponding to the number of the tube they contained. At the end of the experiment, the students removed the tubes and tested the water in the beakers for the presence of nutrients.

32. Sugar would most likely be present in the water in

(F) beaker 1 only

(G) beaker 2 only

(H) beakers 1 and 3 only

(J) beakers 1, 2, and 3

33. Which statement would be a valid inference if vitamin C had been present in the water in each beaker?

(A) The water synthesized vitamin C.

(B) Vitamin C is a small molecule.

(C) The membrane tube produced vitamin C.

(D) The concentration of vitamin C is higher in the beaker than in the membrane tube.

34. Nutrients that are not used as building blocks for the cell may be broken down to release the energy stored in their chemical bonds. This process, which provides cells with energy, is called

(F) chemical synthesis

(G) cell respiration

(H) digestion

(J) homeostasis

35. When organisms break the bonds of organic compounds, the organisms can

(A) use the smaller molecules to plug the gaps in the cell membrane to slow diffusion

(B) use the energy obtained to digest molecules produced by cellular respiration

(C) obtain energy or reassemble the resulting materials to form different compounds

(D) produce more sugar in the mitochondria

Base your answers to questions 36 through 38 on the information and data table below.

The rate of respiration of a freshwater sunfish was determined at different temperatures. The rate of respiration was determined by counting the number of times the gill covers of the fish opened and closed during 1-minute intervals at the various temperatures. The following information was collected.

Temperature (°C)	Gill Cover Opening and Closing Per Minute
10	15
15	25
18	30
20	38
23	60
25	57
27	25

36. According to the data, as the temperature increases, the rate of respiration of the sunfish

(F) increases steadily

(G) decreases steadily

(H) increases, then decreases

(J) decreases, then increases

37. Which title is appropriate for this data table?

(A) The Effect of Temperature on Rate of Respiration in Sunfish

(B) The Effect of Gill Movement on Rate of Respiration in Sunfish

(C) The Relationship Between Temperature and Dissolved Oxygen

(D) The Relationship Between Sunfish Population and Temperature Change in Freshwater Habitats

38. Which statement explains how these observations demonstrate homeostasis?

(F) The sunfish had the greatest amount of gill cover activity at 23°C.

(G) Other sunfish would be expected to respond exactly the same way to the same temperature changes.

(H) As the temperature changed, the sunfish adjusted its gill cover activity.

(J) Sunfish can probably not survive at temperatures above 27°C or below 10°C.

Biologically Important Chemical Processes of Organisms

TOPIC

3

In order to survive, all organisms must keep their biological systems stable, even though they live in a changing environment. For example, your body temperature must stay within a narrow range near 98.6°F or 37°C. If you become too hot or too cold, the biochemical processes that keep you alive will fail.

Biochemical processes are the chemical reactions that occur in living things and are essential to maintaining homeostasis. They are regulated by enzymes made according to instructions coded in the DNA molecules of all organisms. Two very important enzyme-controlled biochemical processes are photosynthesis and respiration.

3.1 Storing Energy: Photosynthesis

VOCABULARY			
ATP	chemosynthesis	glucose	synthesis
biochemical processes	chloroplasts	photosynthesis	

Light Energy to Chemical Bond Energy

Photosynthesis is the process by which light energy is captured and then stored in the chemical bonds of organic molecules such as glucose and other carbohydrates. Plants, algae, and many single-celled organisms carry out photosynthesis. Recall that respiration is the process by which the chemical energy stored in organic molecules is released for use in cells. All living organisms carry out respiration.

The energy for life comes primarily from the sun. In Figure 3-1, notice that photosynthesis is the connection between the energy released by the sun and the energy available to living systems.

The cells of organisms that carry out photosynthesis contain light-capturing molecules. In plant cells, these molecules are located in the **chloroplasts**, which are the organelles where photosynthesis occurs. In Figure 3-2, the chloroplasts are the oval structures. You may have seen these green structures on microscope slides of cells prepared from plant leaves.

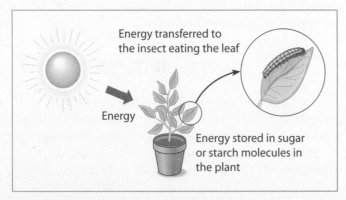

Figure 3-1. Energy transfer: The sun provides energy for most of the life on Earth.

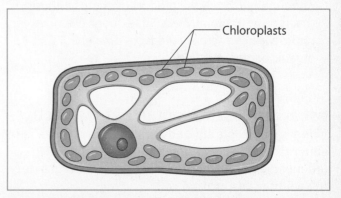

Figure 3-2. Chloroplasts in a typical plant cell: The chloroplasts capture light energy.

Nearly all plants—from mosses to complex angiosperms, use solar energy to convert inorganic molecules—carbon dioxide, and water into any one of several energy-rich organic compounds. One such compound is **glucose**, a monosaccharide or simple sugar. In the equation shown in Figure 3-3, notice that water and carbon dioxide, raw materials from the organism's environment, react to make glucose. Oxygen gas, a byproduct of the process, is released into the environment.

$$\text{light energy} + \text{water} + \text{carbon dioxide} \longrightarrow \text{glucose} + \text{oxygen}$$
$$\text{light energy} + 6\,H_2O + 6\,CO_2 \longrightarrow C_6H_{12}O_6 + 6\,O_2$$

Figure 3-3. Photosynthesis: In the chloroplasts, molecules of water and carbon dioxide are involved in a series of reactions to form glucose and oxygen. The sun provides light energy necessary for the process of photosynthesis to occur.

CHEMOSYNTHESIS **Chemosynthesis** is an energy-storing process used by some bacteria. In this process, the energy needed to make food molecules comes from inorganic compounds rather than sunlight. In chemosynthesis glucose is usually produced, but oxygen is not a byproduct.

How is the glucose used?

Plant cells use products of photosynthesis, such as glucose, in two ways. During cellular respiration, these organic molecules are broken down and energy is released. This energy is used in the production of ATP molecules. Glucose is also used as a raw material for building more complex molecules.

DID YOU KNOW?

Although glucose is the product of photosynthesis that is most frequently used in textbook examples, photosynthesis actually produces a variety of organic compounds.

USING GLUCOSE TO PRODUCE ATP MOLECULES One way both plants and animals use glucose is to generate high-energy molecules known as **ATP** (*a*denosine *tri*phosphate). This process occurs during cellular respiration.

Because cell processes actually "run" on ATP rather than glucose, the transfer of energy from glucose to ATP is essential to both plants and the organisms that consume them. Energy stored in the chemical bonds of ATP molecules is the source of energy for almost all life processes, from obtaining, transforming, and transporting materials to eliminating wastes.

USING GLUCOSE TO BUILD COMPLEX MOLECULES Cells also use glucose as the starting point for the **synthesis** (chemical combining) of many complex organic compounds. For example, plants convert much of the glucose from photosynthesis into starch for storage. Table 3-1 provides some examples of how organisms use a variety of complex molecules.

Table 3-1. Complex Molecules and Their Functions	
Molecule	**Function**
ATP	Supplies chemical energy for cellular processes
DNA	Carries hereditary information
Carbohydrates	Act as energy reserve molecules
Lipids (fats and oils)	Act as energy reserve molecules
Proteins	Aid in growth and repair of tissues

When animals eat plants or other animals, they digest the complex molecules into simpler molecules for their own cells to use. Some of these molecules provide energy for the organism. For example, starches from plants and fats from animals can both be digested and used by the cells for energy. If they are not all needed for energy, the molecules can be stored as fat to provide a food reserve for the animal. Table 3-2 provides a summary of photosynthesis.

DIGGING DEEPER

Since glucose contains only the elements carbon, hydrogen, and oxygen, other elements may be needed to synthesize new compounds. Minerals are a common source of these other elements, including phosphorus for nucleotides and iron for hemoglobin.

Table 3-2. Summary of Photosynthesis	
Energy	The energy comes from sunlight as solar energy and ends up in glucose molecules as chemical bond energy.
Materials used	Carbon dioxide gas and water are used; both molecules come from the environment.
Materials produced	Molecules made from the carbon dioxide and water include molecules of the sugar glucose (a simple carbohydrate) and oxygen gas. Oxygen is actually released as a byproduct of photosynthesis.
Time frame	Photosynthesis occurs in plant cells when light is available, which is generally during the daytime.
Location	Photosynthesis occurs in the chloroplasts of plant cells, algae, and some one-celled organisms when they are exposed to light.
Importance of photosynthesis	Organisms either (1) use glucose to synthesize other molecules they need or (2) break down the glucose to release its stored energy.
Relationship to respiration	The energy originally stored in glucose during photosynthesis is transferred to the chemical bonds of ATP. All cells "run" on the energy released from ATP.

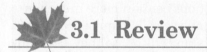

3.1 Review

1. In a plant cell, the synthesis of glucose and other sugar compounds from inorganic raw materials takes place in the (A) cell membrane (B) mitochondria (C) nucleus (D) chloroplasts

2. Which word equation represents the process of photosynthesis? (F) glucose → alcohol + carbon dioxide (G) carbon dioxide + water → glucose + oxygen (H) chlorophyll + water → glucose + alcohol (J) glucose + oxygen → carbon dioxide + water

3. Which activity occurs during the process of photosynthesis? (A) Chemical energy from organic molecules is converted into light energy. (B) Organic molecules are absorbed from the environment. (C) Organic molecules are converted into inorganic food molecules. (D) Light energy is stored as chemical energy in organic molecules.

4. The basic raw materials of photosynthesis are (F) sugar and carbon dioxide (G) oxygen and water (H) water and carbon dioxide (J) oxygen and sugar

5. Which compound is formed as a common product of the process of photosynthesis? (A) DNA (B) sugar (C) chlorophyll (D) carbon dioxide

6. In the test tube shown, what does the snail produce that is used by the plant? (F) oxygen (G) carbon dioxide (H) food (J) eggs

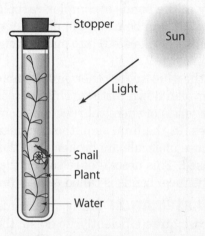

7. Which factor *least* influences the rate of photosynthesis? (A) concentration of carbon dioxide in air (B) time of day (C) number of chloroplasts (D) concentration of nitrogen in the air

8. Without chloroplasts and light energy, the process of photosynthesis in plants would not occur. Specific raw materials must also be available in a plant's environment.

   • Name two raw materials that are necessary for photosynthesis to take place.

   • Explain what happens to these two raw materials during the process.

   • Explain what happens to the light energy.

9. The greenhouse effect leads to global warming by trapping heat in our atmosphere. Carbon dioxide produced through the burning of coal and oil for industrial processes, power generation, and transportation is one of the main atmospheric gases that contributes to the problem. Some people have suggested that planting many long-lived trees along interstate highways could help counteract the greenhouse effect. Explain how doing so could help.

3.2 Releasing Energy: Cellular Respiration

VOCABULARY			
aerobic respiration	**anaerobic respiration**	**cellular respiration**	**gas exchange**

Making ATP

All living things need energy to stay alive. Before the energy in the bonds of complex carbohydrates, such as starch, can be used, the molecules must be broken down (digested) into simpler ones, such as glucose.

Next, the glucose (or other simple molecules) must be broken down further. This process involves a series of chemical reactions controlled by enzymes. In the final step, the chemical bonds of the glucose molecule are broken, and their energy is released. This process of releasing the energy in those chemical bonds is called **cellular respiration**.

AEROBIC RESPIRATION Many organisms break down glucose quite efficiently. To do so, these organisms use oxygen, which must be brought into the organism from the environment. Obtaining oxygen from the environment and releasing carbon dioxide is called **gas exchange**.

MEMORY JOGGER

Sometimes people use the term *respiration* when they really mean *breathing*. *Respiration* is the process that involves oxygen and breaks down food molecules to release energy. *Cellular respiration* refers specifically to the transfer of energy from simple organic molecules like glucose to ATP molecules within cells.

During **aerobic respiration**, cells use oxygen as they break down glucose. They are able to capture much of the energy that is released from the glucose bonds. The captured energy is then used to form new bonds in high-energy molecules known as ATP. Figure 3-4 shows how ATP temporarily stores energy. Most of the energy that the cell fails to capture to make ATP is lost to the environment as heat.

In many organisms, aerobic cellular respiration is completed in organelles called mitochondria.

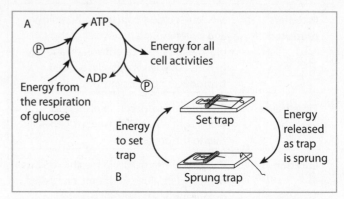

Figure 3-4. Energy storage in ATP molecules: (A) Chemical energy from the breakdown of glucose molecules is used to attach a phosphate (P) to a molecule of ADP. The result is ATP, the cell's energy carrier. When the cell needs energy, the ATP is broken down into ADP. During that process, the phosphate (P), along with the energy that was stored in its chemical bond, is released. (B) A similar form of temporary energy storage occurs when a mousetrap is set. The mechanical energy that is put into the act of setting the trap is stored in the spring. When the trap is sprung, that energy is released.

(See Figure 3-5.) Mitochondria are abundant in animal cells, and cells that require more energy to carry out their functions contain more mitochondria. For example, muscle cells require more energy to function than skin cells do, so they also generally contain more mitochondria.

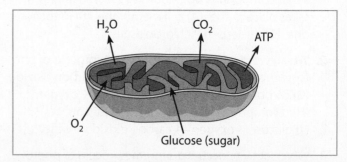

Figure 3-5. Aerobic respiration in a mitochondrion: Partially broken down glucose molecules and oxygen (O_2) enter the organelle and are rearranged, with the help of enzymes. Water (H_2O) and carbon dioxide (CO_2) are released as waste products. The energy that was stored in the glucose is transferred to ATP molecules.

As they generate ATP, mitochondria release carbon dioxide and water molecules as byproducts of the reactions. Most cellular processes use ATP as a direct source of energy. Basically, cells "run" on ATP. Table 3-3 summarizes aerobic respiration.

ANAEROBIC RESPIRATION Some organisms, often simpler ones like bacteria, are **anaerobic**—they do not use oxygen to break down glucose. This results in a much less efficient process, which produces much less ATP. Instead of water and carbon dioxide, anaerobic respiration may produce lactic acid as a waste product. Sometimes alcohol and CO_2 are the waste products of another form of energy release, called fermentation, which does not use oxygen.

Table 3-3. Summary of Aerobic Cellular Respiration

Energy	Comes from the chemical bond energy of glucose molecules; ends up in ATP bonds where it can be utilized for cell activities.
Materials used	Sugar or other energy-rich organic food compounds and oxygen gas from the environment. (Food is obtained through photosynthesis in producers and by feeding in consumers. Oxygen is obtained through gas exchange.)
Materials produced	ATP molecules and two waste products—carbon dioxide gas and water. The release of carbon dioxide into the environment is part of the process of gas exchange.
Time frame	Cellular respiration occurs in all cells (including plant cells) 24 hours a day.
Location	Respiration occurs in the cells of all living things. In many organisms, cellular respiration is concluded in mitochondria, in which ATP is produced more efficiently.
Importance of respiration	All cells "run" on the energy released from ATP. Organisms can use the ATP they make as the source of energy to help them obtain raw materials and nutrients, to transform materials in chemical reactions, to transport materials (for example, active transport), and to eliminate wastes. The energy is also used to allow the organism to grow and to move from one place to another.

3.2 Review

1. Energy for use in cells is stored in the form of (A) chemical bond energy (B) physical energy (C) heat energy (D) mechanical energy

2. In which process do organisms transfer the energy in organic molecules to ATP molecules? (F) excretion (G) cellular respiration (H) autotrophic nutrition (J) photosynthesis

3. Which statement most accurately describes the process of respiration? (A) It occurs only in plants during the daylight hours and usually involves the exchange of gases. (B) It occurs only in plants during the daylight hours and involves the taking in of preformed organic molecules. (C) It occurs continuously in the cells of all organisms and involves the synthesis of carbohydrate molecules. (D) It occurs continuously in the cells of all organisms and often involves an exchange of gases.

4. The process during which energy is released from digested foods is called (F) cellular respiration (G) chemical digestion (H) photosynthesis (J) excretion

5. As a direct result of the life process called cellular respiration in humans, (A) liquid wastes are eliminated from the body (B) food is digested and absorbed into the blood (C) energy is released from digested food within the cells (D) nutrients are transported within the cells

6. Which process involves the transfer of energy from carbohydrates to ATP molecules? (F) photosynthesis (G) respiration (H) digestion (J) chemosynthesis

7. In cellular respiration, the energy released is used to (A) synthesize ATP (B) control the process of diffusion (C) synthesize more glucose (D) produce oxygen molecules

8. Which statement best describes one of the events taking place in the chemical reaction represented below?

$$H_2O + ATP \xrightarrow{\text{enzymes}} ADP + P + energy$$

(F) Energy is being stored as a result of cellular respiration. (G) Energy is being released for metabolic processes. (H) Decomposition is taking place, resulting in the synthesis of ATP. (J) Photosynthesis is taking place, resulting in the storage of energy.

9. Energy released from the cellular respiration of glucose is (A) first stored within ATP (B) stored in the liver as fat (C) turned into fat (D) used directly for body activity

Base your answers to questions 10 through 12 on the diagram of a mitochondrion below.

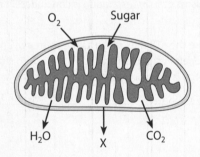

10. The process represented in this diagram is (F) respiration (G) coordination (H) photosynthesis (J) chemosynthesis

11. What term would most appropriately be represented by the "X"? (A) ATP (B) chlorophyll (C) antibodies (D) glucose

12. What is present within the mitochondrion that allows the reaction to occur? (F) enzymes (G) chlorophyll (H) bacteria (J) carbon dioxide

13. The production of energy-rich ATP molecules is the direct result of (A) recycling light energy to be used in the process of photosynthesis (B) releasing the stored energy of organic compounds by the process of respiration (C) breaking down starch by the process of digestion (D) copying coded information during the process of DNA replication

14. Information concerning a metabolic activity is shown below.

$$X \xrightarrow{\text{enzymes}} \text{products} + \text{energy for metabolism}$$

Substance X is most likely (F) DNA (G) ATP (H) oxygen (J) chlorophyll

15. Living organisms must be able to obtain materials, change the materials into new forms, remove poisons, and move needed material from one place to another.

Many of these activities directly require (A) energy released from ATP (B) carbohydrates formed from receptor molecules (C) the synthesis of DNA (D) the breakdown of energy-rich inorganic molecules

Base your answer to question 16 on the following selection from the work of an early scientist.

"A sprig [stem with leaves] of a nettle plant was put in a jar full of air fouled by breathing so as to extinguish a candle; it was placed in a room and left overnight; the next morning the air was found to be as bad as before. At 9 o'clock in the morning, the jar was put in the sunshine and, in the space of two hours, the air was so much corrected that it was found to be nearly as good as common air."

16. What gases a6nd processes were being investigated by the scientist? In your response, include the answers to the following questions:

- The "jar full of air fouled by breathing" probably contained an excess of what gas?

- The fact that "the air was found to be as bad as before" was due to what process taking place in the plant?

- What process did the plant perform to produce air nearly as good as "common air"?

- What gas was produced by the plant in the process that improved the air in the jar?

- What gas was produced by the plant in the dark?

Base your answers to questions 17 through 21 on the following information and data table.

An investigation was designed to determine the effect of temperature on respiration in germinating seeds. Two sets of test tubes were prepared. In each set of two test tubes, one tube contained a number of germinating peas, and the other tube contained an equal number of glass beads. An equal amount of chemical was placed in each tube to absorb the carbon dioxide produced so that the volume of oxygen consumed could be measured.

One set of tubes was placed in a water bath at a controlled temperature of 10°C. The other set of test tubes was placed in a water bath at a controlled temperature of 26°C. Total oxygen consumption was measured every 5 minutes for a period of 20 minutes. The data are summarized below.

Use the information in the table and follow the directions in questions 17 through 19 to construct a line graph on the grid provided.

Data Table

Time (in minutes)	Total Oxygen Consumption (mL)			
	10°C		26°C	
	Beads	Peas	Beads	Peas
0 (Start)	0	0.0	0	0.0
5	0	0.3	0	0.5
10	0	0.6	0	1.0
15	0	0.9	0	1.5
20	0	1.2	0	2.0

17. Label each axis and mark an appropriate scale on each axis.

18. Plot the data for oxygen consumption by peas at 10°C on the grid. Surround each point with a small circle and connect the points.

Example:

19. Plot the data for oxygen consumption by peas at 26°C on the grid. Surround each point with a small triangle and connect the points.

Example:

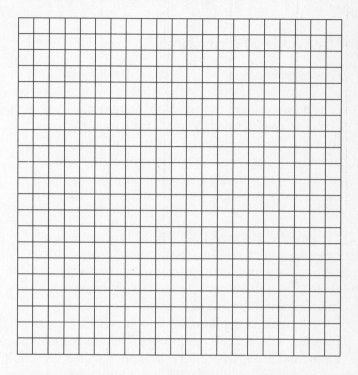

20. State one conclusion that relates the rate of respiration in germinating peas to temperature.

21. State one reason for including the tube containing the glass beads in each set.

3.3 Enzyme Action

VOCABULARY			
catalyst	enzymes	pH	substrate

Biological Catalysts

A **catalyst** is any substance that increases the rate of a chemical reaction without itself being changed or used up during the reaction. **Enzymes** are proteins that act as biological catalysts. Because they are neither changed nor used up, enzymes are capable of carrying out the same function again and again. Without enzymes, the chemical reactions required by cells to maintain homeostasis would progress too slowly to keep the cell alive.

THE FUNCTION OF ENZYMES Biochemical processes, such as digestion (breakdown), synthesis (building up), cellular respiration (energy release), and photosynthesis (energy capture), are made possible by enzymes.

All living organisms contain enzymes. Enzymes interact with specific molecules. The molecule that a particular enzyme interacts with is called its **substrate**. Chemical reactions in living organisms are regulated by many different enzymes that function best at whatever the normal body temperature is for the organism.

IMPORTANCE OF MOLECULAR SHAPE Enzymes have three-dimensional shapes that influence both how they function and how they interact with other molecules. (The same is true for all other proteins, including hormones, antibodies, and receptor molecules on cell membranes.) Enzymes interact with certain substances but not others. The enzyme salivary amylase, for example, acts on starches but not on proteins. In Figure 3-6, notice how the shapes of W, X, and Y fit together precisely to combine two molecules, W and X.

If the arrows in Figure 3-6 were reversed, the reaction would involve splitting molecule Z into two smaller molecules, W and X. This reverse process is digestion.

Each enzyme must have a specific shape to work correctly, and anything that alters that shape will affect the enzyme's ability to function. High temperatures and strong acids or bases can change the enzyme's shape either temporarily or permanently. When this happens, the enzyme cannot function, and the reaction rate will decrease in proportion to the number of enzymes that are altered.

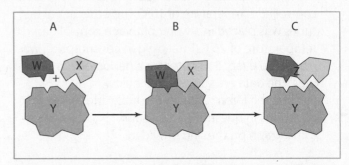

Figure 3-6. Enzymes interact with specific substrate molecules: Enzyme interactions are determined in part by molecular shape. After the two substrate molecules W and X interact with enzyme Y (A), the enzyme forms a temporary physical connection with them (B) and then separates after a reaction has occurred (C). As a result, the molecules W and X have chemically bonded for the synthesis of the new molecule Z.

Enzyme Reaction Rates

Several other factors can either quicken or slow the rate of enzyme action.

TEMPERATURE The enzymes in organisms have an optimum temperature at which they function most efficiently. For human enzymes, this temperature is typically 98.6°F (37°C). For a cat, body temperature is about 101°F, and its enzymes would be expected to work best at that temperature. As the temperature of a cell or organism reaches its optimum level, enzymes and the molecules they are interacting with will move faster and collide more often, causing the reaction rate to increase. Beyond the optimum temperature, the rate falls rapidly because the fragile enzyme molecules begin to change shape or break apart. Trace the rise and fall of an enzyme reaction rate in Figure 3-7.

pH The **pH** of a substance indicates whether a substance is acidic, neutral, or basic. Varying the pH value affects enzyme activity. Many enzymes work best at a pH of about 7, which is neutral.

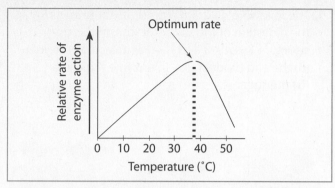

Figure 3-7. **Enzymes and temperature:** Note that the rate of enzyme action is fastest at about 37°C, which is typical of a human enzyme. The reason the rate declines so quickly beyond the optimum is that the higher temperature alters the shape of the enzyme. In this example, by the time the temperature reaches 55°C, all the enzyme molecules have been altered. As a result, they no longer function.

This makes sense, since most body fluids and cells maintain a pH of near 7. However, some parts of organisms have typical pH values that are far from neutral. For example, the environment of the human stomach is extremely acidic and has a pH of 2 or 3; the small intestine, by contrast, has a pH around 8. Enzymes in these locations typically have rates that correspond to the pH of their environment, as shown in Figure 3-8.

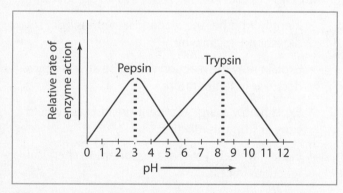

Figure 3-8. **Enzymes and pH:** Pepsin is found in the human stomach and has a pH that matches the acid environment found there. Trypsin is an enzyme that works in the small intestine, where the pH is close to 8. Notice that each enzyme is less effective if the pH is either raised or lowered from its optimum point.

MEMORY JOGGER

A pH of 7 is neutral, the same as pure water. A low pH, such as 1 or 2, indicates a strong acid; a high pH, such as 13 or 14, indicates a strong base. In a typical high school biology laboratory, pH is measured with pH paper treated with various indicator dyes.

CONCENTRATION The concentration of an enzyme or the concentration of the substrate also affects enzyme activity. With an increased amount of enzyme or substrate, the reaction would proceed at a faster rate—but only up to a point. If there is too much enzyme or substrate, the overabundance of either one may interfere with contact between the enzyme and substrate molecules.

3.3 Review

1. Which organelle indicated in the following diagram controls the synthesis of enzymes? (A) 1 (B) 2 (C) 3 (D) 4

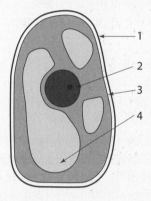

2. Only small amounts of enzymes are required for reactions within cells because enzymes are (F) fragile (G) reused (H) small molecules (J) constantly synthesized

3. Which characteristic allows enzymes to function in a specific way? (A) Enzymes are complex compounds composed of starch. (B) Each enzyme has a characteristic shape. (C) Enzymes are long, complex fats. (D) Each enzyme is made up of four subunits.

4. Which group of organic compounds includes enzymes? (F) proteins (G) carbohydrates (H) sugars (J) starches

5. At which point on the following graph can the rate of enzyme activity be increased by increasing the concentration of sugar molecules? (A) 1 (B) 2 (C) 3 (D) either 2, 3, or 4

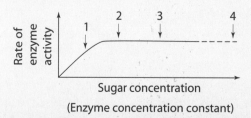

6. Which statement best describes the relationship between enzyme action and temperature shown in the following graph?

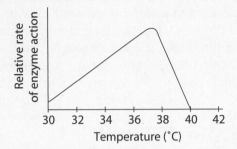

(F) Enzyme synthesis begins at 30°C. (G) Enzyme activity constantly increases with increasing temperature. (H) The pH has a greater effect on this enzyme than temperature does. (J) Enzyme activity increases as the temperature increases from 32°C to 34°C.

7. The enzyme salivary amylase will act on starch but not on protein. This action shows that salivary amylase (A) contains starch (B) is chemically specific (C) is not reusable (D) lacks protein

8. Which statement best describes how enzymes influence chemical reactions in living systems? (F) They become part of the product after the reactions occur. (G) They combine with atmospheric gases to form waste products. (H) They increase the rate at which reactions occur. (J) They absorb water during synthesis and digestion.

9. The following diagram represents three steps in the digestion of the sugar sucrose. In this diagram, structure X is most likely (A) a molecule of oxygen (B) the end product (C) an enzyme molecule (D) the sugar

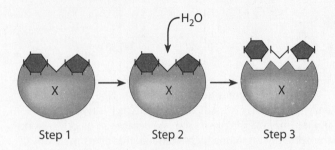

10. The diagram below shows changes that occur during a reaction involving a cellular enzyme.

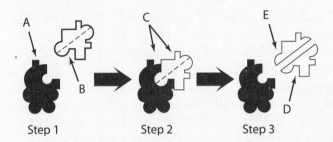

Explain how organisms depend on enzymes such as this one. In your answer be sure to do the following.

• Identify whether the reaction is synthesis or digestion. Explain why.

• Explain how the reaction would be affected by a decrease in temperature.

• Explain how a large temperature increase would slow or stop this reaction.

• Explain why enzymes are important to chemical reactions in cells.

3.4 The Genetic Code

Genes are inherited instructions that are passed from parent to offspring and exist in the form of a chemical code. This genetic code, as the chemical code is called, is contained in the DNA molecules of all organisms. DNA molecules resemble a flexible, twisted ladder consisting of many smaller subunits, as shown in Figure 3-9.

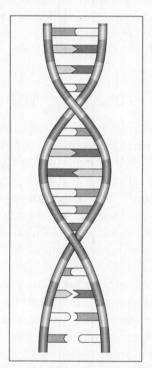

Figure 3-9. Model of a section of a DNA molecule: Notice the twisted-ladder shape and the four different kinds of subunits, called nucleotides, that form the molecule.

DNA Structure

The DNA molecule is made of thousands of smaller subunits called **nucleotides**. Each subunit has three chemical parts: a sugar (deoxyribose), a phosphate, and a nitrogen base. DNA nucleotides vary from one another according to the kind of bases they contain. The nitrogen bases—adenine, guanine, cytosine, and thymine—are represented by the letters A, G, C, and T. The four nucleotides

of DNA molecules are arranged in pairs, each nucleotide forming part of one side and half of one rung of the "twisted ladder," or double helix. Adenine (A) always pairs with the base thymine (T) of another subunit. In a similar way, base G always pairs with base C. Figure 3-10 shows the details of the structure in an untwisted molecule.

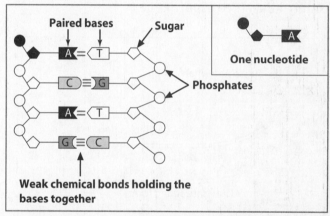

Figure 3-10. Portion of a DNA molecule: *A single nucleotide subunit is shown in the box on the upper right.* The bases of the DNA molecule are arranged in pairs, represented here by letters. The base pairs form the rungs of the twisted DNA ladder. The sugar and phosphate of each nucleotide form the sides of the ladder and are connected by strong chemical bonds. The two sides are held together by weak chemical bonds between the paired bases. Chemical bonds are the links between atoms that hold molecules together.

The discovery of the chemical and structural properties of DNA also revealed how this molecule could contain a coded genetic message. Notice in Figure 3–10 that the sequence of bases on this molecule's left strand, reading from top to bottom, is ACAG. A different DNA molecule might have a sequence in the same position reading GCAG or AACG. The specific sequence of bases in a DNA molecule forms a coded message. The "message" of a single gene is often a sequence of hundreds of bases. The code for an entire human is estimated to be around 3 billion pairs of bases.

DNA Replication

The ability to copy the coded instructions in the DNA molecule is critical to its function. Knowing the chemical makeup and structure of DNA molecules gave scientists an immediate clue to how the molecule could be copied, or replicated. When scientists realized that the bases used weak chemical bonds to pair with each other, they also realized that the DNA could separate at these weak bonds to form two single strands. Each single strand became a template, or pattern, for a new molecule. The new molecule was built by attaching new nucleotides to each template strand, always following the base pairing rules of linking A with T and C with G. The result is the formation of two new molecules whose base pair sequences are exactly alike. (See Figure 3-11.)

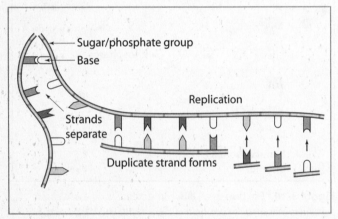

Figure 3-11. The replication of a DNA molecule: This is how cells copy their genetic information to be passed on to two offspring cells when cell division occurs. Both strands are replicated at the same time.

When the structure of DNA was determined, scientists finally understood how cells could copy and transfer information to new cells each time they divide. Replication produces two identical copies of the cell's genetic information, each ready to be passed from the parent cell to two offspring cells during cell division. Offspring cells are commonly called daughter cells.

Proteins and Cell Functioning

The work of the cell is carried out by the many types of molecules the cell synthesizes. Many of these molecules are proteins. Protein molecules are long chains formed from 20 kinds of amino acids arranged in a specific sequence.

The sequence of amino acids in a particular protein influences the shape of the molecule, since some of the amino acid parts are attracted to (and may bond with) other amino acids in the chain. The connections that form between different parts of the chain cause it to fold and bend in a specific way.

The final folded shape of the protein enables it to carry out its function in the cell. For example, many proteins made by a cell become enzymes that regulate chemical reactions. Refer back to Figure 3-6 for a reminder of how an enzyme can interact with a specific substrate molecule.

Proteins are essential to the body's structure and function. Some proteins become parts of organelles, such as the cell membrane. Other proteins include the hormone insulin or the many antibodies that bind to antigen molecules on pathogens. The color of your eyes and skin are also the result of proteins synthesized by your body.

The DNA-Protein Connection

Cells store vast amounts of coded information in their genes. Much of this information is used to make the thousands of proteins that each cell requires for its functions and the structures it contains. The proteins for these structures and functions are made at the ribosomes according to the directions stored in the cell's DNA code.

Because offspring inherit genetic information from their parents, their cells make many of the same proteins. This is what causes the resemblance between some children and their parents. Making many of the same proteins causes both parent and offspring to form similar structures that give them similar features. One example of a protein-dependent trait includes hair texture—curly, straight, or wavy.

If a parent's DNA carries a code for a protein that does not function correctly, the children may also make that defective protein. For example, albino animals do not produce the usual amount of pigment that normally provides eye, hair, or skin color. The condition is caused by a defect in the gene that codes for the protein that produces pigment. If the offspring of albino parents inherit this gene, they too may be unable to produce the normal pigment.

PROTEIN SYNTHESIS The process of synthesizing a protein from DNA begins in the nucleus. There, the DNA code of a particular gene is

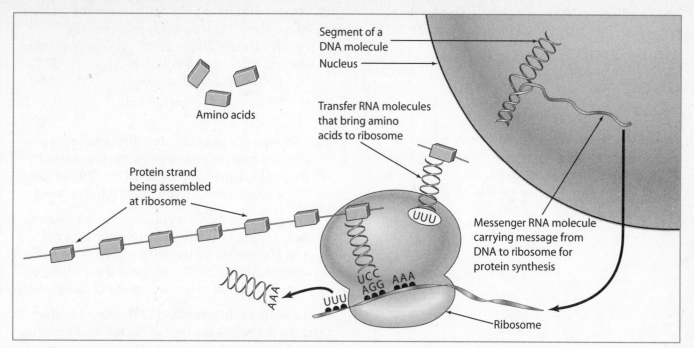

Figure 3-12. **Protein synthesis:** Notice that the DNA in the nucleus supplies the instructions for how to assemble the protein to the messenger RNA molecule. The transfer RNA molecules help assemble amino acids. The whole assembly occurs at a ribosome.

"read" by a special enzyme and used to produce a **messenger RNA** (mRNA) molecule. This mRNA molecule then travels to the ribosomes in the cell's cytoplasm. With the aid of specialized **transfer RNA** (tRNA) molecules, amino acids are moved to the ribosomes for assembly into protein. They are bonded in the order specified by the messenger RNA molecule. In this way, the sequence of amino acids of any protein, and therefore its overall structure, is determined by the gene's DNA sequence in the nucleus. The process is shown in Figure 3-12.

MEMORY JOGGER

RNA molecules, both mRNA and tRNA, are composed of nucleotides that are somewhat different than DNA nucleotides.

RNA nucleotides have a different sugar (ribose) and they have the base U (uracil) instead of T. The base "U" bonds with a base "A" in much the same way the base "T" bonds with the base "A" in DNA.

![maple leaf] **3.4 Review**

1. In a DNA molecule, the letters A, T, C, and G represent (A) bases (B) sugars (C) starches (D) proteins

2. The following diagram represents a portion of a DNA molecule.

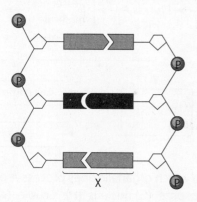

The letter X represents two bases that are (F) identical and joined by weak bonds (G) identical and joined by strong bonds (H) a part of the genetic code of the organism (J) amino acids used to build folded protein molecules

3. The genes an organism possesses are dependent on the (A) types of proteins in the organism's nuclei (B) sequence of bases in the organism's DNA (C) number of ribosomes in the organism's cytoplasm (D) size of the mitochondria in the organism's cells

4. In DNA, the base represented by an A always pairs with the base represented by (F) A (G) T (H) C (J) G

5. The diagram below represents a molecule of
(A) ATP (B) protein (C) carbohydrate (D) DNA

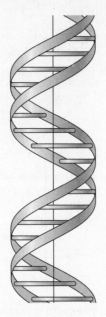

Base your answers to questions 6 and 7 on the following diagram and on your knowledge of biology.

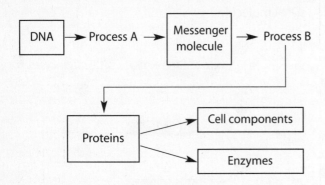

6. Within which organelle does process A occur?
(F) ribosome (G) nucleus (H) vacuole (J) cell membrane

7. Within living cells, which organelles are necessary for process B to occur? (A) ribosomes (B) nuclei (C) vacuoles (D) cell membranes

8. Which statement describes how DNA controls cellular activities? (F) It determines the order of amino acids in protein molecules. (G) It regulates the concentration of molecules on both sides of the cell membrane. (H) It varies the rates of starch synthesis. (J) It coordinates active and passive transport.

9. What is the role of DNA molecules in the synthesis of proteins? (A) They catalyze the formation of bonds between amino acids. (B) They determine the sequence of amino acids in a protein. (C) They transfer amino acids from the cytoplasm to the nucleus. (D) They supply energy for protein synthesis.

10. The sequence of amino acids that makes up a protein molecule is determined by the sequence of (F) bases in DNA (G) glucose in DNA (H) ribosomes in the cytoplasm (J) chloroplasts in the vacuoles

11. The presence of DNA is important for cellular metabolic activities because DNA (A) directs the production of enzymes (B) is a structural component of cell membranes (C) directly increases the solubility of nutrients (D) is a major component of the cytoplasm

For each phrase in questions 12 through 14 select from the list below the type of nucleic acid molecule that is best described by that phrase. A letter may be used more than once.

Types of Nucleic Acid Molecules
(F) Only DNA molecules
(G) Only RNA molecules
(H) Both DNA and RNA molecules
(J) Neither DNA nor RNA molecules

12. Carry genetic information from the nucleus to the ribosomes

13. Are present in the nucleus of the cell

14. Consist of chains of nucleotides

15. During replication, the strands of a double-stranded DNA molecule separate when the bonds between paired bases are broken. In terms of the genetic code, it is important that the molecule separate between the bases and not at some other point.

- Describe how separating between the base pairs maintains the genetic code.

- Explain what happens during replication after the separation of the base pairs.

- Describe the result of the replication process.

16. Identify the two organelles most closely associated with the synthesis of proteins.

17. Assume that a section of double-stranded DNA contains 100 base pairs. If 40 of the pairs contain base C, how many of the pairs would contain base A?

1. Which statement best describes the relationship between cells, DNA, and proteins?

    (A) Cells contain DNA that controls the production of proteins.

    (B) DNA is composed of proteins that carry coded information for how cells function.

    (C) Proteins are used to produce cells that link amino acids together into DNA.

    (D) Cells are linked together by proteins to make different kinds of DNA molecules.

2. Which two organ systems provide materials required for the human body to produce ATP?

    (F) reproductive and excretory

    (G) digestive and respiratory

    (H) respiratory and immune

    (J) digestive and reproductive

3. An enzyme is added to a solution containing starch. The enzyme can digest starch molecules into sugar molecules. The graph below represents data obtained from the experiment on starch digestion.

    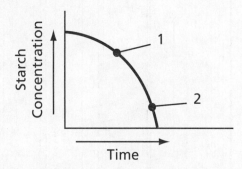

    Which statement best describes point 1 and point 2 on the graph?

    (A) The concentration of sugars is greater at point 1 than it is at point 2.

    (B) The concentration of sugars is greater at point 2 than it is at point 1.

    (C) The starch concentration is the same at point 1 as it is at point 2.

    (D) The starch concentration is greater at point 2 than it is at point 1.

4. The equation below represents a chemical reaction that occurs in humans.

    $$\text{Substance X} + \text{Substance Y} \xrightarrow{\text{enzyme C}} \text{Substance W}$$

    What data should be collected to support the hypothesis that enzyme C works best in an environment that is slightly basic?

    (F) the amino acid sequence of enzyme C

    (G) the amount of substance W produced in five minutes at various pH levels

    (H) the shapes of substances X and Y after the reaction occurs

    (J) the temperature before the reaction occurs

5. Most of the oxygen in our atmosphere comes from processes carried out

    (A) in the soil

    (B) by animals

    (C) in factories

    (D) by plants

6. Two species of bacteria produce different respiratory end products. Species X always produces ATP, water, and carbon dioxide. Species Y always produces ATP, ethyl alcohol, and carbon dioxide. Which conclusion can correctly be drawn from this information?

    (F) Only species X is aerobic.

    (G) Only species Y is aerobic.

    (H) Species X and species Y are both anaerobic.

    (J) Species X and species Y are both aerobic.

7. Plants provide food for animals through the process of

    (A) respiration

    (B) digestion

    (C) photosynthesis

    (D) excretion

8. Which word equation represents the process of photosynthesis?

    (F) starch ⇨ many glucose molecules

    (G) glucose + oxygen ⇨ carbon dioxide + water + energy

    (H) carbon dioxide + water ⇨ glucose + oxygen

    (J) fats ⇨ many monosaccharide molecules

9. Which statement correctly relates the two organisms in the illustration at the right?

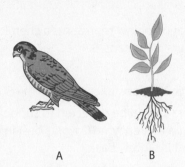

A   B

(A) A carries out cell division, but B does not.

(B) B transports needed organic materials, but A does not.

(C) Both A and B carry out cellular respiration to release energy from organic molecules.

(D) Neither A nor B is able to use energy to combine carbon dioxide and water to make organic compounds.

10. A plant cell that lacks chloroplasts will not

(F) give off oxygen

(G) take in food

(H) give off carbon dioxide

(J) take in water

11. Which process removes carbon dioxide from the atmosphere rather than adding it?

(A) cellular respiration

(B) combustion of gasoline

(C) photosynthesis

(D) deforestation

12. Which process in plants produces carbon dioxide?

(F) respiration

(G) photosynthesis

(H) coordination

(J) digestion

13. What process does the following word equation represent?

$$\text{glucose + oxygen} \xrightarrow{\text{enzymes}} \text{carbon dioxide + water + energy}$$

(A) photosynthesis

(B) breathing

(C) transport

(D) respiration

14. Which of these factors provides most of the weight gain in a growing plant?

(F) sunlight

(G) carbon dioxide

(H) oxygen

(J) soil

15. A small piece of black paper was folded in half and used to cover part of a leaf on a living geranium plant. After the plant was kept in sunlight for several days, the paper was removed. The leaf was then boiled in alcohol to remove the chlorophyll and placed in Lugol's iodine solution, which turns blue-black in the presence of starch. Only the part of the leaf that had *not* been covered turned blue-black.

Which hypothesis was this investigation most likely testing?

(A) Light is necessary for photosynthesis to occur.

(B) Alcohol plus chlorophyll forms Lugol's iodine solution.

(C) Green plants use carbon dioxide in photosynthesis.

(D) Plants use alcohol in the production of chlorophyll.

16. The following diagram represents some events that take place in a plant cell. With which organelle would these events be most closely associated?

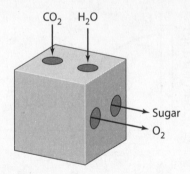

(F) mitochondrion

(G) chloroplast

(H) ribosome

(J) vacuole

17. An enzyme that digests starch will not act upon the sugar sucrose. This fact indicates that enzymes are

(A) specific

(B) synthetic

(C) starches

(D) generalized

18. Which statement best describes the enzyme represented in the following graphs?

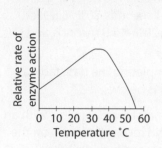 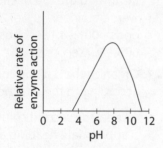

(F) This enzyme works best at a temperature of 30°C and a pH of 8.

(G) This enzyme works best at a temperature of 55°C and a pH of 12.

(H) Temperature and pH have no effect on the action of this enzyme.

(J) This enzyme works best at a temperature near freezing and a pH above 4.

19. Which substance controls each reaction that takes place in both aerobic and anaerobic respiration?

(A) oxygen

(B) enzymes

(C) carbon dioxide

(D) water

20. A final result of the process of anaerobic respiration in animals is the

(F) release of oxygen as a waste product

(G) use of carbon dioxide to form sugars

(H) transfer of chemical energy to a more usable form

(J) enzymatic breakdown of inorganic molecules

Base your answers to questions 21 through 23 on the diagram below, which contains arrows representing different processes occurring in a cell, and on your knowledge of biology.

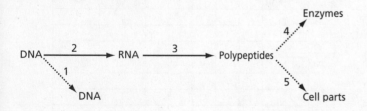

21. Which processes occur in the nucleus?

(A) 1 and 2

(B) 2 and 3

(C) 3 and 4

(D) 4 and 5

22. Process 1 is known as

(F) replication

(G) synthesis

(H) mutation

(J) digestion

23. What is the product of process 3?

(A) a strand of DNA

(B) two complementary strands of DNA

(C) a strand of RNA

(D) a chain of amino acids

24. Twenty-five geranium plants were placed in each of four closed containers and then exposed to the light conditions shown in the data table. All other environmental conditions were held constant for a period of two days. At the beginning of the investigation, the quantity of carbon dioxide (CO_2) present in each container was 250 cm³ (cubic centimeters). The data table shows the amount of CO_2 *remaining* in each container at the end of two days.

Data Table

Container	Color of light	CO_2 (cm³) at start	CO_2 (cm³) remaining after 2 days
1	blue	250	50
2	red	250	75
3	green	250	200
4	orange	250	150

• Identify the independent variable in this investigation.

• What is the problem being investigated in this experiment?

• What other inorganic chemical compound was used by the plants during this investigation?

• Explain what happened to the "missing" CO_2.

Base your answers to questions 25 and 26 on the graph below that illustrates a single species of bacteria grown at various pH levels.

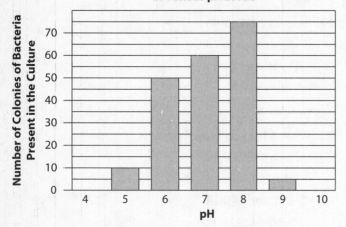

Number of Colonies of Bacteria Present at Various pH Levels

25. The most likely reason there are no colonies in cultures of this species at pH 4 and at pH 10 is that

(A) these bacteria could successfully compete with other species of bacteria at these pH values

(B) there are more predators feeding on these bacteria at pH 4 and pH 10 than at other pH levels

(C) at pH 4 and pH 10 the environment is too acidic or too basic for the bacteria to grow

(D) fertilization cannot occur in these bacteria at pH 4 or pH 10

26. Which statement is supported by data from this graph?

(F) All species of bacteria can grow well at pH 7.

(G) This type of bacterium would grow well at pH 7.5.

(H) This type of bacterium would grow well at pH 2.

(J) Other types of bacteria can grow well at pH 4.

Base your answers to questions 27 and 28 on the information below.

An investigation was carried out to measure the rate of activity of catalase, an enzyme that breaks down hydrogen peroxide. Five 40-mL solutions of the enzyme at concentrations of 20%, 40%, 60%, 80%, and 100% were prepared.

A filter paper disk was placed in each enzyme solution. Each soaked disk from the different enzyme concentrations was then added to different cups containing 30 mL of 1% hydrogen peroxide.

The rate of catalase activity was inferred from measurements of how fast the disks rose from the bottom to the top of each cup. The following data were obtained: 40%–12.1 seconds, 80%–5.8 seconds, 100%–4.1 seconds, 20%–15.8 seconds, and 60%– 9.9 seconds.

27. Organize the data by completing the data table, according to the directions below.

• Label the second column of the data table with an appropriate heading and record that label on the y-axis of the graph. Be sure to include units.

• Complete the data table so that the enzyme percentage increases from the top to the bottom of the table.

Enzyme Concentration (percent)	

Using the information in the data table, construct a line graph on the grid provided, following the directions below.

• Mark an appropriate scale on each axis.

• Plot the data from your data table. Surround each point with a small circle and connect the points.

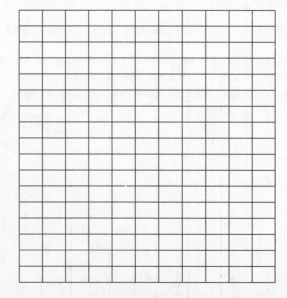

Percentage of Catalase

28. Discuss the functioning of enzymes such as catalase.

- Describe the action of catalase as its concentration changes. Cite data from this investigation in your answer.

- Describe how enzymes such as catalase are affected by changes in pH.

- Describe the effect of temperature changes on the action of enzymes.

- Explain how temperatures around the boiling point of water affect the activity of enzymes, and explain why this happens.

29. You have been asked to demonstrate the effects of different amounts of light on the growth rate of bean plants. State an appropriate hypothesis and then describe the design of an experiment you would conduct to test your hypothesis. You may describe your design by listing the procedures.

30. Compare photosynthesis and aerobic respiration with regard to each of the following

- source of energy

- materials used by each process

- location of each process in the cell

- when each process occurs in plants and animals

Base your answers to questions 31 through 34 on the following diagram and data table and on your knowledge of biology.

A student is studying the effect of temperature on the action of a protein-digesting enzyme that is contained in stomach fluid. An investigation is set up using five identical test tubes. Each test tube contains 40 milliliters of stomach fluid as well as a 20-millimeter glass tube filled with cooked egg white, as shown in the diagram. After 48 hours, the amount of egg white digested in each tube is measured. The data collected are shown in the following table.

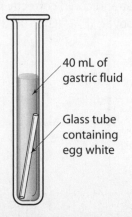

40 mL of gastric fluid

Glass tube containing egg white

Data Table

Tube	Temperature (°C)	Amount of Digestion After 48 Hours
1	4	0.0 mm
2	8	2.5 mm
3	21	4.0 mm
4	37	7.5 mm
5	100	0.0 mm

31. Which is the independent variable in this investigation?

(A) gastric fluid

(B) length of glass tubing

(C) temperature

(D) time

32. What amount of digestion might be expected after 48 hours in a test tube that is identical to the other five test tubes but kept at a temperature of 15°C?

(F) less than 2.5 mm

(G) between 2.5 and 4 mm

(H) between 4.0 and 7.5 mm

(J) more than 7.5 mm

33. The best graph of the results of this investigation would be made by plotting the data on which set of axes?

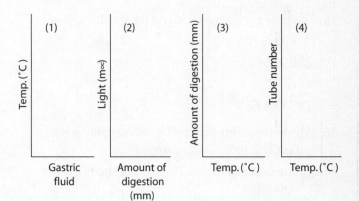

(A) 1

(B) 2

(C) 3

(D) 4

34. The student repeated this same experiment using a glass tube containing potato instead of egg white. After 48 hours, he found no evidence of any digestion. Which statement best explains why no digestion occurred?

(F) The glass tube and potato reacted.

(G) Enzymes are specific.

(H) The temperature was too low.

(J) The pH was too high.

Base your answers to questions 35 through 37 on the following diagram, which represents part of a double-stranded DNA molecule.

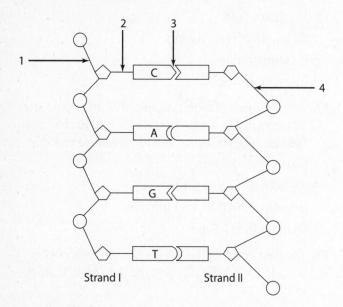

Strand I   Strand II

35. The base sequence of Strand II is most likely

(A) C-G-G-A

(B) C-A-G-T

(C) G-T-C-A

(D) T-G-A-C

36. Which event must occur if a cell containing this molecule is to undergo mitosis?

(F) The bonds at point 3 break, and the molecule replicates.

(G) The molecule separates at point 2, and new bases attach.

(H) The bonds at point 3 break, and the molecule deletes bases.

(J) The bonds at points 1, 2, and 4 break, and new sequences of bases form.

37. If this molecule was used to form a strand of mRNA, which sequence would be found in the mRNA?

(A) G-T-C-A

(B) C-U-C-U

(C) G-U-C-A

(D) G-T-C-U

38. During the winter, many fish eat very little. Some students thought this might be because less oxygen is dissolved in the cold winter water than in the same water during the warm summer months. The students tested the water and found that cold water holds more dissolved oxygen than warm water. They also discovered that the fish have nearly as much food available during the winter as in the summer.

Explain why the fish eat very little during the winter.

39. Animal cells utilize many different proteins. Discuss the synthesis of proteins in an animal cell. In your response be sure to include

• the identity of the building blocks required to synthesize these proteins

• the identity of the sites in the cell where the proteins are assembled

• an explanation of the role of DNA in the process of making proteins in the cell

40. The diagram below represents a portion of DNA.

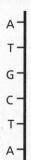

Which DNA strand could correctly pair with the one illustrated above? (F) 1 (G) 2 (H) 3 (J) 4

(1)	(2)	(3)	(4)
G	T	A	C
C	A	T	A
A	C	G	T
T	G	C	G
C	A	T	A
G	T	A	C

Structure and Function in Organisms

The diversity of life on Earth is enormous. At first glance, it may seem that most living things don't have very much in common. Unicellular organisms, such as bacteria, algae, and protozoans, are quite different in size and appearance. The same is true of the simple plants, such as mosses, and animals without backbones, the invertebrates. Complex vertebrates, including humans, have many features in common. Complex plants appear to be very different from the vertebrates. In spite of all these differences, all living things actually have a lot in common.

All organisms have adaptations that enable them to carry out the basic life functions associated with obtaining food, processing and using food, and getting rid of waste products. They must all maintain stability by responding appropriately to environmental changes—both internal and external. Finally, some of each species must reproduce if the species is to continue to survive.

4.1 Adaptations for Nutrition

VOCABULARY			
angiosperms	flagella	locomotion	transport
autotroph	gas exchange	nutrition	vascular tissue
autotrophic nutrition	heterotroph	pseudopodia	
cilia	heterotrophic nutrition	transpiration	

Nutrition

Nutrition includes all the activities by which organisms obtain and process food. Nutrients in food consist of various kinds of large organic molecules, along with some smaller organic molecules and inorganic substances such as water and minerals. Foods furnish living things with the basic compounds needed for energy, growth and repair, and the maintenance of homeostasis.

TYPES OF NUTRITION There are two types of nutrition, autotrophic and heterotrophic. In **autotrophic nutrition** the organism manufactures organic compounds from inorganic raw materials. Such organisms are called **autotrophs**. Most autotrophs, such as algae and green plants, use photosynthesis to store energy in food molecules. Some bacteria are chemosynthetic. Chemosynthesis is another form of autotrophic

nutrition, which uses chemical rather than light energy to make food.

In **heterotrophic nutrition**, the organism cannot make organic compounds from inorganic raw materials. These organisms must obtain organic materials from other living organisms or their products. Such organisms are called **heterotrophs**. Heterotrophs include animals and fungi, along with many unicellular bacteria and protozoans.

Adaptations for Photosynthesis

Some algae may drift from place to place in their watery environment, while other algae have adaptations for moving around. Most plants grow in one place their entire life. To meet their needs, all photosynthetic autotrophs must grow where light is available and where can they also obtain the chemicals they need for survival: water, carbon dioxide, oxygen, and minerals.

Angiosperms, one of the most successful groups of complex plants, have four major organs: roots, stems, leaves, and flowers. The roots, stems, and leaves carry out the basic life functions. Flowers are reproductive organs. (See Figure 4-1.)

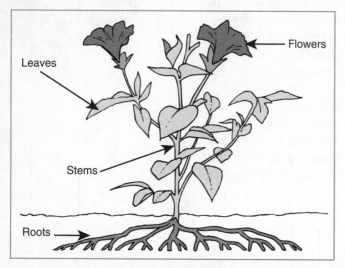

Figure 4-1: **The organs of complex plants.**

The roots are an adaptation for holding the plant firmly in the soil. Roots also have special features that help them absorb water and minerals from the soil and transport them up to the leaves where they are used.

The cells that plants use for transporting water, minerals, and dissolved food form the **vascular tissue** of the plant. Vascular tissue consists of columns of cells that function as tubes for transport. When the amount of food produced by the leaves is more than needed at the time, the plant transports it to the stem, the roots, or both for storage. The stems (trunks) of trees are made up almost entirely of vascular tissue.

DIGGING DEEPER

Much of the food reserves of plants are in the form of large, insoluble starch molecules.

When food is in limited supply, enzymes digest these food reserves to produce small sugar molecules, which can then be transported to where they are needed.

The leaves of green plants are well adapted for photosynthesis. They are usually flat and thin. This allows light to reach most of the cells of the leaf. Leaves are arranged to get the greatest exposure to available light. Openings in leaves called **stomates** enable the plant to exchange gases with the outside environment. Carbon dioxide that diffuses into a leaf through the stomates can then be used for photosynthesis.

Water from the roots moves up to the leaves, where much of it evaporates from the stomate openings in a process known as **transpiration**. Transpiration helps to cool the plant in much the same way as the evaporation of sweat cools our skin. The evaporation of water from the leaf also enables leaf cells to retain the minerals that were dissolved in the water carried up from the roots.

Oxygen, a byproduct of photosynthesis, is used by the plant for respiration, both during the day and at night. During the day some of this oxygen never leaves the plant—it is taken into mitochondria for immediate use in respiration. However, during times of rapid photosynthesis, plants produce more oxygen than is needed, and this excess oxygen diffuses out of the leaves through stomates. Excess oxygen produced by green plants is the source of the oxygen that all animals and other aerobic organisms rely on for survival. Plants must take in oxygen through the stomates at night when no photosynthesis is occurring.

Heterotrophs and Locomotion

Locomotion is the ability to move from place to place. Many heterotrophs rely on locomotion as a means of finding food, escaping enemies, and finding mates for reproduction.

DID YOU KNOW?

Some heterotrophs have adaptations that enable them to remain in one place, much the same as plants. For example, certain species of sea anemones in the ocean attach to rocks and remain there. They catch food that swims by and touches their stinging tentacles. The stingers also protect them from predators. The male sex cells of sea anemones are released into the water and find their way to egg cells of other individuals of their species.

Single-celled protozoans may have one of several adaptations for locomotion. Some, such as amoebas, use **pseudopodia**, which are extensions of their flexible cell membrane that enable them to move in flowing motion. Others use hair-like extensions from their cell membrane called **flagella**. Flagella move back and forth or in a whip-like motion to move these organisms around. Sperm cells of many organisms are often propelled by flagella. **Cilia**, used by paramecia and other protozoans, consist of many very short, hair-like projections from the cell membrane. As cilia move back and forth in a coordinated fashion, the organism swims through the water. (See Figure 4-2.)

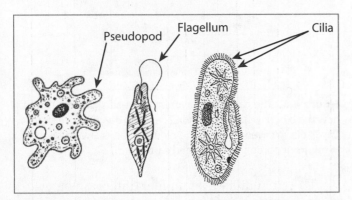

Figure 4-2. Some adaptations for locomotion in protozoans.

Movement in mammals and many other animals involves the interaction of muscles and bones. The human muscular and skeletal systems, shown in Figure 4-3, work together to provide support for the body and to make movement possible. Other vertebrates also have bones and muscles. Insects have muscles attached to the body wall, which is actually an external skeleton. As different groups

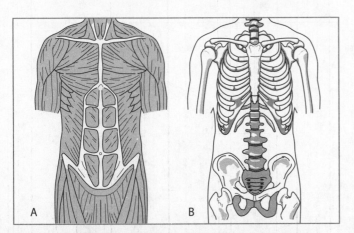

Figure 4-3. The human muscular (A) and skeletal systems (B): Bones provide support; the muscles move the bones of the arms, legs, and other parts of the skeleton.

of muscles contract and relax, they move the parts of the skeleton to which they are attached.

Adaptations for Digestion

Digestion is the process of breaking down large molecules into smaller ones that can enter or leave cells. These end products of digestion are easily transported within an organism.

Bacteria and some other heterotrophs have no mouth and cannot take in food in the same way many animals can. These organisms commonly secrete enzymes to the outside where the enzymes break large food molecules into smaller ones. These molecules can then enter the cell or cells by diffusion or related processes. Fungi and molds often use this method of obtaining food.

MEMORY JOGGER

The food made by plants during photosynthesis is in the form of small molecules and does not require digestion. However, plants often store food in the form of larger molecules, and these require digestion before they can be transported. The process of digestion in plants is similar to the process in animals—it involves the use of specific enzymes.

Heterotrophs have many adaptations associated with digestion. Protozoans may engulf food particles, forming food vacuoles in the cell. Digestion occurs in food vacuoles with the aid of enzymes. In some of the simpler multicellular animals, the mouth only connects to a digestive pouch or sac into which enzymes are released to break down the food.

Like humans, many animals have a tubular digestive system with specialized parts. Teeth are one adaptation some animals have to begin the breakdown process. Other animals, such as birds and some insects, use a muscular gizzard to grind the food into smaller particles. Along the "food tube," specific enzymes and other chemicals are released into the digestive system, and the food is broken down in a specific sequence of steps.

Any food materials that cannot be broken down are eliminated from the body as waste. Cellulose, sometimes called fiber, is one such substance that cannot be digested by humans. In the process of moving through the digestive tract, fiber helps the muscle tissue move the digested and undigested food along.

Notice the similarities between the tubular digestive system of a grasshopper, Figure 4-4, and the digestive system of a human, Figure 4-5. Both have a series of organs that perform specific parts of the digestive process.

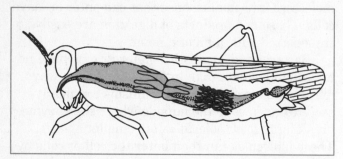

Figure 4-4. The digestive system of a grasshopper is shaded in this illustration.

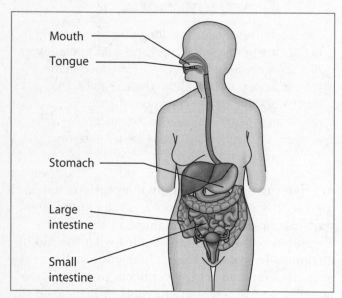

Figure 4-5. The human digestive system

Adaptations for Transport

Circulation involves the movement of materials inside the cell and between parts of a multicellular organism. As mentioned earlier, plants use vascular tissue to move food molecules through the plant for storage or to get the molecules to cells that will use them. Protozoans and other one-celled organisms move materials internally by using cytoplasm as a transport fluid.

Capillaries, small blood vessels of the circulatory system, are found in close association with the digestive system in more complex animals. These blood vessels absorb and transport the

sugars, amino acids, and other molecules that result from digestion. These molecules are then transported throughout the body by the circulatory system to the cells that use them. This is one example of two body systems working together to meet the needs of the organism. The arrows in Figure 4-6 point out some of the main parts of the rather simple circulatory system of an earthworm.

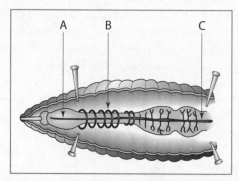

Figure 4-6. The circulatory system of an earthworm. Notice how the blood vessels (A, B, and C) lie along the digestive system. Capillaries involved in absorbing digested food can also be seen in this front portion of a dissected earthworm.

The circulatory system found in complex animals is more intricate than the one in earthworms, but it performs many of the same tasks. It carries digested food and oxygen to cells and carries wastes from the cells to the lungs, kidneys, and skin for excretion. The blood vessels of the circulatory system also carry chemical messengers called hormones, as well as the antibodies that attack foreign substances and provide protection from disease-causing organisms. The human circulatory system, shown in Figure 4-7, includes the heart, blood vessels, and blood.

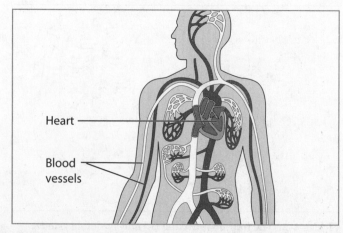

Figure 4-7. The human circulatory system

Cellular Uses for Food Molecules

The cells of all organisms use food for two basic processes: for releasing energy and for growth and repair. The food that circulates in the body and enters cells consists of amino acids, sugars, and other substances.

ENERGY RELEASE Many of the sugar molecules taken in by cells are broken down to release energy and make ATP. This process occurs in mitochondria. If amino acids or the products of lipid digestion are not used in the synthesis of new materials or food reserves, they too may be broken down further and the energy stored in them used to make ATP. Cells require a constant supply of ATP to function, so a constant supply of digested food molecules is needed. Many animals use glucose to synthesize and maintain a reserve of energy-rich carbohydrate molecules in the liver, which can be converted back to glucose and made available quickly when the digestive system cannot provide it.

Gas Exchange Most animals use aerobic respiration to release the energy in the chemical bonds of sugar molecules. This process requires oxygen and produces carbon dioxide as a waste product. Organisms have a variety of adaptations for taking in oxygen and releasing carbon dioxide, a process called **gas exchange**. As one example, a cell membrane is all a protozoan needs to absorb dissolved oxygen from the water it lives in while excess carbon dioxide diffuses out. (See Figure 4-8.)

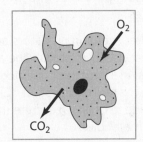

Figure 4-8. Gas exchange in a freshwater protozoan.

Worms live in moist places and oxygen can pass through their thin, moist skin and enter small blood vessels (capillaries) just below the surface. Lungs are an adaptation associated with living in dry environments. Lungs have many moist surfaces and capillaries for gas exchange.

GROWTH AND REPAIR One important use for our food is to replace broken down cells and tissues. This takes place constantly. As animals build or repair tissues, they also grow. Most of the amino acids taken into cells are used to synthesize protein molecules at the ribosomes. Many of the proteins made are enzymes. Many other proteins are synthesized as well, including some that make up muscle tissue, blood cells, hormones, and skin.

The digestive system breaks down the lipids in food to produce easily transported and absorbed molecules. These can be reassembled into new lipid molecules, such as phospholipids for use in cell membranes, or can be stored as fat for an energy reserve.

Plants synthesize a variety of materials from the food they make. Starch is the carbohydrate plants often store in roots and stems. Starch is also stored in seeds where it serves as a source of sugar for a plant embryo until the plant is able to carry out photosynthesis on its own. Plants make cellulose, the material of cell walls, as growth occurs in the plant and new cells are added.

Plants use the minerals they obtain from soil or water. Minerals containing nitrogen, phosphorus, calcium, and other elements are important in the synthesis of necessary organic molecules such as proteins.

Adaptations for Waste Disposal

Excretion is often confused with the removal of the waste products of digestion. **Excretion**, however, is actually the removal of the metabolic wastes produced by the cells of the organism.

In bacteria, protozoans, and other single-celled organisms, excretion typically involves the passage of wastes out of the cell through the cell membrane. Common wastes excreted in this way are carbon dioxide and water from aerobic respiration and nitrogen compounds from protein metabolism. Protozoans living in fresh water often have contractile vacuoles that pump out the excess water that tends to diffuse in from the outside environment.

The simpler animals have many adaptations for waste removal. Worms and others have a moist skin for excreting carbon dioxide. Many animals have specialized groups of cells that form collecting areas and ducts to receive waste products and carry them to the outside. In more complex animals, kidneys and ducts associated with them collect and pass the wastes out of the body. The circulatory system in many animals helps collect the wastes from the body cells and deliver them to the kidneys or other excretory structures for later removal.

Table 4-1. Examples of Adaptations for Some Basic Life Activities			
Function	**Single Celled Organism**	**Multicellular Animals**	**Complex Plants**
Gas exchange	Cell membrane	Respiratory system	Stomates in leaves
Transport of substances	Cytoplasm	Circulatory system	Vascular tissue
Nutrition	Specialized vacuoles	Digestive system	Photosynthesis
Excretion	Cell membrane	Excretory system	Stomates in leaves

In humans and many other animals, the excretory system includes the lungs and kidneys. In some, it may also include sweat glands in the skin. Human excretory organs are shown in Figure 4-9.

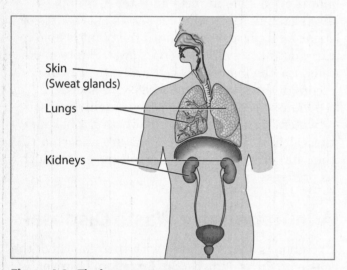

Figure 4-9. The human excretory system

Plants must also excrete wastes. Photosynthesis and cellular respiration both result in the formation of waste products. Other metabolic wastes are produced as well. Plants have evolved ways to use many of these wastes, avoiding the problem of disposal, but some wastes are not useful to the plant. Excess CO_2 and other gases may pass out through the stomates of leaves or openings in stems. Some wastes are retained by the plant—stored safely in special vacuoles—but the increased mass is not a problem since plants do not move around. Some of these wastes may help protect them from attack by insects.

Summing Up—Adaptations for Survival

It is clear that all living organisms have more in common than it would seem. They all require and use food, and they must carry on certain basic activities to stay alive. The different ways these organisms accomplish this reveal many specific adaptations that have evolved over time. Some examples are shown in Table 4-1.

4.1 Review

1. Which statement best describes why enzymes are important to the digestive system? (A) Enzymes form proteins needed in the stomach. (B) Enzymes form the acids that break down food. (C) Enzymes change food substances into molecules that can pass into the bloodstream and cells. (D) Enzymes change food materials into wastes that can be passed out of the body.

2. Which statement best describes the main function of the digestive system in mammals? (F) It rids the body of cellular waste materials. (G) It processes organic molecules so they can enter cells. (H) It breaks down glucose in order to release energy. (J) It changes simple sugars into proteins and carbohydrates.

3. Finding shelter, avoiding predators, and obtaining food are most closely related to the ability of an animal to (A) use structures adapted for movement (B) decrease the rate of digestion (C) transport carbon dioxide to cells (D) excrete the waste products of metabolism

4. The destruction of the vascular tissue in an angiosperm would most directly interfere with the movement of which materials? (F) carbon dioxide out of the leaves (G) water and minerals to the leaves (H) oxygen out of the roots (J) food into the roots

5. A fruit fly is classified as a heterotroph, rather than as an autotroph, because it is unable to (A) transport needed materials throughout its body (B) release energy from organic molecules (C) manufacture its own food (D) excrete wastes

6. Through which process is water lost from the leaves of a plant? (F) transpiration (G) digestion (H) cell division (J) anaerobic respiration

7. Organisms remove metabolic cellular wastes by the process of (A) excretion (B) absorption (C) coordination (D) digestion

8. The diagram below represents a unicellular organism.

Which process is most closely associated with structure X? (F) locomotion (G) circulation (H) reproduction (J) respiration

Use the information below to answer questions 9 and 10.

When a test tube of water containing an aquatic plant is placed near bright light, the plant gives off gas bubbles. When the light is placed at different distances from the plant, the rate of bubbling is affected.

9. Which phrase best describes the independent variable in this demonstration? (A) the concentration of gas in the water (B) the type of aquatic plant in the test tube (C) the amount of water in the test tube (D) the distance of the plant from light

10. Which statement most accurately identifies the gas and the process responsible for its production? (F) It is oxygen gas produced as a result of photosynthesis. (G) It is carbon dioxide gas produced as a result of photosynthesis (H) It is oxygen gas produced as a result of respiration. (J) It is carbon dioxide gas produced as a result of respiration.

11. The following diagram shows an air sac surrounded by the thin-walled blood vessels of a lung.

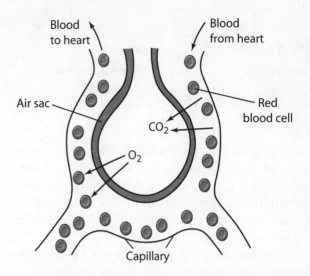

Which two body systems are interacting in the diagram? (A) respiratory and nervous (B) respiratory and circulatory (C) digestive and circulatory (D) reproductive and endocrine

12. How are minerals transported within plants? (F) in solution through the vascular system (G) attached to ATP molecules through the stomata (H) in solution through the guard cells (J) attached to DNA molecules in the vascular system

13. Before being used by individual cells, food must be broken down and distributed throughout the body of a multicellular organism. Name two systems that must interact to accomplish this.

14. Organ systems of the human body interact to maintain a balanced internal environment. As blood flows through certain organs of the body, the composition of the blood changes because of interactions with those organs. State one change in the composition of the blood as it flows through the digestive system.

15. Just like complex organisms, cells are able to survive by coordinating various activities. Complex organisms have a variety of systems, and cells have a variety of organelles that work together for survival. Describe the roles of *two* organelles, and include

   • the names of two organelles and their functions

   • how these two organelles work together

   • the name of an organelle and the name of a system in the human body that have similar functions

4.2 Adaptations for Homeostasis

4.2 VOCABULARY			
AIDS	cancer	negative feedback	stimulus
antibodies	dynamic equilibrium	pathogens	tumor
antigens	guard cells	positive feedback	

Living organisms are always dealing with change. Waste products build up as a result of cell metabolism, disease organisms enter the body, and the environmental temperature falls quickly—all possible ways that things can begin to get out of control.

From bacteria and protozoans to plants and animals, all organisms must respond to such changes on a regular basis. If things don't function properly and the organism does not respond appropriately, it may be unable to survive.

Sensing and Responding to Change

Because an organism's external and internal environment is constantly changing, its homeostasis is constantly threatened. As a result, living things must monitor and respond to changes in the environment. A change in an organism's environment is called a **stimulus**. Failure to detect critical stimuli, either within the organism or in the external environment, could be fatal.

Single-celled organisms are able to detect changes that signal the presence of food or danger. They are sensitive to chemical changes in their environment, such an increase in salt concentration that may be harmful. Some use cilia and others use flagella to move away from the potential danger.

Some protozoans are capable of photosynthesis. One, the euglena, even has an "eye spot" in the cell that is able to detect the presence of light. When it senses light, it uses its flagellum to move toward the light. Freshwater protozoans can also detect when too much water has entered the cell from the surrounding environment and activate their contractile vacuoles to deal with it.

Plants do not have nervous systems, but they are capable of many responses to changes in their environment. Many produce hormones that circulate through the vascular system or pass from cell to cell to regulate activity. The light plants normally receive comes from above the plant. If a plant is given light from one side, as shown in Figure 4-10, plant growth hormones will cause cells on the darker side of the stem to grow longer than those on the lighted side, which results in the stem bending toward the source of light.

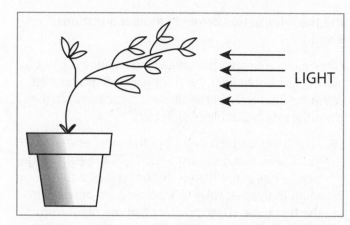

Figure 4-10. **Plant hormones influence growth toward light.**

Plants and some animals can also sense changes in the length of daylight. As seasons change, days get longer or shorter. Detecting these changes is important for animals that migrate or hibernate, for plants that lose their leaves for the winter, and plants that flower at the best time of year for reproductive success.

Multicellular organisms can detect and respond to change at both the cellular and the organismal level. In animals, one such adaptation is a nervous system. Animals exhibit a variety of

Table 4-2: Responses to Environmental Change

Organism	Change (stimulus)	Response
A bacterial species	Temperature falls below a certain point	The bacteria produce a chemical that acts like antifreeze.
Many plants	Air is hot and dry	Stomates in leaves close to conserve water.
Monarch butterflies	Detect bright colors	The butterflies fly toward nearby flowers.
Rabbits	Hear a loud noise	Hormones are released that increase alertness and speed up heart rate in case the rabbit must flee from danger.
Some plants	Feeding by insects	Plants release chemicals with bad taste to repel insect.

different types of nervous systems, ranging from simple to complex. A jellyfish has a very simple net-like system, yet it can sense that an object in the environment is touching it.

DID YOU KNOW?

Jellyfish also have a chemical sense to determine whether the object that touched it is food or not. If the object appears to be food, the jellyfish may fire specialized stinging cells in response and capture the prey. If the organism touching it is too large to be food, the stinging cell response serves as a defense mechanism.

Many animals have sensory organs as part of their nervous system. Eyes, ears, and antennae are all sense organs that have evolved over time. The nervous system of insects allows them to use the senses of sight and smell to find food. The nervous system also coordinates the beating of their wings as they fly toward the food. Many animals can detect changes in temperature, allowing them to respond by shivering, panting, sweating, or other means of keeping their body temperature within normal limits.

The endocrine system is another adaptation for responding to environmental changes—both internal and external. The endocrine system in some complex animals is made of several glands that produce hormones. Hormones are often released into the circulatory system in response to a stimulus detected by the nervous system. In some animals, environmental stimuli trigger the flow of sex hormones. These hormones may stimulate physical or behavioral changes in the animal associated with the breeding season.

Some additional examples of responses organisms have to changes they encounter are shown in Table 4-2.

Dynamic Equilibrium

Organisms have a variety of mechanisms that maintain the physical and chemical aspects of the internal environment within the narrow limits that are favorable for cell activities. Homeostasis is a result of these responses. Homeostasis is not always a steady, unchanging condition. It often involves constant small corrections around a normal level.

Dynamic equilibrium is the term used to describe the small corrections that keep the internal environment within the limits needed for survival. In Figure 4-11, on the following page, notice how these small corrections include a narrow range of variations. Certain microorganisms or diseases can interfere with dynamic equilibrium and therefore with homeostasis. Organisms have mechanisms to deal with such interference and restore the normal state. Homeostatic adjustments have their limits. They can operate only within certain set ranges.

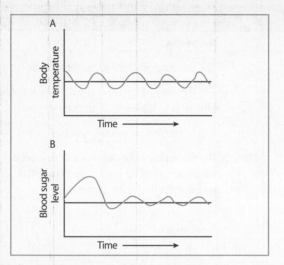

Figure 4-11. **Dynamic equilibrium:** (**A**) Temperature: The body temperature of many mammals and birds shows a regular pattern of slight changes around a "normal" temperature for the organism. The graph represents the slight differences in temperature that are part of a daily cycle. Mechanisms such as shivering, panting, or sweating may help maintain this range.
(**B**) Blood sugar: Normal blood sugar levels show a rise in blood sugar after a meal, but blood sugar level is quickly restored to equilibrium as the hormone insulin prompts glucose to move from the blood to body cells.

Feedback Mechanisms

A feedback mechanism involves a cycle in which the output of a system "feeds back" to either modify or reinforce the action taken by the system. A variety of feedback mechanisms have evolved for helping organisms detect and respond to stimuli. Multi-celled organisms detect and respond to change both at the cellular level and at the organismal level. Their systems detect departures from the normal state and take action to restore homeostasis.

Feedback responses can be simple or complex. A simple feedback response might involve a hormone that regulates a particular chemical process in a cell. A complex feedback response might be an elaborate learned behavior.

POSITIVE FEEDBACK Feedback mechanisms can also be either positive or negative. In systems involving **positive feedback**, a change prompts a response, which leads to a greater change and a greater response.

An early stage of childbirth is a positive feedback system. The first contractions push the baby's head against the base of the uterus, which causes stronger contractions in the muscles surrounding the uterus, which increases the pressure of the baby's head against the base of the uterus, which causes stronger contractions and so on. Eventually the baby is born, and the feedback cycle ends.

NEGATIVE FEEDBACK Negative feedback systems are the most common. In systems involving **negative feedback**, a change prompts a response, which then cancels or reduces the original response. In this case, a change in the environment can prompt system 1 to send a message, often a hormone, to system 2, which responds by attempting to restore homeostasis. When system 1 detects that system 2 has acted, it stops signaling for further action.

A typical house heating system is an example of negative feedback. The furnace has a thermostat that is set to a specific temperature called the set point. When the room cools below the set point, the thermostat sends a message to turn on the furnace. When the room temperature rises above the set point, the thermostat stops sending the message, and the furnace shuts down. (See Figure 4-12.)

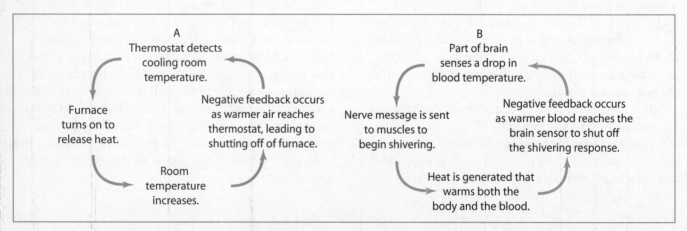

Figure 4-12. **Negative feedback systems:** (**A**) The furnace and thermostat in most houses are part of a negative feedback system.
(**B**) Like the household heating system, the regulation of body temperature is a negative feedback system.

Regulating human body temperature uses a similar system. A structure in the brain detects a blood temperature that is too low. This brain structure then sends a signal to muscles, causing them to contract and relax in rapid cycles. The result is shivering, which generates body heat. When shivering has sufficiently warmed the body and blood, sensors in the brain detect the change, and the signal to shiver stops.

Cell/Organ Feedback Interactions

Maintaining dynamic equilibrium often involves interactions between cells and body organs or systems. For example, certain cells in the body monitor the level of glucose in the blood. When the glucose level is above normal limits, the pancreas, an organ of the endocrine system, secretes insulin. Insulin is a hormone that prompts glucose to move from the blood into body cells, resulting in a lower glucose level in the blood.

Another hormone secreted by the pancreas works in the opposite way. When the glucose level in the blood is too low, this second hormone prompts the release of glucose stored in the liver. The negative feedback process is shown in Figure 4-13.

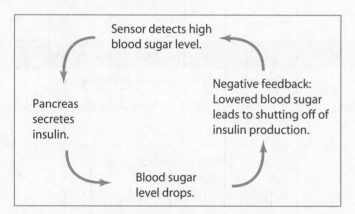

Figure 4-13. Negative feedback involving blood sugar level

Other examples of cell/organ feedback interactions include the following:

- Increased muscle activity often stimulates an increase in heart rate and breathing rate. If this did not occur, the muscles would not receive the increase in blood flow to provide the nutrients and oxygen they need to continue working.

- When leaves detect a water shortage (either due to a drought or just a very hot, dry day), **guard cells**—specialized cells that surround stomate pores on the surface of the leaf—change shape to close the stomates and reduce evaporation. When the stomates are open, water can exit from the leaf, and CO_2 can enter. This situation commonly exists when the sun is shining, the air is warm, and water is available in the soil. With the stomate pores closed, gas exchange is limited and photosynthesis slows down because little CO_2 is available. The process is shown in Figure 4-14.

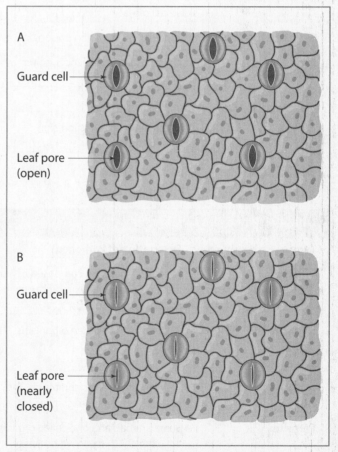

Figure 4-14. Guard cell activity on the surface of a leaf: (**A**) The guard cells have opened the pores (stomates) in the leaf, allowing gas exchange between the leaf and the environment. (**B**) The guard cells have nearly closed the pores in the leaf, thus protecting the leaf from drying out.

Disease and Homeostasis

Disease is any condition that prevents the body from working as it should. As a result, the body may fail to maintain homeostasis. Diseases in humans may be caused by infectious organisms, called pathogens, or result from abnormal cells in the body that lead to cancer. Disease may also result from toxic substances, poor nutrition, organ malfunction, an inherited disorder, or risky personal behavior. All can lead to a disruption of the body's ability to function normally—that is, to maintain homeostasis. Some examples of these kinds of diseases are noted in Table 4-3.

PATHOGENS There are many potentially dangerous disease-causing organisms in the air, water, and food we take in every day. A variety of **pathogens**—viruses, bacteria, fungi, and other parasites—can interfere with normal functioning and cause serious illness. Plants and other animals can also be infected by these kinds of organisms. Some examples of pathogens and diseases they can cause are shown in Table 2-4.

CANCER Certain genetic mutations in a cell can result in uncontrolled cell division called **cancer**. Exposing cells to certain chemicals and radiation increases mutations and thus increases the chance of cancer. In this disease, genes that control and coordinate a cell's normal cycle of growth and division are altered by mutation. As a result, the cell begins to divide abnormally and uncontrollably. The result is a mass of abnormal cells called a **tumor**.

PROTECTION AGAINST DISEASE Plants, animals, and other living organisms are vulnerable to disease. Humans and other complex animals have the advantage of possessing a well-developed immune system. Plants and many simple animals also have a variety of adaptations that help protect them from pathogens.

Pathogens, foreign substances, and cancer cells have molecules on their outer surfaces that usually identify them to the immune system.

Table 4-3. Causes of Disease

Cause of Disease	Examples
Inherited disorders	Down syndrome, cystic fibrosis, sickle cell disease
Exposure to toxins	Lead poisoning, radiation poisoning
Poor nutrition	Scurvy (vitamin C deficiency), goiter (iodine deficiency)
Organ malfunction	Heart attack, diabetes
High-risk behaviors	Lung cancer, drug addiction, skin cancer, AIDS

Table 4-4. Pathogens and Disease

Type of Pathogen	Description of Pathogen	Examples of Disease Caused by Pathogen
Viruses	Viruses are particles composed of nucleic acid and protein. They reproduce when they invade living cells.	Examples include the common cold, influenza, and AIDS.
Bacteria	Bacteria are one-celled organisms.	Bacterial illnesses include poisoning (from the toxins given off by some bacteria), strep throat, and food poisoning.
Fungi	Fungi include yeasts and molds. They eat by absorbing organic substances.	Examples include athlete's foot and ringworm.
Parasites	Some animals and one-celled organisms are parasites that survive by living and feeding on other organisms.	Parasites include leeches and tapeworms. Malaria and heartworm (a parasitic worm that lives in dogs and cats) are caused by parasites.

These molecules, called **antigens**, trigger a response from the immune system. Toxins, the poisonous wastes of certain pathogens, also can act as antigens.

All cells have potential antigens on their surfaces, but the immune system can usually tell the difference between the molecules of "self" cells, which belong to the body, and "non-self" (foreign) cells, which come from outside the body. When cells of our immune system recognize foreign antigens, specialized white blood cells and antibodies attack the cells bearing those antigens.

WHITE BLOOD CELLS AND ANTIBODIES Some white blood cells are specialized to surround and engulf invading pathogens that are recognized as a threat. Others produce **antibodies**—proteins that either attack the pathogens or mark them for killing. The marked pathogens may then be killed by other white blood cells. In Figure 4-15, notice the Y-shaped antibodies that match the shape of antigens.

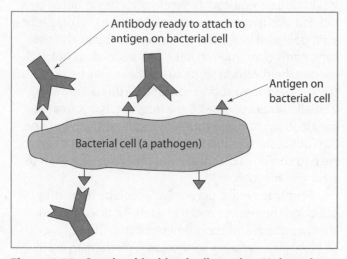

Figure 4-15. Certain white blood cells produce Y-shaped antibodies: The antibodies match the shape of certain antigens on pathogens or abnormal proteins on cancer cells. Note that the antibodies and antigens are not drawn to scale. They would be *much* smaller than the pathogen.

Most of the antibodies and white blood cells that attack an invader break down soon after they have defended the body. However, some specialized white blood cells remain. These cells are capable of quickly dividing and producing more antibodies of the same kind to fight off later invasions by the same invader.

DAMAGE TO THE IMMUNE SYSTEM The immune system may weaken because of age or other factors. Stress and fatigue, for example, can lower our resistance and make us more vulnerable to disease. Some viral diseases, such as **AIDS**, result from an attack on the immune system. Damage from the disease may leave the person with AIDS unable to deal with infections and cancerous cells. A weakened immune system is one reason that people with AIDS often die of infections that a healthy immune system would easily destroy.

 4.2 Review

1. A similarity between the nervous system and the endocrine system in humans is that they both (A) are composed of the same type of cells (B) are composed of many glands (C) help to maintain homeostasis (D) secrete chemicals directly into the blood

2. In complex animals, the activity of the body systems is coordinated by (F) the secretion of hormones and the nervous system (G) the interaction of nerve impulses with the excretory system (H) the movement of digested food by the circulatory system (J) the secretion of hormones and the circulatory system

3. Some plants respond to light with a sudden enlargement of their leaf pores. This response is important because it enables the plant to increase its intake of (A) carbon dioxide (B) water (C) oxygen (D) nitrogen

4. An increase in the blood's level of a thyroid gland hormone decreases the release of a hormone that stimulates the thyroid gland. This mechanism illustrates (F) negative feedback (G) enzyme action (H) immune response (J) positive feedback

5. Maintenance of the pH of human blood within a certain range is an example of (A) chemical digestion (B) synthesis (C) respiration (D) dynamic equilibrium

6. In the human body, homeostasis can be illustrated by the effects of insulin on the amount of (F) proteins digested (G) amino acids absorbed into the blood (H) oxygen transport to the lungs (J) glucose in the blood

7. The following chart shows the amount of oxygen and carbon dioxide exchanged through the skin and lungs of a frog over the course of one year.

The lowest rate of gas exchange is most likely the result of (A) increased mating activity (B) elevated

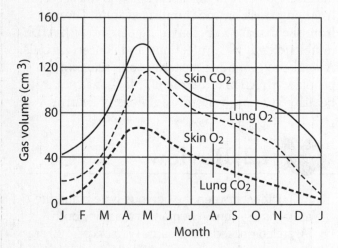

body temperature (C) environmental conditions (D) competition with other species

8. When a person is suffering from an infection, such as strep throat or chicken pox, his blood usually shows a significant increase in the number of (F) enzymes (G) antibodies (H) hormones (J) sugars

9. The body makes chemicals that can help destroy harmful viruses and bacteria. These chemicals are called (A) antibodies (B) vaccines (C) hormones (D) antibiotics

10. Uncontrolled cell division is known as (F) dynamic equilibrium (G) cancer (H) antibody production (J) homeostasis

11. The resistance of the body to a pathogen is called (A) immunity (B) antigen (C) cancer (D) infection

12. During hot weather and vigorous exercise, people sweat. As the water on their skin evaporates, the water molecules absorb heat energy. Why is this process important to the individual?

13. In desert environments, organisms that cannot maintain a constant internal body temperature, such as snakes and lizards, rarely go out during the hot, sunny daylight hours. They stay in the shade, under rocks, or in burrows during the day. Explain how this behavior helps maintain homeostasis in these organisms.

14. Explain the importance of cell-to-cell communication in a multicellular organism, such as a human.

Base your answer to this question 15 on the following technical passage.

Lyme Disease

Since 1980, the number of reported cases of Lyme disease in the United States has been increasing. The vector (carrier) of Lyme disease is the black-legged tick, *Ixodes scapularis*. The disease is spread from infected animals to ticks that bite these animals. Humans bitten by these ticks may then become infected.

The symptoms of Lyme disease do not always occur immediately after a tick bite. An individual may develop a skin rash several days to weeks after being bitten by a tick. Flu-like symptoms, such as headaches, muscle aches, joint pain, and fever, may also develop. Generally, these symptoms clear up even if the individual does not seek medical help. Also, in some cases, there may be no symptoms other than a sudden onset of arthritis. However, in a small number of cases, if the infection is not treated, it may lead to chronic arthritis, disorders of the heart and nervous system, or in a few cases, death. A blood test can help to confirm a diagnosis, and antibiotics are used to treat the infection.

People may take preventive action by frequently checking themselves and their pets for ticks, tucking their pant legs into socks when walking through woods or high grass, wearing light-colored clothing to aid in spotting a tick, and using insect repellent.

15. Summarize some of the key information in the passage.

- Explain how Lyme disease is transmitted.

- Describe one way that people might protect themselves from Lyme disease.

- Describe two symptoms that may occur if a person has Lyme disease.

- Identify one danger of ignoring any symptoms that may develop after a tick bite.

4.3 Adaptations for Reproduction

VOCABULARY			
asexual reproduction	egg	meiosis	species
binary fission	fertilization	mitosis	sperm
budding	genes	sex cells	
chromosomes	heredity	sexual reproduction	

A **species** is a group of closely related organisms that share certain characteristics and can produce new individuals through reproduction. For any species to survive past a single generation, reproduction is essential. All individuals eventually die, but the species continues because individuals reproduce. When individuals reproduce, their offspring begin a period of development that ends in adulthood. Once an individual reaches adulthood, it is usually able to reproduce and continue the species for another generation.

When organisms reproduce, parents pass on specific genetic instructions, called **genes**, to their offspring. The genes present in an organism determine which traits or characteristics the offspring will have. All organisms—whether they are animals, plants, or members of one of the other kingdoms—pass their genetic characteristics along in this manner. Because of this transfer of genetic information, offspring tend to resemble their parents.

Heredity and Genes

Heredity is the passing of genetic information from one generation to the next through reproduction. The hereditary information (DNA) is organized in the form of genes located in the chromosomes of each cell. **Chromosomes** are structures found in cell nuclei that contain DNA and therefore carry the genetic information. (See Figure 4-16.) The DNA molecules carry the genetic information of the cell.

Types of Reproduction

There are two methods of reproduction associated with living organisms: asexual and sexual. **Asexual reproduction** involves just one parent and results in one or more offspring that are genetically

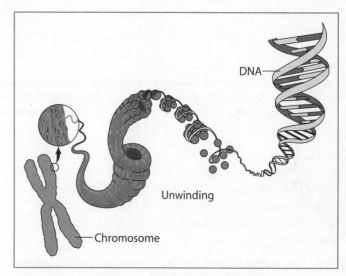

Figure 4-16. Chromosomes contain DNA: Notice that the chromosome contains one very long double strand of DNA.

identical to that parent. **Sexual reproduction** involves two parents and results in offspring that have some genetic material (DNA) from each parent. The result is an organism that may be similar to one or both parents, but is not identical to either.

ASEXUAL REPRODUCTION Organisms that reproduce asexually produce their offspring in a variety of ways. Unicellular organisms often divide into two cells of equal size, thus producing two new individuals. This process is called **binary fission**. The parent in this case *becomes* the offspring! Other organisms, such as molds and mushrooms, produce spores—special cells that have a complete set of genetic information. These individual spores can each develop into a new member of the species. Still others reproduce by **budding**, producing outgrowths of the body called buds, which later detach to become separate individuals. Many plants can develop from parts that are either broken off intentionally by humans or separated

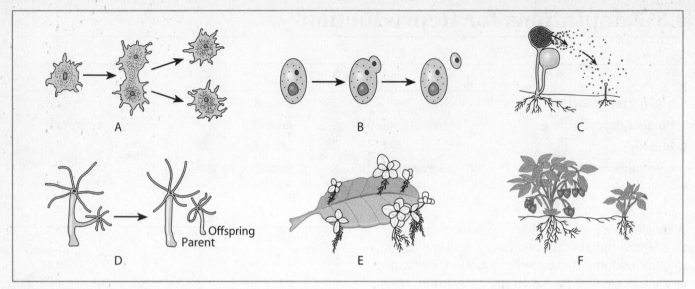

Figure 4-17. **Examples of asexual reproduction:** (**A**) An amoeba divides to form two new amoebas by binary fission. (**B**) A yeast cell forms a bud and eventually divides into two cells that are different sizes but genetically alike. (**C**) Mold spore cells reproduce the mold. (**D**) This animal forms a bud that later separates from the parent. (**E** and **F**) Some plant offspring develop attached to the parent, but later separate to become independent individuals.

naturally from the parent plant. In every case, organisms produced by asexual reproduction have only one parent, and they have the same genetic information as the parent. Figure 4-17 shows some examples of asexual reproduction.

SEXUAL REPRODUCTION In **sexual reproduction**, offspring receive half of their genes from one parent and half from the other. The genes from each parent are carried on chromosomes in **sex cells**, which are also known as gametes, or egg or sperm cells. These sex cells combine in the process called **fertilization**. In this way, each parent supplies half of the genetic information needed to form a complete individual. The **sperm**, which is the sex cell from the father, provides half of the information; the **egg**, which is the sex cell from the mother, provides the other half.

Offspring produced by sexual reproduction, therefore, possess genes inherited from each parent's gametes. Since the offspring get only half of their DNA from each parent, they will not be identical to either of the parents. Also, since each one gets a unique combination of genes from its parents, it will differ from its siblings (brothers and sisters).

Animals rely on a moist environment, either outside in water or internally, for the sperm to swim to the egg for fertilization. Following fertilization, an embryo forms and develops either internally, as in mammals, or externally, as in birds, insects, and many other animals.

Angiosperms and other complex plants also reproduce sexually. Pollen is produced in flowers and released. Pollen is light enough to be carried by the wind, insects, or other animals. Pollination occurs when pollen from the male part of a flower eventually reaches the female part of the same or another flower of the same species. The pollen then produces a pollen tube that provides a way for the male sex cell, the sperm nucleus, to get to the egg nucleus, where fertilization occurs.

Next, the fertilized egg nuclei and other parts of the flower progress through of a series of stages that results in the formation of seeds. Each fertilized egg nucleus normally develops into an embryo plant, enclosed in a seed. In angiosperms the seeds are enclosed in a fruit.

Cell Division

Cell division is the orderly separation of one cell into two. Before a cell divides, the genetic information in the DNA of the cells is duplicated. During cell division, one copy of this information is distributed to each new cell. As a result, each new cell has all the information it needs to function properly.

One-celled organisms use cell division for asexual reproduction. Multicellular organisms mainly use cell division for growth and for tissue repair where cells must be replaced. This process, by which a cell's genetic material divides, creating two complete sets of the cell's genetic material, is known as **mitosis**. Mitotic cell division produces two cells that each have a full set of identical genes and chromosomes—unless an error occurs somewhere along the way.

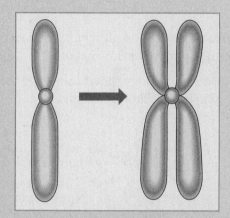
A second type of cell division is meiosis. **Meiosis** divides the genetic material in a way that results in the production of the sex cells required by organisms that reproduce sexually. Each sex cell produced by meiotic division has only half the genetic material needed for a cell to function properly. Meiosis is covered in detail in Topic 5.

Mitotic Division

During the process of mitotic cell division, the double-stranded chromosomes that are visible split into two identical single strands (see Figure 4-19) and move apart to opposite ends of the cell.

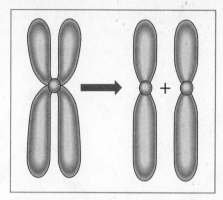

Figure 4-19. Chromosome during mitosis: When cells divide, each double-stranded chromosome separates into two identical single strands.

The process concludes when the cytoplasm divides, resulting in two smaller but genetically identical cells. Mitotic cell division in plants is illustrated in Figure 4-20.

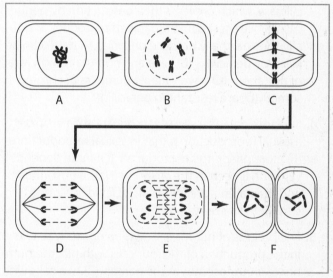

Figure 4-20. Mitotic cell division: The chromosomes in cell A have replicated, forming the double-stranded chromosomes that are finally visible in the cell at stage B. The four chromosomes line up single-file in stage C. Then the strands separate and move apart at stages D and E. The final result is two cells, shown at stage F, each with four single strands of chromosomes containing identical genetic information in their nuclei.

 **4.3 Review**

1. Which statement best describes the process of asexual reproduction? (A) It involves two parents. (B) It requires the combination of sperm and egg. (C) It results in variation in the offspring. (D) It involves the production of genetic copies.

2. A student using a compound light microscope to observe a cell saw a number of threadlike nuclear structures resembling those shown below.

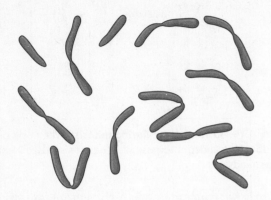

These threadlike structures are composed primarily of (F) fat (G) glucose (H) DNA (J) ATP

3. Some bacteria produce an enzyme known as penicillinase, which prevents their destruction by penicillin. Since these same organisms reproduce asexually, they normally produce offspring that (A) can be killed by penicillin (B) have an abnormally high rate of mutation (C) have variable numbers of chromosomes (D) are resistant to penicillin

4. In plants, one way sexual reproduction differs from asexual reproduction is that in sexual reproduction (F) more offspring are produced (G) more genetic variation is seen in the offspring (H) the offspring and the parents are identical (J) fewer offspring survive to maturity

5. The process of mitotic cell division normally results in the production of (A) four cells with half the number of chromosomes as the parent (B) two cells with the same number of chromosomes as the parent (C) two cells with only one chromosome from each parent (D) one cell with a replicated set of matched chromosomes

6. A man cuts some stems from several plants that are growing in his garden. He places the stems in wet sand until they grow roots, and then he transplants them to new pots. This method of reproducing plants is most like (F) sexual reproduction (G) asexual reproduction (H) natural selection (J) fertilization

7. Which process is represented in the following photographs?

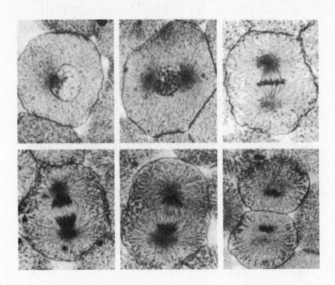

(A) mitotic cell division (B) zygote formation (C) fertilization (D) recombination

8. The following diagram shows some steps involved in preparing tissue cultures in plants.

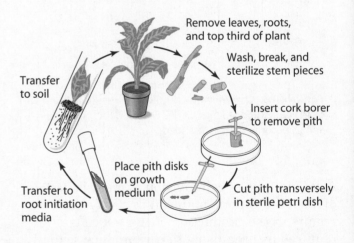

Transfer to soil

Remove leaves, roots, and top third of plant

Wash, break, and sterilize stem pieces

Insert cork borer to remove pith

Cut pith transversely in sterile petri dish

Place pith disks on growth medium

Transfer to root initiation media

Compare the genetic makeup of the offspring plants that are transferred to the soil to that of the parent plant that provided the stem pieces.

Topic 4: Assess Your Understanding

1. Communication between cells is affected if there is decreased ability to produce

   (A) digestive enzymes and gametes

   (B) antibodies and chloroplasts

   (C) hormones and nerve impulses

   (D) antibiotics and stomates

2. Feedback mechanisms are best described as processes that help

   (F) reduce hormone levels to below normal in the blood

   (G) destroy hormones in the blood

   (H) directly control muscle contraction in the leg

   (J) keep body conditions near a normal, steady state

3. The ability of certain hormones to attach to a cell is primarily determined by the

   (A) receptor molecules in the cell membrane

   (B) proteins in the cytoplasm of the cell

   (C) amount of DNA in the cell

   (D) concentration of salts outside the cell

4. The diagram shows some of the specialized organelles in a single-celled organism.

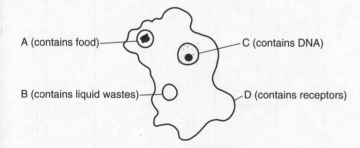

A (contains food)

C (contains DNA)

B (contains liquid wastes)

D (contains receptors)

   • Write the letter of *one* of the labeled organelles and state the name of that organelle.

   • Explain how the function of the organelle you selected assists in the maintenance of homeostasis.

   • Identify a system in the human body that performs a function similar to that of the organelle you selected above.

5. The circulatory and endocrine systems in the human body interact to maintain homeostasis. Describe

   • the function of the circulatory system

   • the function of the endocrine system

   • how these two systems interact to maintain homeostasis

6. Nerve cells are essential to an animal because they directly provide

   (F) communication between cells

   (G) transport of nutrients to various organs

   (H) regulation of reproductive rates within other cells

   (J) an exchange of gases within the body

7. The organism represented below is multicellular, heterotrophic, and completely aquatic. Which other characteristics could be used to describe this organism?

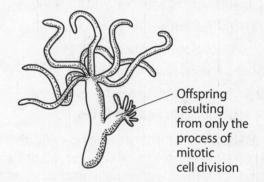

Offspring resulting from only the process of mitotic cell division

   (A) It carries out photosynthesis and needs oxygen.

   (B) It deposits cellular wastes on land and decomposes dead organisms.

   (C) It reproduces asexually and is a consumer.

   (D) It reproduces in a water habitat and is a producer.

8. A characteristic shared by all enzymes, hormones, and antibodies is that their function is determined by the

   (F) shape of their molecules

   (G) DNA they contain

   (H) inorganic molecules they contain

   (J) organelles present in their structure

9. Which statement accurately compares cells in the human circulatory system to cells in the human nervous system?

(A) Cells in the circulatory system carry out the same life function as cells in the nervous system.

(B) Cells in the circulatory system are identical in structure to cells in the nervous system.

(C) Cells in the nervous system are different in structure from cells in the circulatory system, and they carry out different specialized functions.

(D) Cells in the nervous system act independently, but cells in the circulatory system function together.

10. Inhaling carbon monoxide reduces the ability of the blood to carry oxygen. This can lead to brain damage. Which three systems of the human body interact in this situation?

(F) digestive, circulatory, and respiratory

(G) reproductive, digestive, and circulatory

(H) respiratory, circulatory, and nervous

(J) respiratory, reproductive, and nervous

11. The body defends against harmful flu viruses with

(A) red blood cells and hormones

(B) white blood cells and antibodies

(C) white blood cells and enzymes

(D) red blood cells and antibodies

12. A scientist wishes to determine how effective a vaccine is in protecting rats against a contagious disease. Which experimental procedure should the scientist use to determine the vaccine's effectiveness?

(F) Expose 100 rats to the disease and then vaccinate them all.

(G) Give vaccinations to 50 of the 100 rats and then expose all 100 to the disease.

(H) Give vaccinations to 100 of the rats and expose them all to the disease.

(J) Vaccinate 50 of the 100 rats and then expose only the 50 vaccinated rats to the disease.

13. Two organs are considered to be a part of the same body system if the organs

(A) are located next to each other

(B) work independently of each other

(C) work together to carry out life functions

(D) are made up of cells with organelles

14. The diagram below shows the interaction between blood sugar levels and pancreatic activity.

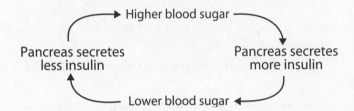

This process is an example of

(F) a feedback mechanism maintaining homeostasis

(G) an immune system responding to prevent disease

(H) the digestion of sugar by insulin

(J) the hormonal regulation of gamete production

15. All of the human organs shown in the diagram interact to help carry out the

(A) removal of waste products

(B) digestion of food

(C) production of hormones

(D) coordination of body movements

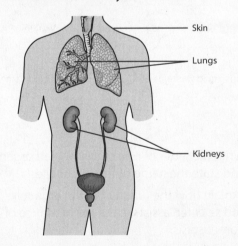

16. The circulatory system helps to maintain homeostasis by interacting with the

(F) nervous system and transporting chemicals produced by nerve cells from one cell to another

(G) respiratory system and producing oxygen for gas exchange

(H) digestive system by removing undigested food from the stomach

(J) excretory system in helping to regulate body temperature through sweating

17. Which structure in a cell corresponds with the function of the human lungs?

(A) nucleus

(B) vacuole

(C) cell membrane

(D) mitochondrion

18. The respiratory and the digestive systems are important in the maintenance of homeostasis. Select one of these two systems and

• name the system and state *one* possible malfunction of that system

• explain how the malfunction disrupts homeostasis

• describe *one* way the malfunction could be prevented or treated

19. The body usually responds to foreign material by forming

(A) hormones

(B) antibodies

(C) vaccines

(D) antigens

20. Bacteria that can survive without oxygen are described as

(F) aerobic

(G) heterotrophic

(H) anaerobic

(J) saprophytic

21. Some deep-sea bacteria live near submerged volcanoes and make their own food using energy derived from minerals coming from the volcanoes. These bacteria would be classified as

(A) heterotrophic

(B) photosynthetic

(C) autotrophic

(D) synthetic

22. Which two organ systems provide materials required for the human body to produce ATP?

(F) reproductive and excretory

(G) digestive and respiratory

(H) respiratory and immune

(J) digestive and reproductive

23. The graphs below show the changes in the relative concentrations of two gases in the air surrounding a group of mice. Which process in the mice most likely accounts for the changes shown?

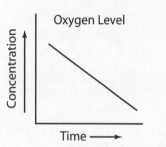 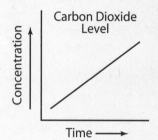

(A) active transport

(B) respiration

(C) evaporation

(D) photosynthesis

24. By which process is the potential energy of organic molecules transferred to a form of energy that is usable by the cells?

(F) digestion

(G) photosynthesis

(H) hydrolysis

(J) respiration

25. The exchange of oxygen and carbon dioxide between internal leaf cells and the external environment will occur most efficiently if

(A) the surfaces of these cells are dry and the stomates are closed

(B) these cells are dry and the stomates are open

(C) the surfaces of these cells are moist and the stomates are open

(D) these cells are moist and the stomates are closed

26. The size of the openings in a leaf through which gases move in and out is controlled by the

(F) root cells

(G) chloroplasts

(H) chromosomes

(J) guard cells

27. The diagram below represents a cell that will undergo mitosis.

Which diagram best illustrates the daughter cells that result from a normal mitotic cell division of the parent cell shown?

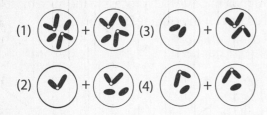

(A) diagram 1

(B) diagram 2

(C) diagram 3

(D) diagram 4

28. Many different feedback mechanisms have evolved over time. These mechanisms allow an organism to respond to changes in both its internal and external environment. Select an organism and explain how feedback allows it to respond to environmental changes:

- Identify the organism and a specific feedback process it uses.
- Describe how this feedback process works within that organism.
- Explain how the feedback specifically helps the organism maintain homeostasis.

29. When microscope slides are stained to show blood cells, the small red blood cells that appear on the slides are much more numerous than the large white blood cells. This supports the concept that

(A) the body's need for white blood cells is less than its need for red blood cells

(B) red cells are more numerous because they are smaller than white blood cells

(C) the nuclei of the white blood cells help them work more efficiently than the red blood cells, which lack nuclei

(D) each kind of cell is present in the numbers best suited to meet the needs of the body

30. Which statement most accurately describes the process of respiration?

(F) It occurs only in plants during the daylight hours and involves the exchange of gases.

(G) It occurs only in plants during daylight hours and involves the synthesis of organic molecules.

(H) It occurs continuously in the cells of all organisms and involves the exchange of gases.

(J) It occurs continuously in the cells of all organisms and involves the synthesis of organic molecules.

31. Human growth and sexual development are controlled by

(A) nerves

(B) hormones

(C) the digestive system

(D) the excretory system

32. Explain how the endocrine system acts to affect blood sugar levels.

- Identify the specific substance produced by the endocrine system.
- Explain the role of this substance in relation to blood sugar.
- Identify how this control system uses feedback to maintain homeostasis.

33. A student is frightened by a loud noise, which results in a hormone being released into the blood. The hormone causes the student's heart to beat rapidly. The two systems that work together to cause this reaction are the endocrine system that secretes the hormone and the

(A) nervous system

(B) reproductive system

(C) excretory system

(D) digestive system

34. Which important human process is represented in the following diagram?

(F) coordination

(G) digestion

(H) excretion

(J) cell respiration

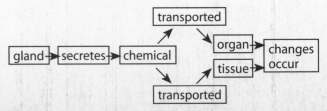

Inheritance of Traits: Genetic Continuity

In the process of sexual reproduction, offspring receive half of their genetic information from each parent. This requires a way to divide the genetic information from each parent in half. There must also be a process to ensure that offspring will receive a full set of genetic instructions that will enable them to develop and function normally. In addition, there must be a way for the genetic instructions to be carried out. And, as in all biological processes, sometimes things go wrong. Scientists now have a good understanding of how each of these things occur—giving us much knowledge about the way traits are expressed and passed from one generation to the next.

5.1 Introduction to Heredity

VOCABULARY			
alleles	embryo	homologous chromosomes	zygote
differentiation	gametes		

Sexual Reproduction and Inheritance

GENES AND ALLELES The cells of most organisms contain a specific number of chromosomes. For example, humans normally have 46 chromosomes in every body cell, while a fruit fly has 8. These chromosomes are in pairs, with the two chromosomes of each pair carrying genes for the same traits. (An exception to this is the sex chromosomes. These are discussed in Section 5.3.)

In sexual reproduction, the **gametes** (sperm and eggs) each have one half of the organism's genetic information. They contain only one chromosome of each pair that is present in the body cells of that organism. However, a full set of genetic information is needed to produce a complete individual. When sperm and an egg combine during fertilization, the chromosomes are paired up once again. At this point all of the required genetic information is present in the fertilized egg and development can proceed.

The two chromosomes forming each pair are called **homologous chromosomes**. They carry genes for the same traits and can be recognized by particular features, including basic shape and size.

If a gene for eye color is located on one of these two paired chromosomes, another gene for eye color will be in the same location on the other chromosome of the pair. The specific DNA information contained in the gene is known as an allele.

Alleles are different forms of a gene associated with an inherited trait. For example, the gene for blood type in humans has several different alleles: one for type A, one for type B, and one for type O. Each of these alleles has a different base sequence in the section of the DNA molecule that is the blood type gene. The two alleles on homologous chromosomes may be the same or they may differ. In the case of blood type, several combinations are possible.

MEMORY JOGGER

Each gene is a specific sequence of nitrogen bases along a portion of a DNA molecule. These genes usually code for the production of a specific protein. It is the proteins an organism synthesizes that make the organism unique.

Some traits that an organism inherits are readily observable. These include traits such as hair color, leaf shape, flower scent, and wing structure. The overall structure of the body is also an observable trait that is inherited from the parents. Some children, for example, inherit long, slender toes or large ear lobes.

Other traits are not so obvious. Less obvious traits may involve how some of the body's chemicals function. Examples include the ability to produce insulin, the types of receptors present on a cell membrane, and whether an individual can make a specific respiratory enzyme.

The traits inherited by an individual are determined by the alleles present for one pair of genes or on several pairs of genes. It is also true that a single pair of genes can sometimes influence more than one trait. Table 5-1 lists several of these variations.

Table 5-1. Human Traits Inherited with Different Numbers of Gene Pairs	
Trait	**Number of Gene Pairs Involved in Determining the Trait**
Cystic fibrosis	Single gene pair
Skin color	Multiple gene pairs
Sickle cell disease	Single gene pair affecting multiple traits

ZYGOTE FORMATION At fertilization, the gametes unite to form a **zygote**—a fertilized egg cell that contains all of the genetic information needed by the offspring. Since each sex cell contains a unique combination of genetic material, the result of the random combination of any sperm with any egg explains the variation found in offspring produced by sexual reproduction. This variation plays a key role in evolutionary change and species survival.

The zygote contains all the information necessary for growth, development, and eventual reproduction of the organism. The zygote divides by mitosis to form a multicellular organism. Fertilization, zygote formation, and some early mitotic divisions that occur in development are illustrated in Figure 5-1.

DNA and Individuality

GENE EXPRESSION Although an individual's body cells all originally come from a single cell, the body is made up of many types of cells. Each body cell's nucleus—whether it is a nerve cell, skin cell, or bone cell—has a complete set of identical genetic instructions for that individual.

During the early stages of development, the cells that are formed by mitotic division begin to undergo **differentiation**, which simply means that they become different from one another. This leads to the formation of specialized cells, which form the tissues, and then the organs, of multicellular organisms. In an **embryo**, an organism in an early stage of development, all the genetic information in each cell starts out the same.

For years, scientists wondered how cells with identical genetic instructions could be so different. The answer is that each kind of cell uses only some of the genetic information it contains. A cell uses only the instructions it needs to operate its own kind of cell.

Different genes are activated or deactivated in certain cells, causing them to make only some of the many proteins they are capable of synthesizing. When a gene is actively producing its protein, scientists say that the gene is expressed. For instance, genes for building all of a person's enzymes are in the chromosomes of each cell, but a muscle cell expresses only some of them. The cell therefore produces only the enzymes and other proteins that make it a muscle cell. As a result,

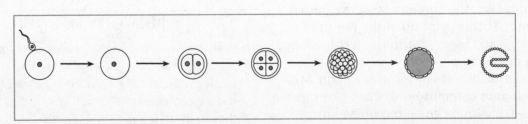

Figure 5-1. Fertilization, zygote formation, and early development: Note that all cell divisions here are by *mitotic* division.

muscle cells become different from others that may express other genes and develop into skin cells, bone cells, or any of the other specialized cells of the organism.

ENVIRONMENTAL EFFECTS There is much evidence that gene expression can be modified through interaction with the environment. The selective activation of genes in a cell may continue as conditions change throughout life. For instance, chemical signals from within the cell or from other nearby cells may activate a particular gene. Hormones are one kind of molecule that can activate parts of a cell's DNA code, leading to the production of a particular protein.

An organism's external environment can also affect the way some genes are expressed in the organism. For example, fruit flies that have genes to develop curly wings will develop straight wings if they are raised in an environment that is cooler than normal.

Another example of an environmentally produced gene modification is a plant grown without light. Such a plant is white instead of green because sunlight is needed to stimulate the gene that produces chlorophyll.

In some animals, such as the Himalayan rabbit, the outside temperature can cause the activation or inactivation of the genes for fur color. When the rabbit's body area is cold, black fur grows. If the same body area becomes warm, white fur grows instead. (See Figure 5-2.) The environment can also influence human genes. For example, in studies of genetically identical twins who were raised in different environments, each twin displayed differences that could only be explained by the influence of the environment on gene expression.

Figure 5-2. Body temperature and fur color in the Himalayan rabbit: From what you know about the activation and inactivation of the genes for fur color in this animal, why do you think the ears, feet, nose, and tail are black?

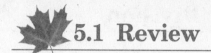 **5.1 Review**

1. Which is primarily composed of DNA? (A) proteins (B) genes (C) nerve secretions (D) fluid in vacuoles

2. Which cell structure includes all of the others? (F) nucleus (G) gene (H) DNA (J) chromosome

3. If the sperm cells of a fish have 12 chromosomes, how many chromosomes would be found in the cells forming the scales of the fish? (A) 6 (B) 12 (C) 24 (D) 48

4. The individuality of an organism is determined by the organism's (F) amino acids (G) nitrogen bases (H) DNA base sequence (J) order of ribosomes

5. The development of specialized tissues and organs in a multicellular organism directly results from (A) cloning (B) meiosis (C) differentiation (D) evolution

6. The following data table summarizes the results of an experiment using red and white primrose plants grown under different temperature conditions.

The Effect of Temperature on Primrose Flower Color

Temperature in Degrees C	Color Coded in DNA	Actual Color Expressed
21°	Red	Red
	White	White
31°	Red	White
	White	White

Which conclusion can be drawn from this data table? (F) Color in primroses is determined only by gene action. (G) Many traits are not inherited. (H) Gene exchanges occur only when the plants are grown at lower temperatures. (J) There is an interaction between environment and heredity.

7. Complex organisms produce sex cells that unite during fertilization, forming a single cell known as (A) an embryo (B) a gamete (C) a clone (D) a zygote

5.2 Meiotic Division

Meiotic cell division is the process by which sexually reproducing animals and plants produce sex cells that contain one half of the normal number of chromosomes for that organism. This means that the sex cells will each provide half of the genetic instructions received by the offspring at the time of fertilization.

Meiotic division begins with a cell that has the full number of chromosomes typical of the species. Depending on the species, the cell contains one or more pairs of chromosomes, carrying paired genes that determine the traits of the organism. Because replication of DNA occurs in preparation for meiotic division, the chromosomes are double-stranded, with identical alleles on the two strands. Figure 5-3 shows an example.

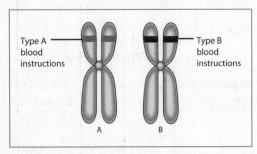

Figure 5-3. **Two chromosomes with different information:** These two chromosomes differ in the specific information they carry. Each strand of chromosome A has the allele (instructions) for type A blood, while each strand of chromosome B has the allele for type B blood. Information for many other traits coded in the genes of these two chromosomes will be different, too.

During the first phase of meiotic division, the double-stranded chromosomes line up in pairs in the center of the cell. The two chromosomes of each pair (still double-stranded) then separate, moving to opposite ends of the cell. Following this separation, the cell divides physically to form two cells.

The second phase involves the division of each of these two new cells. This time, however, the chromosomes line up in single file in the center of

each cell. Each chromosome still consists of two strands. The strands soon separate and move to opposite ends of each of the dividing cells.

When the process is complete, four cells will have been formed, each having half the number of chromosomes of the organism's body cells. Each contains only one member of each original chromosome pair. Meiotic cell division is illustrated in Figures 5-4 and 5-5.

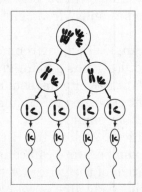

Figure 5-4. **Meiotic cell division in the testes of males:** Note the *four* double-stranded chromosomes (two pairs) present in the original cell. The pairs separate from each other during the first division—resulting in *two* chromosomes in each of two cells. In the next division, the double-stranded chromosomes separate, leaving each final cell with *two* single-stranded chromosomes. These four cells can develop further into sperm cells in male individuals.

Notice that the formation of cells during meiotic division, in which each cell has half the usual number of chromosomes, is very different from the duplication and distribution of a full set of chromosomes that occurs in mitotic division.

Meiotic division in females involves the same number of divisions and chromosome changes as in males. However, instead of producing four cells of equal size, the cytoplasm in a cell destined to become an egg cell divides unequally. This results in one large egg cell and three small nonfunctioning cells called polar bodies. Meiotic division in females is shown in Figure 5-5.

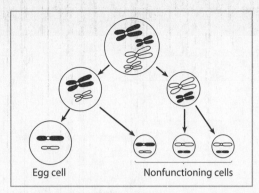

Figure 5-5. Meiotic cell division in the ovaries of females: This process is different from sperm cell formation because the cytoplasm divides unequally, resulting in one large egg cell and three smaller cells that do not function. The egg cell is the one with the most cytoplasm.

Meiosis as a Source of Variation

SORTING OF GENES The events that occur during meiosis do more than simply divide chromosomes into smaller sets and form smaller cells. Meiosis is responsible for much of the genetic variation among the sex cells of each individual. For example, the two members of each pair of chromosomes may carry different alleles, so the way the different pairs randomly line up *in relation to other pairs* leads to many possible combinations in the sex cells that result. Two combinations are shown

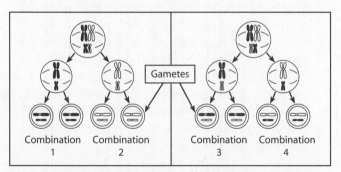

Figure 5-6. Two equally likely combinations of chromosomes lined up for meiotic division: A pair of chromosomes can be arranged in two ways when they pair up at the start of meiosis. This helps increase genetic variation. How many combinations do you see in the gametes? How would more pairs of chromosomes affect the number of possible arrangements?

in Figure 5-6. Notice the position of the black chromosomes of each original pair shown.

CROSSING OVER Another way variation can arise is by the exchange of parts of chromosomes, called **crossing over**. This occurs as chromosomes pair up during the first division. The result is shown in Figure 5-7. Upper and lower case letters are used to indicate different alleles. After separation, each set is unique. This means that there are no two sperm or egg cells, even from the same parent, that are alike.

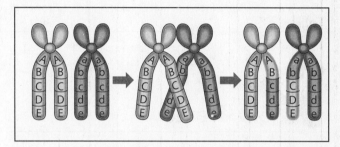

Figure 5-7. Result of exchanging parts between chromosomes: When chromosomes line up in pairs during meiosis (left), their strands often connect or cross over (middle) and then separate in a way that parts are exchanged (right). The result of crossing over is that all four strands carry different combinations of alleles.

RECOMBINATION Recall that in sexual reproduction, a sperm and egg combine at the time of fertilization. As a result of the events of meiosis, each sperm and each egg contain a unique combination of genetic instructions. At fertilization, the full species number of chromosomes is restored—and event known as **recombination**. This exclusive combination of thousands of genes at fertilization produces offspring that may resemble either or both parents in many ways but will not be identical to either of them.

Summary

There are ways in which mitotic and meiotic cell division are similar and ways in which they differ. Table 5-2 on the next page provides a comparison of some of the more important differences.

Table 5-2. Summary of Mitotic and Meiotic Cell Division

Points of Comparison	Mitotic Division	Meiotic Division
Number of cell divisions	One	Two
Exchange of genetic material between chromosomes	No	Yes
Number of functioning cells produced from original	Two	Four sperm (in males) or one egg (in females)
Genetic makeup of final cells produced	Same as original cell	Highly variable gametes produced, each containing half of the genetic information of the original cell
Function of cells produced in multicellular organisms	Growth or replacement of body cells	Combine to form the zygote for reproduction

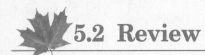 **5.2 Review**

1. The species chromosome number of orangutans is 48. Which diagram represents normal fertilization in orangutans?

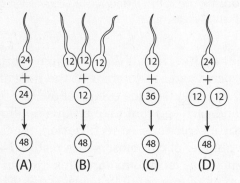

2. A normal body cell of a fruit fly contains eight chromosomes. Which of these correctly pairs the chromosome number with how they were produced? (F) four chromosomes: meiosis (G) four chromosomes: mitosis (H) eight chromosomes: meiosis (J) eight chromosomes: mitosis

3. Compared to the number of chromosomes in a normal human body cell, the number of chromosomes in a normal sperm cell is (A) the same (B) twice as great (C) half as great (D) four times as great

4. An exact duplication of the complete set of chromosomes of a cell, followed by the separation of these duplicate sets into two new cells, is known as (F) mitotic cell division (G) zygote formation (H) meiotic cell division (J) fertilization

5. In sexually reproducing species, the number of chromosomes in each body cell remains the same from one generation to the next as a direct result of (A) meiosis and fertilization (B) mitosis and mutation (C) differentiation and aging (D) homeostasis and dynamic equilibrium

6. The process of meiosis followed by fertilization is necessary to maintain the species chromosome number of a sexually reproducing species. For instance, a species with 24 chromosomes in each body cell normally has offspring that also have 24 chromosomes in their body cells.

Explain the specific way that meiotic cell division and fertilization interact to help maintain the species chromosome number. In your answer be sure to describe

• what happens to the chromosomes during meiosis

• how meiosis affects the number of chromosomes present in a cell

• what happens to the chromosomes during fertilization

• how fertilization affects the number of chromosomes present in a cell

7. When organisms reproduce sexually, the species number of chromosomes is maintained. This can be demonstrated with a diagram like the one below. Complete the diagram by filling in the blanks with the appropriate information.

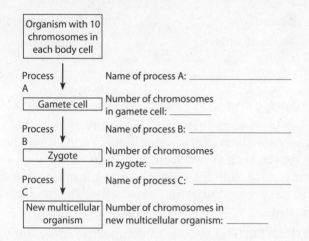

Name of process A: _____

Number of chromosomes in gamete cell: _____

Name of process B: _____

Number of chromosomes in zygote: _____

Name of process C: _____

Number of chromosomes in new multicellular organism: _____

8. The following diagram represents the sequence of events in a cell undergoing normal meiotic cell division.

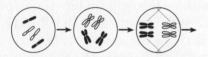

- How many cells will finally be produced?

- How many chromosomes will be in each cell?

- Sketch one of the final cells, showing its chromosomes.

9. Sexually produced offspring often resemble but are not identical to their parents. Explain why they resemble their parents but are *not* identical to either parent.

- Name the process that reduces the genetic material in the gametes of an organism.

- Describe the process that returns the genetic material to the full amount.

- Explain how the process of sexual reproduction results in offspring that are genetically different from each other and their parents.

- Compare the appearance of a parent organism that reproduces asexually with the appearance of its offspring.

10. Crossing over occurs between

(F) homologous chromosomes (G) non-homologous chromosomes (H) gametes (J) cells

5.3 Gene Expression

Foundations of Inheritance

Around 1850, Gregor Mendel studied the inheritance of specific traits in pea plants. The traits he observed occurred as contrasting characteristics. For example, a plant could be either tall or short; its seeds were either smooth or wrinkled; its flowers were either purple or white, and so on. Mendel crossbred plants with contrasting characteristics and did a mathematical analysis of the results for several generations.

From his observations, Mendel concluded that the characteristics of the offspring were the result of inheriting certain factors from the parents. The results of a particular cross could be predicted by the laws of inheritance that Mendel derived: the laws of dominance, segregation, and independent assortment. When large numbers of offspring are produced, these laws predict the ratios of characteristics that are expected to be observed in each generation.

Mendel's work was ignored and forgotten until it was rediscovered in 1900. Then it was noticed that the distribution of chromosomes during meiotic cell division was related to the factors of heredity that Mendel proposed. Breeding experiments with fruit flies showed that each chromosome carries many hereditary factors. These were named genes. It was also learned that genes are arranged along the chromosomes at specific positions and may have different forms called alleles. The separation of alleles during meiosis and their recombination during fertilization account for the laws of heredity that Mendel observed.

Major Genetic Concepts

DOMINANCE If a zygote receives two different alleles for a particular trait, and only one of the alleles is expressed, that allele and its trait are said to be **dominant**. The allele for the gene that is present but not expressed is called **recessive**.

SYMBOLS FOR ALLELES Generally, a capital letter is used to represent a dominant allele. The lowercase form of the same letter represents the recessive trait. For example, T stands for the dominant allele for height in pea plants, tallness, and t represents the recessive allele for height, shortness.

GENOTYPE The genetic makeup of an individual for a particular trait is referred to as its **genotype** and, when dealing with dominant and recessive traits, it is represented by two letters. A tall pea plant that has two alleles for tallness is said to be **homozygous** for the trait and its genotype is TT. A short pea plant would also be homozygous. Its genotype is represented by tt. If the two alleles for the trait are different, Tt, the genotype is **heterozygous** or **hybrid**.

PHENOTYPE The traits that appear in an individual are its **phenotype**. Individuals with different genotypes may have the same phenotype. For example, a pea plant that is homozygous tall (TT) has the same appearance as one that is heterozygous (Tt) for tallness. For the recessive genotype to show, the individual must be homozygous recessive. Only pea plants with the tt genotype are short.

If an individual that is homozygous for a dominant trait is crossed with an individual that is homozygous for the corresponding recessive trait, all of the offspring are heterozygous for the trait. Because of the **law of dominance**, the phenotype of the offspring is the same as the phenotype for individuals that are homozygous dominant. For example, if a homozygous tall (TT) pea plant is crossed with a homozygous short (tt) pea plant, all of the offspring will possess the heterozygous (Tt) genotype. The phenotype of all of the offspring will be tall. The parents in such a cross are called the P_1 generation. The offspring are called the F_1 generation.

Segregation and Recombination

SEGREGATION When a heterozygous individual produces gametes, homologous chromosomes are separated and distributed at random in their gametes. Half of the gametes receive the chromosome carrying the dominant allele and half receive the chromosome carrying the recessive allele. For example, a heterozygous black guinea pig (Bb) produces equal numbers of gametes with the dominant allele (B) and with the recessive allele (b). The process is called **segregation**.

RECOMBINATION When gametes from these heterozygous (Bb) parents fuse during fertilization, each type of gamete from one parent has an equal chance of combining with either type of gamete from the other parent. There are four possible combinations. If the parents are F_1 pea plants with the genotype Tt, the four combinations possible in the offspring are: 1 TT, 2 Tt, and 1 tt.

The genotype ratio for the F_2 generation is 1 : 2 : 1. The phenotype ratio is 3 : 1 (3 tall to 1 short). The reappearance in the F_2 generation of genetic types not present in the F_1 generation is called recombination. Segregation and recombination account for the reappearance of the recessive trait in the F_2 generation, since the original alleles are separated from each other.

PUNNETT SQUARES The results of a particular genetic cross can be predicted using a diagram called a **Punnett square**. The genotypes of the gametes of one parent are placed over the columns of the square and the genotypes of the gametes of the other parent are placed next to the rows.

Where the rows and columns intersect, possible combinations are recorded. The ratios of the genotypes and phenotypes of the offspring can then be determined. In a monohybrid cross, each square represents a 25% chance of occurrence. (See Figure 5-8.)

	T	t
T	TT	Tt
t	Tt	tt

Genotype	Phenotype
25% TT	75% tall
50% Tt	25% Short
25% tt	

Figure 5-8. **Punnett square showing a hybrid cross.**

INDEPENDENT ASSORTMENT Mendel studied seven traits in pea plants. The genes for those traits happened to all be on different chromosomes. Therefore, the segregation of the alleles for one trait is independent of the segregation of any of the others. These traits are inherited independently of any of the others.

Mendel's law of **independent assortment** states that traits are inherited independently. This law applies only to traits that are controlled by genes on non-homologous chromosomes.

GENE LINKAGE If the genes for two different traits are located on the same chromosome, the genes are said to be linked. Alleles that are linked tend to be inherited together. Since a chromosome usually carries thousands of genes, every gene is linked to a large number of other genes. It is the chromosomes that assort independently during meiosis, not the genes.

Linked genes may be separated, however, when crossing over occurs during meiosis. See Figure 5-7 on page 5-5 for a review of this process and note that some genes that are linked at the start are not linked when the process is completed. By separating linked genes on a chromosome, crossing over contributes to variation among offspring.

SEX CHROMOSOMES In the cells of many mammals, there is one pair of chromosomes, the **sex chromosomes**, that determines the sex of the individual. In humans and many other mammals, females have two of the same kind (XX) while males have two distinct sex chromosomes (XY).

The X chromosome is larger and carries more genes than the smaller Y chromosome. All of the other chromosomes are called **autosomes**. Human body cells contain 22 pairs of autosomes and the one pair of sex chromosomes.

Since female cells contain XX, eggs contain one X chromosome. Since male cells contain XY, half of the sperm carry an X chromosome and the other half carry a Y chromosome.

During fertilization, an egg nucleus containing an X chromosome fuses with a sperm nucleus, which may contain either an X or a Y. If the sperm nucleus carries an X, the zygote will be XX, and it develops into a female. If the sperm nucleus carries a Y chromosome, the zygote is XY and it develops into a male. (See Figure 5-9 on the next page.)

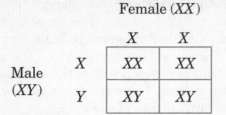

Female (*XX*)

		X	*X*
Male (*XY*)	*X*	*XX*	*XX*
	Y	*XY*	*XY*

Figure 5-9. **Sex determination in humans**

SEX LINKAGE The *X* chromosome carries some genes that do not have corresponding alleles on the *Y* chromosome. The expression of these genes is therefore affected by the sex of the individual. Traits controlled by these genes are said to be **sex-linked genes**.

DID YOU KNOW?

- Sex linked traits are often represented with the sex chromosome and a superscript that indicates whether that chromosome carries the dominant or recessive allele: X^H is a chromosome with the dominant allele for normal blood clotting, X^h is one with the recessive hemophilia allele.
- Sometimes, the letter N is used for the normal condition, with the letter n used for the disorder: X^N and X^n.
- Since the *Y* chromosome does not have the gene, it has no superscript.

Since females are *XX*, they have two alleles for each sex-linked trait. One allele is present on each *X* chromosome. If the two alleles for the trait are different, one recessive and the other dominant, the recessive trait is not expressed.

Males, however, are *XY*. They have only one allele for each sex-linked trait, since the *Y* chromosome does not have an allele for that trait. Therefore, recessive alleles on the *X* chromosome in males will always be expressed. Thus, certain recessive, sex-linked traits appear more often in males than in females.

EXAMPLES OF SEX-LINKED TRAITS Hemophilia, a disorder characterized by the poor clotting ability of blood, is a recessive, sex-linked trait in humans. Colorblindness is another. **Carrier** females carry one recessive allele for these disorders without showing the condition because the dominant, normal allele on the other chromosome is expressed. If a woman is heterozygous for a sex-linked trait,

there is a 50% probability that she will transmit the trait to her sons. Females show the trait only when they are homozygous recessive—when both *X* chromosomes carry the recessive allele. (See Figure 5-10.)

Carrier Mother
(X^HX^h)

		X^H	X^h
Normal Father (X^HY)	X^H	X^HX^H	$X^H X^h$
	Y	X^HY	$X^h Y$

Figure 5-10. **Inheritance of sex-linked trait:** Notice how a son would have a 50% chance of inheriting hemophilia when the mother is a carrier. The probability that a daughter would have the condition is 0%.

Human Heredity

Some knowledge of how human genetic traits are inherited has been obtained by studying the characteristics of many members of related families through several generations. This leads to the construction of **pedigree** charts, which show the presence or absence of certain traits in the members of each generation.

Genetic counselors interpret human pedigree charts. From the information provided by these charts, they can infer the genotypes of certain members of a family. It is often possible to determine the presence of recessive genes in "carriers." The pedigree in Figure 5-11 on the next page represents three generations of a family.

- The father in the P_1 generation (shaded) expressed the trait of interest.

- The original couple had 4 children, a boy and a girl who expressed the trait and a boy and a girl who did not.

- The two daughters in the F_1 generation married. One of the daughters had three children and the other had two.

- The original couple has five grandchildren.

- If the pedigree represented a family with a sex-linked trait, female carriers of the trait would be half shaded to indicate that they carried one normal allele for the trait and one allele for the disorder.

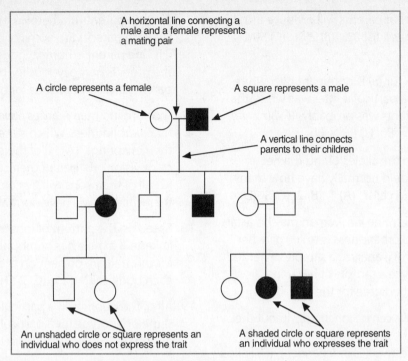

Figure 5-11. Interpreting a Pedigree Chart

This technique would be used when constructing pedigree charts for families with a history of colorblindness or hemophilia. Males would never be carriers, since a male has only one X chromosome.

For example, if colorblindness runs in the family, a male would have either an allele for normal color vision or one for colorblindness on his single X chromosome. A male would be either $X^C Y$ or $X^c Y$. A female would have one of three different combinations. Since a female has two X chromosomes, she could be homozygous $X^C X^C$ for normal color vision, or heterozygous $X^C X^c$ for normal color vision, or colorblind $X^c X^c$.

5.3 Review

1. If a trait that is not evident in the parents appears in the offspring, the parental genotypes are most likely (A) homozygous recessive (B) homozygous dominant (C) homologous (D) heterozygous

2. The phenotype of a mouse's fur can best be determined by (F) mating the mouse with another mouse (G) crossing over (H) looking at it (J) biochemical techniques

3. Genes for a trait are located at corresponding positions on homologous chromosomes. Which term best describes these genes? (A) alleles (B) phenotypes (C) genotypes (D) hybrids

4. An individual possesses two identical alleles for a certain trait. For this trait, the individual is said to be (F) heterozygous (G) homozygous (H) hybrid (J) mitotic

5. Curly hair in humans, white fur in rats, and needlelike spines in cacti all partly describe an organism's (A) alleles (B) chromosomes (C) genotype (D) phenotype

6. Which statement describes how two organisms may show the same trait yet have different genotypes? (F) One is homozygous dominant and the other heterozygous. (G) Both are heterozygous for the dominant for the trait. (H) One is homozygous dominant and the other homozygous recessive. (J) Both are homozygous for the dominant trait.

7. In cabbage butterflies, white color (W) is dominant and yellow color (w) is recessive. If a homozygous white cabbage butterfly mates with a yellow cabbage butterfly, all of the offspring are white. Which cross represents the genotypes of the parents? (A) $Ww \times ww$ (B) $WW \times Ww$ (C) $WW \times ww$ (D) $Ww \times Ww$

8. Genes carried only on an X-chromosome are said to be (F) hybrid (G) dominant (H) segregated (J) sex-linked

9. What is the chance that parents will produce a child with XY chromosomes? (A) 0% (B) 25% (C) 50% (D) 100%

10. In guinea pigs, black fur (*B*) is dominant over white fur (*b*). If one half of a particular litter was white, the genotype of the parents was probably (F) *bb* × *bb* (G) *Bb* × *bb* (H) *Bb* × *Bb* (J) *BB* × *bb*

11. With respect only to the alleles *G* and *g*, a heterozygous female could normally have how many different kinds of egg cells? (A) 1 (B) 2 (C) 3 (D) 4

12. The best way to determine if a woman may be a carrier of the trait for colorblindness is to (F) give her an eye examination (G) analyze a sample of her red blood cells (H) analyze a sample of her urine (J) check her family pedigree for the trait

13. When one of two traits can be inherited without the other, the genes for these two traits are said to be (A) dominant (B) recessive (C) independent (D) linked

14. The pedigree below shows the incidence of Huntington's disease in a family. Huntington's has been found to be a dominant trait.

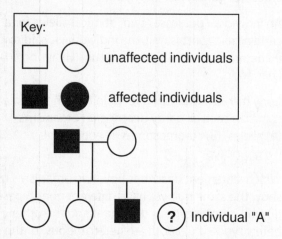

Key:

□ ○ unaffected individuals

■ ● affected individuals

Individual "A"

What is the chance that individual "A" will be afflicted with Huntington's? (F) 25% (G) 50% (H) 75% (J) 100%

15. In humans, the gene for red hair and the gene for freckles are often inherited together because both genes are located on the same chromosome. Which concept is best illustrated by this observation? (A) gene linkage (B) independent assortment (C) dominance (D) hybridization

16. Brown eye color is dominant to blue eye color in humans. What is the probable genetic makeup of two brown-eyed parents who have a blue-eyed child?

(F) Both parents are heterozygous for eye color.
(G) Both parents are homozygous for brown eyes.
(H) One parent is homozygous for brown eyes while the other is homozygous for blue eyes. (J) Both parents are homozygous for blue eyes.

17. A colorblind man marries a woman who is a carrier for colorblindness. Which statement best describes their offspring? (A) All of their sons will have normal color vision. (B) Half of their sons will be colorblind. (C) All of their sons will be colorblind. (D) None of their children will have normal color vision.

18. Based on the pattern of inheritance known as sex linkage, if a male has hemophilia, how many genes for this trait are present on the sex chromosomes in each body cell? (F) 1 (G) 2 (H) 3 (J) 4

19. All of the puppies in a particular litter can have the same phenotype for a particular trait but a different genotype. Explain how this is possible.

- Construct a Punnett square that shows the genotypes of the parents and the possible genotypes of the puppies.

- Indicate which puppies would have the same phenotype.

- Explain how the puppies indicated can have the same phenotype for the selected trait but possess different genotypes.

20. A genetic disorder is caused by a recessive allele (*m*). The allele for the unaffected condition (*M*) is dominant. A woman who is heterozygous for the disorder marries a man who is unaffected. The woman underwent testing because there was a history of the disorder in her family. Even though there is no history of the disorder in the man's family, he was also tested and found to be heterozygous for the disorder. The couple would like to have a child, but they are concerned that their child will inherit the disorder.

- Construct a Punnett square with the genotypes of the woman and the man, and the possible genotypes of their child.

- Identify the probability that the child will inherit the disorder.

- Identify the probability that the child will *not* inherit the recessive allele (*m*).

- Explain how the man can carry the recessive allele and not have anyone in the family affected with the disorder.

5.4 Applying Genetic Knowledge

VOCABULARY			
biotechnology	cloning	gene splicing	karyotype
chromosome mutation	gene mutation	genetic engineering	mutation

Mutations

A **mutation** is any change in the genetic or hereditary material of a cell. Inheritable mutations are those that occur in the sex cells of an organism and can be passed on to future generations. Non-inheritable mutations occur in the body cells of an organism. The number of body cells with the mutation increases as these cells divide, but they cannot be passed on to the offspring of the organism.

Types of Mutations

GENE MUTATIONS Genes are actually segments of DNA molecules. Any alteration of the DNA sequence of a gene is a **gene mutation**. These mutations often change the normal message carried by the gene. Many mutations involve the substitution of one nitrogen base for another. This often causes a different amino acid to be placed in a particular position in the protein the gene codes for.

Some mutations involve the insertion of an additional base into an existing DNA sequence. This affects all of the code past the change, just as skipping a blank on the answer sheet for a test can cause all of the remaining answers to be shifted to the next blank, making most of them wrong. The deletion of a base from the normal gene sequence would also alter all the code past the change. Some mutations occur when the bases within a gene are accidentally rearranged. This, too, alters the genetic code. Figure 5-12 shows several ways that DNA can mutate.

All of these alterations are random and can occur anywhere along the molecule, making the result of the change almost impossible to predict. However, when a DNA sequence is changed, it is quite likely that the protein it codes for will be assembled incorrectly. If some amino acids are replaced by others, or if their sequence is different,

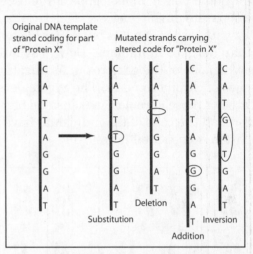

Figure 5-12. Mutation of DNA: The DNA on the left is part of the original template strand that codes for protein X. The four strands on the right show the DNA that would result from several types of mutations.

the way the protein folds may be different. Incorrect folding means that the protein's shape would not be normal. This could cause the protein to malfunction. One mutation caused by a substitution is sickle cell disease. (See Figure 5-13.)

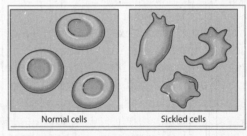

Figure 5-13. Effects of a substitution mutation: Normal red blood cells are round. The abnormal cell shapes are due to a substitution mutation that forms a defective protein, which in turn changes the cell's shape.

Mutations can cause such serious changes that the cell may die. However, if a mutated cell does survive and can replicate its DNA, its changed instructions will be copied and passed on to every cell that develops from it. In sexually reproducing organisms, only mutations found in sex cells can be inherited by offspring.

CHROMOSOME MUTATIONS **Chromosome mutations** involve a change in the structure of a chromosome or the number of chromosomes. The effects of a chromosome mutation can often be seen in the phenotype because many genes are involved. One type of chromosome mutation results when a pair of homologous chromosomes fails to separate during meiosis. This results in gametes with either one less or one more chromosome than normal. In humans, Down's syndrome occurs when one of the gametes in fertilization has two copies of chromosome 21. The zygote develops with three of these chromosomes instead of two. Therefore, all the cells of the individual have an extra chromosome. See Figure 5-14.

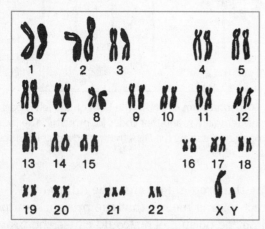

Figure 5-14: **Karyotype of a Down's syndrome individual:** Notice the three copies of chromosome 21. Also notice the X and Y chromosomes, indicating that this is a male individual.

Sometimes during meiosis, an entire set of chromosomes fails to separate. This may result in individuals that have an extra set of chromosomes. If they have three, rather than two of each chromosome, they are said to be triploid. In plants, this may result in individuals that are larger and more vigorous than normal. Certain commercially valuable varieties of cotton, wheat, and apples have an extra set of chromosomes. Sometimes plants with this mutation are sterile and produce fruits that contain no seeds.

As a general rule, animals cannot survive with missing or extra chromosomes, but triploid grass carp have been artificially produced. These fish are now being used in some ponds to eat certain types of aquatic vegetation whose growth is hard to control by other means. The triploid fish cannot

reproduce, so even if they manage to spread to other bodies of water, they eventually die without leaving offspring that could otherwise become an ecological problem.

MUTAGENIC AGENTS Certain environmental factors can cause mutations to occur at a greater rate than normal. One cause is radiation—such as X-rays, ultraviolet rays, and radiation from radioactive materials. Certain chemicals, such as asbestos, can also cause mutations.

Genetic Engineering

Genetic engineering is a relatively new technology that humans use to alter the genetic instructions in organisms. However, the idea of altering organisms to have more desirable traits is not new. In fact, **biotechnology**—the application of technology to biological science—has been producing useful products for thousands of years. Cheese and bread are just two examples of "biotech" products made with the use of microbes.

Throughout recorded history, humans have also used selective breeding, which produces domestic animals and new varieties of plants with desirable traits. Many meat products, for example, come from animals that have been bred to contain less fat. In addition, many of the fruits and vegetables we consume have been selectively bred to be larger, sweeter, hardier, or even juicier. To breed a better plant, farmers might select a bean plant that produces many pods and then cross-breed it with a bean plant that resists fungal infections. The farmers would expect to eventually get seeds that would grow into bean plants with both features.

Gene Manipulation

In recent years, plants and animals have been genetically engineered by manipulating their DNA instructions. The result of this genetic manipulation is new characteristics and new varieties of organisms. Through this process, we have been able to produce plants with many beneficial traits. For example, plants can now contain genes with the instructions for making chemicals that kill the insects that feed on them. Scientists have also engineered bacteria that can be used to clean up oil spills or that produce human growth hormone.

The basic method that alters genes in organisms uses special enzymes. **Gene splicing** uses these enzymes to cut DNA segments in a way that allows the segments to be moved and attached to the DNA of a new organism. Once in the new organism, the transferred genes direct the new organism's cells to make the same protein product as the original organism. For example, when we move a human insulin-producing gene into a bacterial cell, the bacterium—and all of its offspring—will produce human insulin. This provides a way to produce large quantities of a hormone at low cost. Genes for other human proteins have also been inserted into bacterial cells, as illustrated in Figure 5-15.

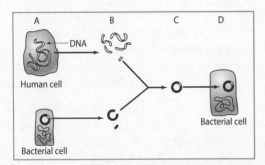

Figure 5-15. Genetic engineering using bacteria: (A) A special enzyme is used to cut a segment of DNA from a human cell and a circular piece of DNA (a plasmid) from a bacterial cell. (B) When the piece of human DNA is mixed with the open loop of bacterial DNA, they join in a closed loop. (C) That loop is then inserted into another bacterial cell (D), which will produce the desired protein. The information contained in the loop will be duplicated every time the cell divides, so that the resulting large number of bacteria will produce the protein in great quantities.

Other enzymes have been found that can be used to make many copies of segments of DNA. These can be used to increase the amount of DNA available from a tiny sample. This procedure is helpful even when only a drop of blood or saliva is found at a crime scene. By copying and re-copying the DNA in the sample, criminal investigators can produce a sample that is large enough to test. The test results may identify or clear suspects.

CLONING **Cloning** is a technique that accomplishes the same end result as asexual reproduction. It is a way of making identical genetic copies. For example, if you cut a piece of stem from a plant and it grows roots and develops into a new plant, you have produced a genetically identical copy of the original plant. It could be called a clone of that plant.

Recently, however, it has also been possible to produce clones of animals that ordinarily only

reproduce sexually. This is done by inserting a nucleus from a "parent" organism's body cell (one that has a complete set of genetic information from that individual) into an egg cell from which the nucleus has been removed. The result is an egg that now contains not 50% but 100% of the genetic information from a single parent. If this new egg cell with all of its genes can be made to develop normally, the resulting offspring is a clone of the individual that donated the original cell nucleus. In mammals, the egg would be implanted and would develop inside the body of the female. Cloning has been accomplished with animals as complex as sheep and pigs.

Applications of Biotechnology

The health care field has much to gain through our increasing knowledge of genetics and biotechnology. New methods enable us to locate and determine the base sequence of genes that cause diseases. Once we have a better understanding of the gene's specific defect, we may be able to develop ways to treat victims of the disease. In some cases, we may be able to alter the DNA in affected cells and cure the person.

Because of such mutations, people with genetic diseases are sometimes unable to produce certain hormones, enzymes, or other body chemicals. At times, we can extract these chemicals from animals, such as sheep and cattle. However, these extractions can be expensive, and the chemicals may contain contaminants that cause side effects. If scientists can produce the chemicals using genetically engineered organisms, the missing chemicals may be produced relatively inexpensively and in a pure enough form to avoid the side effects associated with chemicals obtained from animal sources.

5.4 Review

1. A dog breeder can determine that the sudden appearance of hairlessness in a puppy is a mutation if the dog (A) is still hairless after 5 years (B) shows no change in the hairless condition after its diet is changed (C) develops other conspicuous differences from the parent (D) is bred and the trait is capable of being inherited

2. Which mutation could be passed on to future generations? (F) a gene change in a liver cell (G) cancer caused by excessive exposure to the sun (H) a chromosomal alteration during gamete formation (J) random breakage of a chromosome in a leaf cell of a maple tree

3. Mutations can be transmitted to the next generation if they are present in (A) brain cells (B) sex cells (C) body cells (D) muscle cells

4. Overexposure of animals to X-rays is dangerous because X-rays are known to damage DNA. A direct result of this damage is cells with (F) unusually thick cell walls (G) no organelles located in the cytoplasm (H) abnormally large chloroplasts (J) changes in chromosome structure

5. Plants with desirable qualities can be rapidly produced from the cells of a single plant by (A) cloning (B) gamete fusion (C) meiosis (D) crossing over

Base your answers to questions 6 through 9 on the following diagrams.

Diagram A represents the chromosomes in the nucleus of the body cell of a worm. Diagrams B through G represent chromosomal arrangements that may occur in other cells produced by this worm.

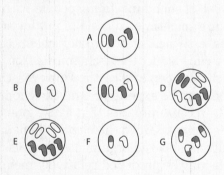

6. If meiosis failed to occur in both male and female worms, the zygote nucleus would resemble diagram (F) E (G) G (H) C (J) D

7. If genes were exchanged between a single pair of chromosomes during gamete formation, the gamete nucleus would most closely resemble diagram (A) F (B) B (C) C (D) G

8. The nucleus of a normal zygote formed when fertilization occurs in this species would most likely resemble diagram (F) F (G) E (H) C (J) D

9. The nucleus of a mature gamete from a female worm would most likely resemble diagram (A) E (B) B (C) C (D) D

10. Genetic engineering is used in the biotechnology industry to (F) eliminate all infections in livestock (G) synthesize hormones such as insulin and human growth hormone (H) increase the frequency of fertilization (J) eliminate asexual reproduction

11. The insertion of a human DNA fragment into a bacterial cell might make it possible for (A) the bacterial cell to produce a human protein (B) the cloning of the human that donated that DNA fragment (C) humans to become immune to an infection by this type of bacteria (D) the cloning of this type of bacteria

12. Orchid plants reproduce slowly and take many years to produce flowers when grown from seeds. One technique that can be used to reproduce rare orchid plants more rapidly is (F) sexual reproduction (G) fertilization (H) selective breeding (J) cloning

13. In recent research, the DNA that codes for a different key enzyme was removed from each of three different species of soil bacteria. A new bacterium, containing DNA for all three key enzymes, could be produced by (A) selective breeding (B) screening for mutations (C) genetic engineering (D) random alteration

14. The technique illustrated in the diagram is known as (F) genetic engineering (G) protein synthesis (H) crossing over (J) gamete formation

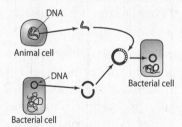

15. Describe two examples of how an understanding of genetics is making new fields of health care (treatment or diagnosis) possible.

16. How could a change in the sequence of nitrogen bases in a DNA molecule result in a gene mutation?

17. The technology of genetic engineering has allowed humans to alter the genetic makeup of organisms. Describe one example of such an alteration.

Base your answers to questions 18 through 22 on the following technical passage.

Advances with Cells and Genes

Recent advances in cell technology and gene manipulation have allowed scientists to perform some interesting experiments, including splicing human DNA into the chromosomes of bacteria. The altered bacteria express the added genes.

Bacteria reproduce rapidly under certain conditions. This means that bacteria with the gene for human insulin could multiply rapidly, resulting in a huge bacterial population capable of producing large quantities of human insulin.

The traditional source of insulin has been the pancreases of slaughtered animals. Continued use of this insulin can trigger allergic reactions in some humans. The new bacterially produced insulin is actually human insulin. As a result, it does not produce many side effects.

The bacteria used for these experiments are *E. coli*, bacteria common to the digestive system of many humans. Some scientists question these experiments and are concerned that the altered *E. coli* may accidentally get into water supplies.

Rate each of the statements in questions 18 through 22, based on the information provided. Decide whether each statement is true, false, or if not enough information is given in the passage to determine this. Note that questions 18 through 22 have only 3 choices.

18. Transplanting genetic material into bacteria is a simple task. (A) this statement is true according to the passage (B) this statement is false according to the passage (C) not enough information is given in the passage to determine this

19. Under certain conditions, bacteria reproduce at a rapid rate. (A) this statement is true according to the passage (B) this statement is false according to the passage (C) not enough information is given in the passage to determine this

20. The continued use of insulin from animals may cause harmful side effects in some people. (A) this statement is true according to the passage (B) this statement is false according to the passage (C) not enough information is given in the passage to determine this

21. The bacteria used in these experiments are normally found only in the nerve tissue of humans. (A) this statement is true according to the passage (B) this statement is false according to the passage (C) not enough information is given in the passage to determine this

22. Bacteria other than *E. coli* are unable to produce insulin. (A) this statement is true according to the passage (B) this statement is false according to the passage (C) not enough information is given in the passage to determine this

Base your answers to questions 23 and 24 on the information below.

Some geneticists are suggesting the possibility of transferring some of the genes that influence photosynthesis from an productive variety of crop plant to a less productive crop plant. The goal is to develop a new variety with improved productivity.

23. To produce this new variety, the project would most likely involve (A) genetic engineering (B) a gene mutation (C) chromatography (D) vaccinations

24. Which technique would most likely be used to produce large numbers of genetically identical offspring from this new variety of plant? (F) cloning (G) sexual reproduction (H) electrophoresis (J) selective breeding

1. Children born to the same parents are usually very different from each other. Which process is primarily responsible for these differences?

   (A) mitosis

   (B) meiotic division

   (C) asexual reproduction

   (D) cloning

2. Hereditary information for most traits is generally located in

   (F) genes found on chromosomes

   (G) chromosomes found on genes

   (H) the ribosomes of sperm cells

   (J) the mitochondria in the cytoplasm

3. What is the technique of genetic engineering in which DNA is transferred from the cells of one organism to the cells of another organism?

   (A) gene splicing

   (B) chromatography

   (C) electrophoresis

   (D) selective deleting

4. A change that alters the base sequence in an organism's DNA is a

   (F) mutation

   (G) replication

   (H) clone

   (J) zygote

5. Bacteria in culture A produce slime capsules around their cell walls. A biologist removed the DNA from some of the bacteria he took from culture A. He then injected it into bacteria in culture B, which normally do not produce slime capsules. After the injection, bacteria with slime capsules began to appear in culture B. What conclusion could best be drawn from this investigation?

   (A) The bacteria in culture A cannot reproduce.

   (B) The slime capsules of bacteria in culture B contain DNA.

   (C) Bacteria reproduce faster when they have slime capsules.

   (D) DNA is most likely involved in the production of slime capsules.

6. In which situation could a mutation be passed on to the offspring of one of the organisms listed in the following table?

   Chromosomes in a Body Cell

Name of Organism	Number of Chromosomes in Each Body Cell
Human	46
Fruit fly	8

   (F) Ultraviolet radiation causes fruit-fly wing cells to undergo uncontrolled division, resulting in cells with 9 chromosomes.

   (G) A cell in the wall of the human uterus undergoes a change, resulting in cells with 47 chromosomes.

   (H) A primary sex cell in a human forms a sperm that contains 23 chromosomes.

   (J) A cell in the ovary of the fruit fly undergoes a chromosomal change that results in 5 chromosomes per egg cell.

7. The diagram illustrates what happens to the fur color of a Himalayan rabbit after prolonged exposure to a low temperature.

   The change in fur color is most likely due to

   (A) the effect of heredity on gene expression

   (B) the arrangement of genes on chromosomes

   (C) environmental influences on gene action

   (D) mutations resulting from a change in the environment

Base your answers to questions 8 through 10 on the diagram below.

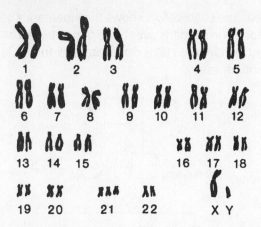

8. The arrangement of chromosomes in the diagram is called a

(F) karyotype

(G) phenotype

(H) genotype chart

(J) pedigree chart

9. The arrangement of chromosomes shown can be used as a test to identify

(A) colorblindness

(B) hemophilia

(C) Down's syndrome

(D) blood type

10. The chromosomes shown indicate that this person is a

(F) normal male

(G) normal female

(H) male with a genetic disorder

(J) female with a genetic disorder

11. Which parental pair will produce a colorblind female?

(A) homozygous normal-vision mother and a colorblind father

(B) colorblind mother and normal-vision father

(C) heterozygous normal-vision mother and normal-vision father

(D) heterozygous normal-vision mother and colorblind father

Base your answers to question 12 on the following information and data table.

Certain chemicals cause mutations in cells by causing chromosomes to break. Cells containing such broken chromosomes are mutated cells. Certain nutrients, such as beta carotene (a form of vitamin A), have the ability to prevent this kind of chromosome breakage.

In the investigation, varying amounts of beta carotene per kilogram of body weight were added to the diets of hamsters. A mutation-causing chemical was also added to the diets of the hamsters.

The results of an investigation of the effect of beta carotene in preventing chromosome damage are presented in the following data table.

The Effect of Beta Carotene on Cell Mutation in Hamsters

Amount of Beta Carotene per Kilogram of Hamster's Body Weight	Percentage of Mutated Cells
0 mg	11.5
20 mg	11.0
30 mg	8.0
40 mg	7.0
50 mg	4.5
75 mg	3.5
100 mg	2.0
150 mg	1.2

12. Based on this information and data

- State an appropriate conclusion regarding the use of beta carotene. Use experimental data to support your conclusion.

- Explain why each hamster used in the experiment had to be weighed before it was given the beta carotene.

- Evaluate the statement, "Taking other vitamins, such as vitamin E, will affect chromosome mutation rates in humans." State whether or not this is a valid statement. Support your answer with an explanation.

13. Mendel developed basic principles of heredity by

(A) examining chromosomes

(B) using X-rays to cause mutations

(C) analyzing large numbers of offspring

(D) observing crossing over during meiosis

14. The process of crossing over takes place between

(F) homologous chromosomes and results in new gene combinations

(G) non-homologous chromosomes and results in an increased gene mutation rate

(H) homologous chromosomes and results in an increased gene mutation rate

(J) non-homologous chromosomes and results in new gene combinations

15. In minks, the gene for brown fur (*B*) is dominant over the gene for silver fur (*b*). Which set of genotypes represents a cross that could produce offspring with silver fur from parents that both have brown fur?

(A) *Bb* × *Bb*

(B) *BB* × *bb*

(C) *BB* × *Bb*

(D) *Bb* × *bb*

16. In pea plants, the gene for smooth seeds is dominant over the trait for wrinkled seeds. When two hybrids are crossed, which results are the most probable?

(F) 75% smooth and 25% wrinkled seeds

(G) 100% smooth seeds

(H) 50% smooth and 50% wrinkled seeds

(J) 100% wrinkled seeds

17. In certain rats, black fur is dominant over white fur. If two rats, both heterozygous for fur color, are mated, their offspring would be expected to be

(A) four different genotypes and two different colors

(B) two different genotypes and three different colors

(C) three different genotypes and two different colors

(D) three different genotypes and three different colors

Use the information in the chart to answer questions 18 and 19.

The pedigree chart below shows the inheritance of handedness in humans over three generations. The allele for right-handedness (*R*) is dominant over the allele for left-handedness (*r*).

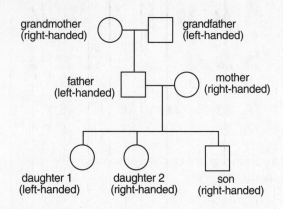

18. For which individual is *Rr* the most probable genotype?

(F) grandfather

(G) grandmother

(H) father

(J) daughter 1

19. Which two individuals have identical genotype for handedness?

(A) grandmother and grandfather

(B) mother and father

(C) mother and son

(D) daughter 1 and daughter 2

20. In squirrels, the gene for gray fur (*G*) is dominant over the gene for black fur (*g*). Fifty percent of a large litter of squirrels is gray. Which parental cross most likely produced this litter?

(F) *GG* × *gg*

(G) *GG* × *GG*

(H) *Gg* × *gg*

(J) *gg* × *gg*

21. Mendel developed the principle of independent assortment when studying the inheritance of seven different traits in pea plants. Modern geneticists explained this principle by inferring that each of these traits

(A) is located on different chromosomes

(B) is linked to the others on homologous chromosomes

(C) fails to separate during meiosis

(D) fails to separate during mitosis

22. Which process is illustrated by the diagram below?

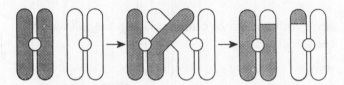

(F) crossing over

(G) independent assortment

(H) codominance

(J) dominance

23. The pedigree below shows the occurrence of red-green colorblindness in three generations of a family.

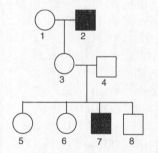
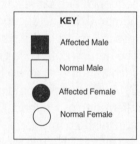

KEY
- Affected Male
- Normal Male
- Affected Female
- Normal Female

Individual 1 comes from a family with no history of red-green colorblindness. Using this information and the fact that red-green colorblindness is a sex-linked trait, do the following.

• Construct a Punnett square with the genotypes of individuals 1 and 2 to determine the genotype of individual 3.

• Identify the probability that individual 3 is a carrier.

• Identify the probability that individual 4 is a carrier.

• Explain why it is more likely that a son born to individual 5 will be colorblind than a son born to individual 7 if both individuals marry people with no family history of colorblindness.

24. In guinea pigs, rough hair is dominant over straight hair. If two heterozygous pigs are crossed, the largest number of any one genotype of offspring would probably be (F) homozygous straight hair (G) homozygous rough hair (H) heterozygous straight hair (J) heterozygous rough hair

25. Base your answer to this question on the technical passage below.

The Plight of the Monarch

Along with producing most of the corn consumed by humans and livestock, the U.S. Corn Belt also produces about half of the monarch butterflies that migrate between Canada and Mexico. During migration, the butterflies mate and lay their eggs. The caterpillars that hatch from these eggs immediately begin to feed on milkweed leaves. This is what monarch butterflies have done successfully for decades. Now it seems that this behavior could cause their extinction.

Cornell University scientists have discovered that the increased use of genetically engineered corn is the problem. Caterpillars feeding on milkweed dusted with pollen from this corn die. The new strain of corn has been engineered to include the bacterial gene that codes for the production of a toxin called *Bt*. *Bt* functions as a natural pesticide and kills European corn borer caterpillars, which are responsible for the destruction of millions of ears of corn every year. The use of *Bt* corn saves crop growers from having to purchase and apply toxic chemical pesticides.

Originally, everyone thought that *Bt* corn was the answer to many financial, environmental, and health issues associated with pesticide use. However, in the Cornell University study, nearly half of the monarch butterfly caterpillars fed milkweed dusted with *Bt* corn pollen died within four days. None of the caterpillars in the control group died.

Analyze the use of the *Bt* gene.

• Corn plants that contain the *Bt* gene in their cells make the toxin that kills corn borer caterpillars. Explain how the gene enables the plants to make the toxin.

• Explain the benefit to farmers of using *Bt* engineered corn.

• Pollen is the male sex cell. It performs the same role in plants as sperm does in animals. Explain why it is reasonable to expect pollen produced by the genetically engineered corn plants to carry the *Bt* gene.

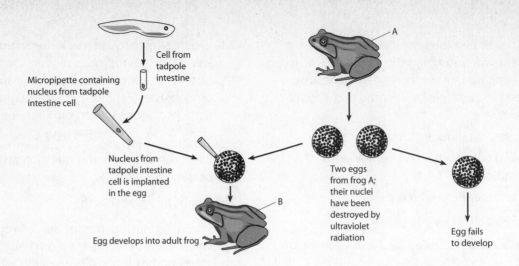

Cell from tadpole intestine

Micropipette containing nucleus from tadpole intestine cell

Nucleus from tadpole intestine cell is implanted in the egg

Egg develops into adult frog

A

Two eggs from frog A; their nuclei have been destroyed by ultraviolet radiation

B

Egg fails to develop

Base your answers to questions 26 and 27 on the diagram above, which represents an experiment using cells from a frog and a tadpole.

26. An inference that can be made is that

(F) adult frog A can develop only from an egg and a sperm

(G) adult frog B will have the same genetic traits as the tadpole

(H) fertilization must occur in order for frog eggs to develop into adult frogs

(J) the nucleus of a body cell fails to function when transferred to other cell types

27. Other scientists used a nucleus from a frog sperm cell instead of an intestinal cell and no adult frog developed. The sperm cell nucleus did not work because

(A) it lacked a full set of chromosomes

(B) it contained a full set of chromosomes

(C) a sperm cell has much less cytoplasm than an intestinal cell

(D) ultraviolet radiation would destroy sperm cell chromosomes and not intestinal cell chromosomes

28. In cats, a pair of X-chromosomes will produce a female, while an X-chromosome and a Y-chromosome will produce a male. A single pair of alleles controls fur color. The alleles for orange fur and for black fur are located on the X-chromosome only. Tortoiseshell cats have one allele for orange four and one for black fur. Which statement is true?

(F) Only female cats can be tortoiseshell.

(G) Only male cats can be tortoiseshell.

(H) Males need two alleles to have orange fur.

(J) Males need two alleles to have black fur.

Base your answer to question 29 on the following technical passage.

Genetic engineering is a technique used by scientists to combine or splice genetic material from different organisms. Gene splicing involves changing the normal base sequence of DNA by cutting a section of DNA and introducing another gene. The technique may involve the use of the bacterium *E. coli*. The bacterium has one large chromosome and several small plasmids, which are ring-shaped pieces of DNA found in the cytoplasm.

Genetic engineers have been able to extract plasmids from *E. coli*. Restriction enzymes are used to cut the DNA of the plasmid at designated places in the base sequence. The same enzymes are used to cut a section of human DNA. This section of human DNA is then placed into the space in the cut DNA of the bacterial plasmid. The human DNA codes for the synthesis of a product such as human growth hormone. The spliced bacterial DNA, which now contains a piece of human DNA, is referred to as a hybrid. This hybridized plasmid is then transplanted into *E. coli*. When the bacterium reproduces, the hybrid DNA will replicate. The offspring will possess the ability to synthesize the human growth hormone.

29. Summarize the process described in the passage and include answers to the following.

• What is a bacterial plasmid?

• What is a hybrid plasmid?

• How do genetic engineers remove sections from human DNA for splicing into bacterial DNA?

• What is one benefit of gene splicing?

• Why isn't it necessary to continue splicing the gene for human growth hormone into *E. coli* once cultures of the bacteria with the spliced gene are established?

Evolutionary Change

Extensive evidence indicates that life on Earth began more than three billion years ago. Fossils found in ancient rocks have given us many clues to the kinds of life that existed long ago. The first living organisms were simple, single-celled organisms. Over time, more complex single-celled creatures developed. Then, about a billion years ago, increasingly complex, multicellular organisms began to appear. Today we find a great variety of life on Earth, with modern organisms ranging from very simple to very complex.

6.1 The Theory of Evolution

VOCABULARY		
evolution	fossil record	geologic time

The idea that species change over time is known as **evolution**. The theory of evolution is accepted as the central theme of modern biology. It helps biologists understand how the variations among individuals can lead to changes in an entire species, and even how new species can arise from earlier ones.

Since it was first suggested by Charles Darwin, the concept of evolution has been refined by massive amounts of evidence offered by thousands of scientists. So much evidence has been collected that evolution now has the stature of a theory, which in scientific terms means a concept that has been tested and confirmed in many different ways and can be used by scientists to make predictions about the natural world.

The theory of evolution helps biologists understand the similarities—such as bone structure and biochemistry—that exist among different organisms. For instance, many related species possess similar proteins because they have similar DNA sequences. Scientists now use an analysis of the sequence of bases in DNA from different organisms to measure the degree of relatedness between them.

In a similar way, the amino acid chains of proteins in related organisms are very similar but not identical. Therefore, comparing amino acid sequences is another way to determine how closely species are related.

Evolution does *not* necessarily produce long-term progress in any set direction. Instead,

evolutionary change appears to be more like the growth of a tree. Notice in Figure 6-1 that some branches survive from the beginning with little or no change. Some die out altogether. Others split repeatedly, with each new branch representing a new species.

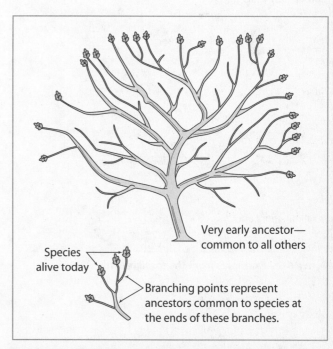

Very early ancestor—common to all others

Species alive today

Branching points represent ancestors common to species at the ends of these branches.

Figure 6-1. Evolution modeled as the growth of a tree: Evolutionary changes in species are like the growth of a tree in which some twigs grow and branch, while others die. The tips of the living twigs represent species that are alive now.

The theory of evolution also helps to explain the history of life that is revealed by the **fossil record**, which is a collection of fossils that provides clues to the history of Earth's organisms.

The fossil record spans much of **geologic time**—the billions of years of Earth's history—revealing many changes in environments as well as species. Figure 6-2 shows examples from the fossil record through geologic time.

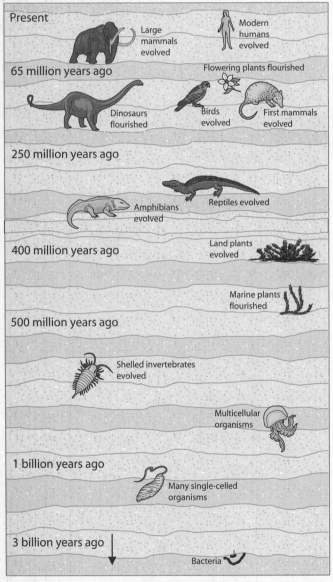

Figure 6-2. Examples from the fossil record

 **6.1 Review**

1. Evolution is the process of the (A) development of one-celled organisms from mammals (B) change in species over long periods of time (C) embryonic development of modern humans (D) changing energy flow in food webs

2. The chart below shows the amino acid sequence in the same part of a hemoglobin molecule of five different mammal species.

Comparison of Hemoglobin in Five Mammals

Mammal Species	Sequence of Amino Acids in a Section of the Molecule
Human	Lys-Glu-His-Iso
Horse	Arg-Lys-His-Lys
Gorilla	Lys-Glu-His-Lys
Chimpanzee	Lys-Glu-His-Iso
Zebra	Arg-Lys-His-Arg

According to the information provided, the closest evolutionary relationship most likely exists between the (F) human and the chimpanzee (G) human and the gorilla (H) chimpanzee and the gorilla (J) horse and the zebra

3. The following diagram represents possible lines of the evolution of primates.

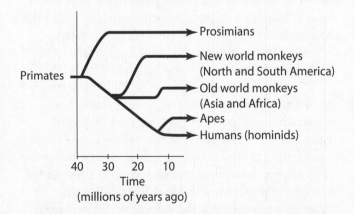

Which inference can best be made based on the diagram? (A) Adaptations for living in trees are inherited by all primates. (B) Humans and apes have a common ancestor. (C) The embryos of monkeys and apes are identical. (D) The period of development is similar in most primates.

4. Which phrase best defines evolution? (F) an adaptation of an organism to its environment (G) a sudden replacement of one community by another (H) the isolation of organisms from each other for many years (J) a process of change in species over a period of time

5. Scientists hypothesize that cabbage, broccoli, cauliflower, and radishes developed along a common evolutionary pathway. Which observation would best support this hypothesis? (A) Fossils of these plants were found in the same rock layer. (B) Chloroplasts of these plants produce a gas. (C) These plants live in the same environment. (D) These plants have similar proteins.

6. The theory of biological evolution includes the concept that (F) species of organisms found on Earth today have adaptations not always found in earlier species (G) fossils are the remains of present-day species and were all formed at the same time (H) individuals may acquire physical characteristics after birth and pass these acquired characteristics on to their offspring (J) the smallest organisms are always eliminated by the larger organisms within the ecosystem

7. The study of fossils has allowed scientists to (A) describe past environments and the history of life (B) study present ocean temperatures at different depths (C) analyze the chemical composition of sedimentary rocks and minerals (D) describe the details of the process by which life began on Earth

8. The diagram below shows the results of a test that was done using DNA samples from three bears of different species. Each DNA sample was cut into fragments using the same enzyme and then placed in the wells as indicated below. The DNA fragments were then separated using gel electrophoresis. The gray bands indicate the results.

Bear 1   Bear 2   Bear 3   ⇐ wells

- Which *two* bears are most closely related? Support your answer with data from the test results.

- Identify one additional way to determine the evolutionary relationship of these bears.

9. Theories of evolution attempt to explain the diversification of species existing today. The essentials of Darwin's theory of natural selection serve as a basis for our present understanding of the evolution of species. Recently, some scientists have suggested two possible explanations for the time frame in which the evolution of species occurs.

Gradualism proposes that evolutionary change is continuous and slow, occurring over many millions of years. New species evolve through the accumulation of many small changes. Gradualism is supported in the fossil record by the presence of transitional forms in some of the evolutionary pathways.

Punctuated equilibrium is another possible explanation for the diversity of species. This explanation proposes that species exist unchanged through long periods of stability, typically several million years. Then, during briefer intervals of geologic time, significant changes occur and new species may evolve. Some scientists use the apparent lack of intermediate forms in the fossil record in many evolutionary pathways to support the concept of punctuated equilibrium.

Compare gradualism and punctuated equilibrium.

- Describe one major difference between gradualism and punctuated equilibrium.

- Explain what may result from the accumulation of small variations, according to the concept of gradualism.

- Describe what fossil evidence would support the concept of punctuated equilibrium.

6.2 The Mechanics of Evolution

Darwin did not only suggest that species evolve, he also suggested a description of how evolution occurs. Darwin thought that the mechanism of evolution was like the process of artificial selection practiced by breeders of plants and animals. (See Figure 6-3.)

Figure 6-3. Racehorses are bred for speed and stamina: When humans breed plants or animals, they select specific traits, such as speed, flower color, or resistance to disease. In a similar way, "nature" selects any trait that increases an organism's ability to survive and reproduce.

Darwin used the term **natural selection** to indicate that the process of evolution was controlled by "nature" rather than by people. In the process of natural selection, individuals that survive are able to breed and pass their genetic information to the next generation. Those that are not as successful in the environment often die without leaving any offspring.

Overview of Evolution

Darwin's ideas are easy to understand. In any environment, an individual may be born with a characteristic that gives it an advantage that will help it survive the pressures of living in a particular environment and reproduce—such as being stronger or faster. In general, individuals that prove to be well adapted to their environment will be more likely to survive than those who are not. Those that do survive can pass their favorable characteristics on to many of their offspring. As a result, these useful adaptations, which first appeared randomly, are likely to become more and more common with each generation. Similarly, characteristics that reduce an individual's chance of surviving and reproducing will tend to decrease over time.

The long-term result of natural selection is a change in the frequency of certain traits in a population. Beneficial traits tend to become more common; harmful traits tend to become less common. As the frequency of a trait in a population increases or decreases over time, it can be said that the species is evolving.

Note that the population—not the individual—changes as a result of evolution. An individual does not evolve; each one is born with genetic information that may or may not help it survive and reproduce. As natural selection leads to changes in the composition of a population, that population may have more individuals with a certain favorable characteristic than it did earlier.

Interactions and Evolution

The driving force behind evolution is the interaction between individual organisms and their environment. Conditions that are vital to the process of evolution include

- the potential for a species to increase its numbers, known as **overproduction**
- the finite (limited) supply of resources needed for life
- the genetic variation of offspring due to mutation and genetic "shuffling"
- the selection by the environment of those offspring that are better able to survive and reproduce

All of these conditions, which are explained in the rest of this section, are involved in the process of evolutionary change.

OVERPRODUCTION In each generation, a species has the potential to produce more offspring than can possibly survive. Species with high reproductive potential include bacteria, insects, dandelions, and rabbits. (See Figure 6-4.)

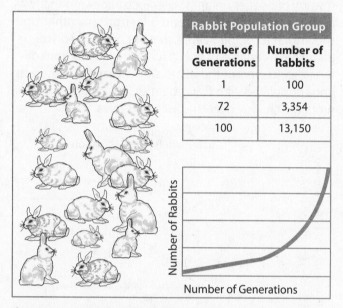

Rabbit Population Group	
Number of Generations	**Number of Rabbits**
1	100
72	3,354
100	13,150

Number of Rabbits (y-axis)
Number of Generations (x-axis)

Figure 6-4. Overproduction: Rabbits are known for their high reproductive potential.

If all the offspring of these organisms survived, they would overrun Earth. However, that does not happen. Scientists have learned that in stable environments the population of a species remains about the same from one year to the next. For example, no matter how many deer are born in one year, at the same time the next year, there will be about the same number of deer as there was the year before. Similarly, some fish species lay millions of eggs, but by the next year, the population of that species is the same as it was the previous year. This happens because not all of the new individuals that are born or hatched will survive to adulthood.

THE STRUGGLE FOR SURVIVAL Overproduction leads to competition among the members of a species. Not all offspring survive long enough to reproduce. In many cases, chance determines which offspring survive. For example, wind may

blow a dandelion seed to a patch of fertile soil or into a lake. A deer may be born in a wildlife preserve or in the path of a forest fire.

But chance is not the only factor that determines which offspring will survive and which will die. The offspring all have to cope with environmental conditions such as temperature, disease, parasites, and predators. They also need resources such as oxygen, water, food, and shelter. However, the supply of these resources is finite. If they are to survive, organisms of the same species must compete for limited resources.

Depending on their success as competitors, individuals will get the resources they need to survive or they will not. Those that are the best suited to their environment are more likely to survive. Many of the losers in this struggle for resources will die before they have a chance to reproduce.

VARIATION The new traits that can lead to evolution come from normal variation within a species. As shown in Figure 6-5, organisms within a species are never exactly alike. For example, some adult grasshoppers have longer legs than others; some have a lighter body color. In any group of gray squirrels, some have sharper or longer claws, lighter or darker fur, bigger or smaller ears, and so on. The differences among offspring are due to **genetic variation**—the unique combination of traits each organism inherits from its parents.

Some variations give individuals an advantage over others in their struggle for resources. Any trait that helps an organism survive and reproduce under a given set of environmental conditions is

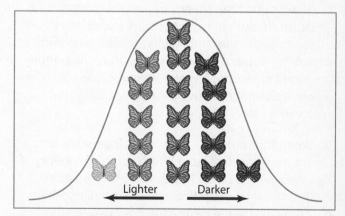

Lighter ← → Darker

Figure 6-5. Genetic variation: In this example, a species of green butterflies might have individuals that vary in color from very dark green to very light green.

said to have **adaptive value**. For example, a rabbit's ability to blend in with its surroundings may allow it to escape capture by a fox. The coloration it inherited has adaptive value for the rabbit, allowing it to escape predators and survive. When the fox population is high, this adaptation may be especially valuable to rabbits that inherited it.

SELECTION BY THE ENVIRONMENT As Darwin proposed with his idea of natural selection, traits with an adaptive value in a specific environment give individuals in that environment a competitive advantage. If the beneficial trait is passed to the offspring, they too are more likely to survive and reproduce. The proportion of individuals with these advantageous characteristics will increase because they are better able to compete than individuals without the beneficial trait. Eventually, nearly all the individuals in the population will have the beneficial trait. This change in the characteristics present in a population over time is evolution.

Although some evolution may occur without much change in the environment, it is usually the adaptation of a species to changes in its environment that brings about evolution. Therefore, a changing environment is often the driving force for evolutionary change.

6.2 Review

1. The process of natural selection is based on the assumption that (A) environmental changes will cause changes in body structure in individuals (B) most changes from generation to generation are the result of mutations (C) part of the population of organisms always remains stable (D) different traits inherited by offspring have different survival value.

2. When lions prey on a herd of antelope, some of the antelope are eliminated. Which part of the theory of evolution can be used to describe this situation? (F) asexual reproduction of the fittest (G) isolation (H) survival of the best adapted (J) new species development resulting from mutation

3. In Yellowstone National Park, some species of algae and bacteria can survive and reproduce in hot springs at temperatures near the boiling point of water. The ability to survive and reproduce at these temperatures is an example of (A) extinction (B) artificial selection (C) adaptation (D) reproductive isolation

Base your answers to questions 4 and 5 on the following information and graph.

A study of beetles on an isolated oceanic island that was formed by volcanic action and is far from any other land shows that all of the beetles that are presently on the island are incapable of flying. A study of fossils from different rock layers of the island shows that the island was once populated with flying beetles. The graph shows the probable change over the last 5,000 years.

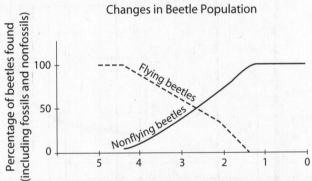

4. The loss of flying ability by the beetle is most probably the result of (F) predators eating the beetles' wings (G) beetles not using their wings (H) genetic changes in the beetles (J) lack of vegetation for the beetle to feed on

5. The graph indicates that the non-flying beetles probably (A) were better adapted to the environment (B) arrived from other islands 5,000 years ago (C) mutated and produced flying beetles (D) became extinct about 1.5 thousand years ago

Base your answers to questions 6 and 7 on the following information and diagram.

The diagram represents a small island divided by a mountain range. The mountain range prevents populations 1 and 2 from making contact with each other. At one time in the past, however, lowlands existed in the area indicated, and the ancestors of Population 1 and Population 2 were members of the same population.

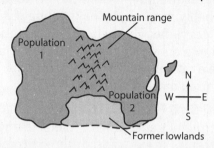

6. The organisms of Population 1 and Population 2 are now incapable of interbreeding and producing offspring. Which biological process most likely caused this situation to occur? (F) artificial selection (G) cloning (H) natural selection (J) asexual reproduction

7. Over many years, the climate on the west side of the island has undergone drastic changes while the climate on the east side has remained the same. It is most likely that Population 2 will (A) migrate and intermix with Population 1 (B) become extinct (C) have evolved more than Population 1 (D) have evolved less than Population 1

Base your answers to questions 8 and 9 on the following information and graph.

Scientists studying a moth population in a wooded area of Maryland recorded the distribution of moth wing color as shown in the following graph. While observing the moths, scientists noted that the moths spent most of the day resting on trees and looking for food during the night. The woods contained trees with a bark color that was predominantly brown.

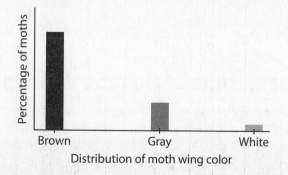

8. A fungal infection affected nearly all trees in the woods so that the color of the tree bark was changed from brown to a gray-white color. Which graph shows the most probable results that would occur in the distribution of wing color in this moth population after a long period of time?

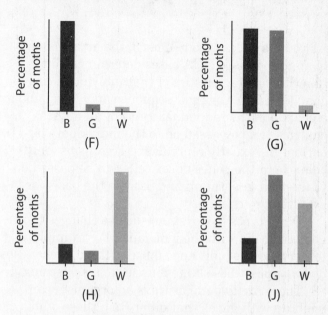

9. As a result of the fungal infection, the change in moth wing color distribution would most probably occur by the (A) production of sex cells by mitosis (B) natural selection of favorable variations (C) eating of pigments in fungus spores (D) production of mutations as a result of eating the fungus

10. Every spring, each mature female fish of a particular species produces several million eggs. However, the total population of this species remains at around 10,000 from one year to the next.

   • Explain why this fish population remains approximately the same from one generation to the next.

   • Explain how this overproduction of offspring relates to the process of natural selection and contributes to the evolution of this species.

11. Genetic variation is the basis of evolution. Explain the relationship between genetic variation and evolution.

   • Identify *two* different sources of genetic variation in a plant or animal population.

   • Explain how genetic variations within a species can lead to evolutionary change.

6.3 Variation: Sources and Results

As you may recall from Topic 3, the arrangement of an individual's DNA bases determines all the inherited characteristics of that individual. Any change in bases or their sequence may bring about a change in the individual. But not all of those changes can be passed on to the individual's offspring. In sexually reproducing organisms, only changes in the genes of sex cells can be passed on to the next generation and become the basis for evolutionary change.

Other types of variation (such as changes to body cells) die with the individual. For example, a father who has built huge muscles through exercise does *not* pass those large muscles to his offspring.

There are two major ways an organism can wind up with genes that differ from those of its parents. Some genetic variations arise because of mutations in the genes of an organism. Others are due to "genetic shuffling," the routine sorting and recombination of genes that occurs during sexual reproduction.

MUTATION A mutation is a change in the base sequence of a DNA molecule. When mutations occur, they occur as random events that cannot be predicted. Some mutations occur as errors in DNA as cells function, but radiation and some chemicals can also cause them. Mutations are an important source of new genes.

When mutations occur in body cells, they affect only that individual. However, a mutation in a single-celled organism or in the sex cells of a multicellular organism can be passed on to offspring. In organisms that reproduce sexually, only mutations in the genes of sex cells can become the basis for evolutionary change.

Most mutations are harmful and may affect the offspring so severely that it cannot survive. However, some mutations benefit the individual and can increase its chance of surviving, reproducing, and passing the mutation to the next generation. A beneficial mutation may lead to the evolution of a new species. For example, the ancestors of polar bears probably had dark fur. If a mutation resulted in a bear with white fur, that bear probably would have died young if it had lived in Maryland. However, if the mutation occurred in a snowy environment, the white fur would be a useful mutation, allowing the bear to stalk its prey more effectively.

GENETIC SHUFFLING The sorting and random recombining of genes during meiosis and fertilization results in new and different combinations of genes. These genes can be passed on to individual offspring.

The process is similar to shuffling and dealing cards. The deck stays the same, but nearly every hand will be slightly different because of mixing and rearranging during shuffling. At fertilization, even more variety is introduced because now cards from "two decks" are combined. Although mutations provide new genetic instructions, genetic shuffling is the main source of the variation that exists among the members of any sexually reproducing species.

MEMORY JOGGER

Recall that at the beginning of meiotic cell division the chromosomes line up and can exchange parts. What ends up in each gamete is partly the result of this shuffling, just as any hand of cards dealt to you is affected by shuffling the deck. As a result of this shuffling, the gametes (sperm and egg) each contain a unique combination of genetic information. Since any sperm may combine with an egg, the number of possible combinations becomes enormous.

The Results of Genetic Variation

The changes that result from mutation or genetic shuffling in the sex cells may affect the offspring in several ways. Most of the changes can be categorized as structural, functional, or behavioral.

STRUCTURAL CHANGE The structure of any organism is the result of its species' entire evolutionary history. There are millions of examples of variations that have resulted in structural changes. For example, the polar bear (like other bears) has thick fur that keeps it warm in its cold environment. Polar bears, however, have evolved an extra protection from the cold. The soles of their feet are also mostly covered with thick fur. This extra fur not only keeps their skin off the ice but also improves traction.

The theory of evolution has helped scientists explain many of the structural variations and anatomical similarities found in organisms. Some organisms have **homologous structures**—structural parts that appear similar even though they may have different functions in different organisms. The forearm bones of many mammals and birds are homologous. For example, in Figure 6-6, notice that each forelimb has one thick "long" bone, two thinner "long" bones, and a "hand" with five digits.

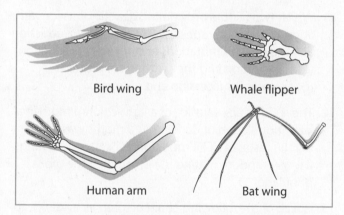

Figure 6-6. Homologous bone structures of different species: The limbs shown above are from different species and have different functions, but they share many structural similarities. They are all made of the same types of bones and are attached in a similar way. The whale flipper is actually *much* larger than the other limbs.

Homologous structures can be explained with the concept of **common ancestry**: an early ancestor of *all* these animals most likely had a limb structure similar to this. Then, at some point in the past, limbs began to vary, evolving into arms, legs, wings, or flippers.

Structures that are no longer used by modern organisms, called **vestigial** structures, also give scientists clues to the evolutionary history of a species. Some snakes, for example, have tiny,

nonfunctional leg bones—an indication that they probably evolved from four-legged, lizard-like ancestors.

FUNCTIONAL CHANGE Molecular or biochemical changes affect how an organism works. These are functional changes. For example, all working muscles emit an extremely tiny electrical output. In some eels, however, that electrical output has evolved into an adaptation that helps it find and capture food. The muscles of these eels can produce a massive shock that stuns or kills their prey.

Changes in DNA often lead to functional changes. One example is a mutation in the DNA of certain one-celled organisms that led to their ability to make enzymes that digest wood. Another is the evolution of the ability of some snakes to make a poisonous venom.

BEHAVIORAL CHANGE Behaviors have also evolved through natural selection. Many of the specific behaviors we find in species today have become common because they resulted in greater reproductive success.

- Fighting among the males of a walrus population for a harem of females is one evolved behavior. Because of the fighting, the stronger, healthier male mates with the most females.

- The correct rate of "blinking" allows males and females of firefly species to find each other. A different pattern or rate of blinking would isolate the individual from potential mates.

The Importance of Variation

If environmental conditions change, organisms that have adapted to those conditions may die. If all the members of the species had exactly the same combination of characteristics, an environmental change could be devastating, wiping out the entire species. The variation of organisms within a species increases the likelihood that at least some members of the species will survive in a changed environment.

Once the diversity present in a species is lost, it is next to impossible to get it back. Today's endangered species have such small populations that biologists worry that they may not have the genetic diversity to adapt to even slight changes in their environment.

 **6.3 Review**

1. Which statement is basic to the theory of evolution by natural selection? (A) In general, living organisms maintain a constant population from generation to generation. (B) Changes in living organisms are almost completely the result of mutations. (C) Natural variations are inherited. (D) There is little competition between species.

2. Which statement is *not* included as part of our modern understanding of evolution? (F) Sexual reproduction and mutations provide variation among offspring. (G) Traits are transmitted by genes and chromosomes. (H) More offspring are produced than can possibly survive. (J) New organs are formed when organisms need them.

3. The changes in the foot structure in a bird population over many generations are shown in the following diagram.

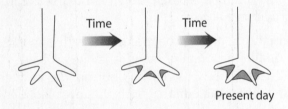

These changes can best be explained by the concept of (A) natural selection (B) extinction (C) stable gene frequencies (D) cloning

4. Which pair of structures are homologous? (F) wing of an insect and wing of a bird (G) tentacle of a hydra and flipper of a whale (H) front leg of an insect and bones in the leg of a human (J) bones in the front leg of a dog and bones in the wing of a bat

5. Sexual reproduction is related to evolution because sexual reproduction (A) occurs only in more recently evolved forms of animal life (B) increases the chances of extinction of different species (C) increases the chances for variations to occur (D) is the more usual kind of reproduction

6. Evolution could not occur without genetic variations. These variations will not be acted upon by natural selection unless they (F) produce unfavorable characteristics (G) produce favorable characteristics (H) are found in the fossil record (J) affect the organisms' appearance or functioning

7. Mutations can be transmitted to the next generation if they are present in (A) hormones (B) gametes (C) body cells (D) muscle cells

8. In most populations, the individuals that produce the greatest number of offspring are (F) always the strongest (G) usually the best adapted (H) those that have only inheritable traits (J) those that are the most intelligent

9. The presence of some similar structures in all vertebrates suggests that these vertebrates (A) all develop at the same rate (B) evolved from different animals that appeared on Earth at the same time (C) all develop internally and rely on nutrients supplied by the mother (D) may have an evolutionary relationship

10. Which of the following is produced by mutation and is essential for evolution to occur? (F) stability in the genetic code of organisms (G) additional DNA in an organism (H) a struggle for existence (J) variations in organisms

11. Which two factors provide the genetic basis for variation within many species? (A) asexual reproduction and meiosis (B) mutations and sexual reproduction (C) competition and the synthesis of proteins (D) ecological succession and mitosis

12. The sudden appearance of a light-colored moth in a large population of dark-colored moths was probably the result of (F) a mutation (G) random mating (H) non-random mating (J) isolation of the moth population

13. Which of the following could be used as evidence to show that two different species of organisms most likely developed from a single common ancestor? (A) They eat the same types of food. (B) They have different digestive enzymes (C) They lived during the same time period. (D) They contain similar amino acid sequences.

14. Many animal species in danger of extinction have small populations and therefore lack genetic diversity because of the inbreeding that results. Explain how the lack of genetic diversity found in such populations might hinder the survival of these species.

   • Explain why inbreeding reduces the genetic diversity of offspring.

   • Describe the importance of genetic diversity to the survival of a species in a changing environment.

6.4 Patterns of Change

Evolution seems to follow certain patterns that appear repeatedly in the fossil record. For example:

- Changes in species are often related to environmental change.
- Species with short reproductive cycles that produce many offspring tend to evolve more quickly than species with long life spans and few offspring.
- The failure to adapt to a changing environment may result in the extinction of the species.

The Rate of Evolution

Most of the diversity of life on Earth today is believed to be the result of natural selection occurring over a vast length of geologic time. The amount of change seems to be linked to changes in the environment.

Minimal environmental change often results in stable populations. Rapid environmental change often leads to rapid changes in species. However, for any species, it may take millions of years to accumulate enough differences from its ancestors to be classified as a new or different species. As shown in Figure 6-7, some species have hardly changed in many millions of years. Others have changed so much that the relationships may not be obvious.

The rate of evolutionary change may also be influenced by the number of offspring produced by a species. Those that have few offspring and live a long time generally evolve quite slowly. Those that have brief life spans and numerous offspring can change so quickly that evolution may occur in just a few years.

One example of rapid change involves the evolution of antibiotic resistance by pathogenic bacteria. When a population of millions of bacteria is exposed to an antibiotic, there is a chance that a few might have a gene that makes them resistant to the antibiotic. This gene probably occurred as a chance mutation at some earlier time. It was most likely present in some of the bacteria before the antibiotic

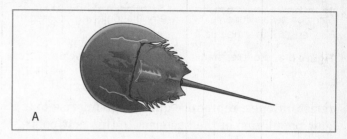

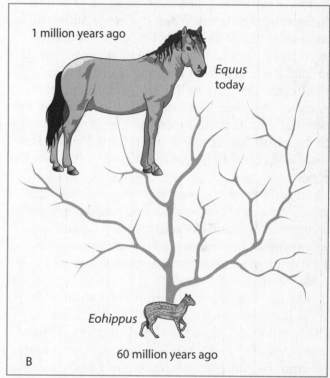

Figure 6-7. The rate of evolution: For some species, the rate of evolutionary change has been very slow. For example, the horseshoe crab **(A)** has shown little change from fossils of its ancestors that lived 300 million years ago. However, the horse **(B)** has evolved tremendously over the past 60 million years.

was used, and its appearance was totally unrelated to the presence of the antibiotic. The antibiotic could kill almost all of the bacteria except for a few that escape exposure to the antibiotic. The ones with the resistance gene would also survive.

Because most of the competition is eliminated by the antibiotic, the few survivors, including the

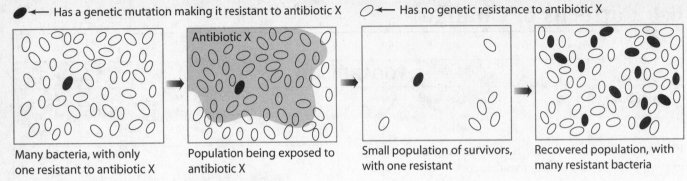

← Has a genetic mutation making it resistant to antibiotic X   ← Has no genetic resistance to antibiotic X

Many bacteria, with only one resistant to antibiotic X

Population being exposed to antibiotic X

Small population of survivors, with one resistant

Recovered population, with many resistant bacteria

Figure 6-8. How resistance to antibiotics can develop

resistant ones, reproduce quickly, giving rise to a new population of the bacteria. In this new population, a higher proportion of individuals is now resistant to the drug. When the same antibiotic is used on the descendants of this new population, even more resistant bacteria will survive. Now the proportion of resistant bacteria is even higher.

In this case, the antibiotic has become an agent of selection. The antibiotic did not cause the original mutation that made the bacteria resistant to the antibiotic. It merely determined which bacteria would live to reproduce. Figure 6-8 shows the process.

Insects also have short reproductive cycles and produce many offspring. Many insect species have changed significantly in response to pesticide use. For example, the widespread use of the pesticide DDT led to insect species becoming resistant in just a few years.

As was the case with bacteria and antibiotics, there may have been a few DDT-resistant insects in the population before the chemical was ever used. They probably had a random mutation that had no adaptive value before the use of DDT. Once the DDT was sprayed, nearly all of the nonresistant insects were killed, leaving a high proportion of resistant insects to repopulate the area. Later, if DDT was sprayed again, it was less effective against the resistant offspring of the survivors of the earlier spraying.

As a result of these kinds of rapid evolutionary events, we are finding more and more bacteria that are resistant to antibiotics and more and more insect species that are resistant to our pesticides. This has created many problems in the fields of medicine and agriculture and will continue to be a problem in the future.

Extinction

Extinction is the disappearance of an entire species. Any time the death rate of individuals within a species is greater than the birth rate, extinction is a possibility. Generally, extinction occurs when the environment changes.

Temperatures change; sea levels rise and fall. Grasslands become deserts; clear lakes become polluted. The variation of organisms within a species increases the likelihood that at least some members of the species will survive the changing environmental conditions. However, when the adaptive characteristics of a species are insufficient to allow its survival in a new environment, the species will become extinct.

The fossil record shows that throughout geologic time, millions of species have evolved, survived for a while, then failed to adapt successfully, and finally became extinct. It is a surprisingly common process. In fact, from the number of fossils of extinct organisms found, it is apparent that most of the species that ever lived on Earth are now extinct.

6.4 Review

1. The shark has changed very little in the last 50 million years. Which statement best explains why this is the case? (A) The shark is well adapted to its relatively unchanged environment. (B) Sharks have a high reproductive rate and show little change in their genetic makeup from one generation to the next. (C) Sharks need to change only if humans are present in their environment. (D) Sharks have high rates of mutation and genetic recombination.

2. Throughout the history of Earth, which factor has probably been the chief cause of the extinction of various species? (F) people's interference with nature (G) failure to adapt to environmental changes (H) warfare within the species (J) volcanic eruptions

3. Compounds like the pesticide DDT may bring about the evolution of new strains of organisms by (A) destroying food producers (B) acting as an agent of natural selection (C) mixing two different sets of genes (D) creating new ecological niches

4. Many animals exist today in a form that is almost identical to the form they had a million years ago.

   What is the most probable explanation for this lack of evolutionary change? (F) Genetic mutations have occurred among these animals. (G) The environment of these animals remained about the same. (H) These animals reproduce by sexual reproduction. (J) Complex organisms evolved into simpler ones.

5. A certain plant species, found only in one particular stream valley in the world, has a very shallow root system. An earthquake causes the stream to change its course so that the valley in which the plant species lives becomes very dry. As a result, the species dies out completely.

   The effect of this change on this plant species is known as (A) evolution (B) mutation (C) extinction (D) succession

Base your answers to questions 6 and 7 on the following information.

Scientist Joshua Lederberg discovered that, in a large population of *Escherichia coli,* about 1 in 10 million of the offspring was naturally resistant to the antibiotic streptomycin. When these naturally resistant bacteria were isolated and grown separately, they soon formed a larger population. The entire population so formed was also naturally resistant to streptomycin.

6. The formation of the large streptomycin-resistant population is based on (F) variations and survival of the fittest (G) mutations and asexual reproduction (H) sexual reproduction and no mutations (J) survival of the fittest and cloning

7. According to modern evolutionary theory, the resistance to streptomycin probably resulted directly from (A) culturing the *Escherichia coli* (B) changes in temperature under which *Escherichia coli* are grown (C) a change in the DNA of *Escherichia coli* (D) the presence of streptomycin

8. Fossil evidence indicates that many species have existed for relatively brief periods of time and have then become extinct.

   Which statement best explains the reason for their short existence? (F) These organisms lacked the energy to produce mutations. (G) Humans modify plant and animal species through the knowledge of genetics. (H) These organisms lacked variations having adaptive value. (J) Within these species, increasing complexity reduced their chances of survival.

9. Cockroaches that are resistant to many common household insecticides are more numerous than those that are killed by these same insecticides. Scientists explain the increased numbers of insecticide-resistant cockroaches with the following:

   Variations that have a high survival value tend to be passed on to the next generation of organisms in greater number than those variations that have low survival value.

   Describe how the above statement explains the increase in insecticide-resistant cockroaches.

   • Identify the variation that is present in the cockroach population and describe how this variation most likely came about.

   • Explain how the use of insecticides is associated with the fact that the resistant cockroaches outnumber the nonresistant cockroaches.

10. Scientists have observed thousands of female leatherback turtles laying eggs. Each turtle exhibits the same behavior. When she first comes to the beach to lay her eggs, she digs a hole, lays her eggs in the hole, and then covers the eggs with sand.

   She then travels about 100 meters away from the first hole and digs another. She doesn't lay any eggs in this hole, but goes through the same process of covering the hole just as if there had been eggs present. In the past, some leatherbacks may have only dug one hole and laid their eggs in it.

   Provide an explanation for how this behavior may have evolved.

   • Propose a hypothesis to explain why the female leatherback today digs two holes.

   • Describe, in terms of evolution, how this modern behavior may be explained.

1. How does natural selection cause change in a population?

   (A) The members of the population are equally able to survive environmental change.

   (B) The members of the population differ so that only some survive when the environment changes.

   (C) The members of the population cause environmental changes and adapt to them.

   (D) All the members of the population adapt to environmental changes.

2. Which mutation could be passed on to future generations?

   (F) a gene change in a liver cell

   (G) cancer caused by excessive exposure to the sun

   (H) a chromosomal alteration during gamete formation

   (J) random breakage of a chromosome in a leaf cell of a maple tree

3. A trait with low survival value to the members of a population will most likely

   (A) undergo a series of mutations in succeeding generations

   (B) cause the reproductive rate of the individual to increase

   (C) decrease in frequency from one generation to the next

   (D) remain unchanged in frequency through many generations

4. Over a period of 45 million years, various groups of hoofed mammals called Titanotheres showed a continuous increase in body and horn size before they eventually became extinct. Scientists are presently attempting to learn more about the evolution of these animals.

   • Provide a description of how changes in the environment might have resulted in the changes observed in Titanotheres.

   • Describe what information the fossil record could provide these scientists.

   • Explain how environmental changes could have led to the extinction of Titanotheres.

5. The process by which a species passes out of existence is known as

   (A) endangerment

   (B) deforestation

   (C) extinction

   (D) adaptation

6. The diagram below illustrates the change that occurred in the frequency of body pattern traits shown by an insect population over ten generations.

First generation

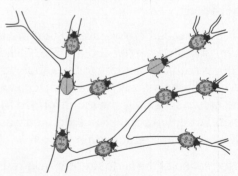

Tenth generation

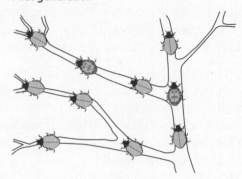

A probable explanation for this change would be that over time there was

   (F) a decrease in the adaptive value of the spotted trait

   (G) an increase in the adaptive value of the spotted trait

   (H) an increase in the population of the insect

   (J) a decrease in the mutation rate of the gene for body pattern

7. A change in genetic material that produces variation in a species may be the result of

   (A) the struggle for survival

   (B) the overproduction of a species

   (C) a mutation

   (D) competition

8. The fact that a healthy deer can outrun a timber wolf is an example of

   (F) mutation

   (G) isolation

   (H) non-random mating

   (J) natural selection

9. A maple tree releases hundreds of seeds in a single season. This is an example of

   (A) a mutation

   (B) isolation

   (C) overproduction

   (D) non-random mating

10. The DNA sequences found in two different species are 95% the same. This suggests that these species

   (F) are evolving into the same species

   (G) contain identical proteins

   (H) may have similar evolutionary histories

   (J) have the same number of mutations

Base your answers to questions 11 through 14 on the paragraph below.

Two different species of crickets inhabited a meadow. One species of cricket had a straw-colored body and made up 90% of the total cricket population. The other species of cricket had a dark red body and made up 10% of the population. This proportion between the species had been constant for many years.

   A new variety of grass with purple blades appeared in the meadow. The purple grass was better adapted to the meadow environment than the native green grass and replaced the green grass within a period of 50 years.

11. The appearance of the purple grass was most likely the result of

   (A) asexual reproduction

   (B) genetic engineering

   (C) cloning

   (D) mutation

12. What is the most likely reason for the large proportion of straw-colored crickets in the original population?

   (F) The straw-colored crickets were larger and killed off most of the red crickets.

   (G) Few natural enemies of the straw-colored crickets lived in the meadow.

   (H) More straw-colored crickets than red were able to survive in the green grass.

   (J) Red-colored crickets were not a part of the fossil record for the meadow.

13. Which graph most likely indicates the percentages of the straw-colored crickets (%S) over the 50-year period?

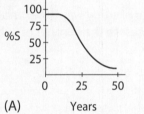

(A)   Years

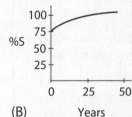

(B)   Years

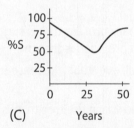

(C)   Years

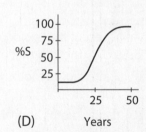

(D)   Years

14. The evolutionary concept that would explain the changes taking place during the 50-year period in both the crickets and grasses is called

   (F) common ancestry

   (G) natural selection

   (H) homeostatic balance

   (J) selective breeding

Base your answers to questions 15 through 17 on the information below.

The bark of trees around Manchester, England, was mostly light in color before the Industrial Revolution. Light-colored peppered moths that rested on the trees were camouflaged from bird predators, while dark-colored peppered moths were easily preyed upon. After a few years of industrialization, the tree bark became darkened from pollution. The table below represents a change in the number of light- and dark-colored moths within the peppered moth population over a period of six years from the beginning of industrialization.

End of Year	Number of Light Moths	Number of Dark Moths
1	556	64
2	237	112
3	484	198
4	392	210
5	246	281
6	225	357

15. At the end of which year of study was the number of dark-colored moths closest to the number of light-colored moths?

(A) 1

(B) 2

(C) 5

(D) 6

16. An aspect of the evolutionary process that is suggested by the information provided is that the

(F) light-colored moths will eventually increase in number

(G) darker moths appeared when the tree trunks became lighter

(H) changing environment caused a darkening of the pigments of the moths

(J) darker moths increased in number when the environment became more favorable for their traits

17. The biological concept that is most closely associated with the changes in the peppered moth population in England is known as

(A) natural selection

(B) positive feedback

(C) asexual reproduction

(D) homeostatic control

18. A hawk has a genetic trait that gives it much better eyesight than other hawks of the same species in the same area.

Explain how this could lead to evolutionary change within this species of hawk over a long period of time. In your answer, be sure to include an explanation of

• competition within the hawk population

• survival of various individuals in the population

• how the frequency of the better-eyesight trait would be expected to change over time within the population

• what would most likely happen to the hawks having the better-eyesight trait if they also had unusually weak wing muscles

19. According to most scientists, which sequence best represents the order of biological evolution on Earth?

1	2	3
The diversity of multicellular organisms increases.	Simple, single-celled organisms appear.	Multicellular organisms begin to evolve.

(A) 1 → 2 → 3

(B) 2 → 3 → 1

(C) 2 → 1 → 3

(D) 3 → 1 → 2

20. In an area in Africa, temporary pools form where rivers flow during the rainy months. Some fish have developed the ability to use their ventral fins as "feet" to travel on land from one of these temporary pools to another. Other fish in these pools die when the pools dry up.

What can be expected to happen in this area after many years?

(F) The fish using ventral fins as "feet" will be present in increasing numbers.

(G) "Feet" in the form of ventral fins will develop on all fish.

(H) The fish using ventral fins as "feet" will develop real feet.

(J) All of the varieties of fish will survive and produce many offspring.

21. Some behaviors, such as mating and caring for young, are genetically determined in certain species of birds. These behaviors most likely exist because

(A) birds do not have the ability to learn

(B) individual birds need to learn to survive and reproduce

(C) these behaviors helped birds to survive in the past

(D) within their lifetimes, birds developed these behaviors

22. Humans have modified some animal species by breeding only those that possess certain desirable traits. As a result, we have racehorses and greyhounds that are faster than their ancestors.

In a similar way, many animals have been modified naturally. The giraffe has long forelegs and a long neck, head, and tongue, which make it well adapted for browsing (feeding) in the higher branches of trees. Therefore, the giraffe can obtain food that is beyond the reach of other animals, especially during droughts.

Ancient populations of giraffes varied in the relative lengths of their body parts. Those giraffes that were able to browse the highest were more likely to survive. They mated, and their offspring often inherited the structural characteristics suitable for high browsing. The giraffes that could not reach the food supply most likely died of starvation and therefore did not produce as many offspring as those that could reach higher.

Animal traits are selected for, both artificially by humans and through natural means. Compare artificial and natural selection.

- Describe how the type of selection for traits in animals such as greyhounds and racehorses is different from the type of selection for traits that occurs in animals such as giraffes.

- Describe two specific events in sexual reproduction that can be the source of the variations selected for in both giraffes and racehorses.

- Provide an example of each of the following from the passage above: variation within species, struggle for existence, and survival of the fittest.

23. A large population of cockroaches was sprayed with a newly developed, fast-acting insecticide. The appearance of some cockroaches that are resistant to this insecticide supports the concept that

(A) species traits tend to remain constant

(B) variation exists within a species

(C) insecticides cause mutations

(D) the environment does not change

24. A scientist discovered that in a large population of *E. coli* bacteria, a few of the bacteria were resistant to the antibiotic streptomycin. By adding streptomycin to the population, she soon obtained a large population that was resistant to streptomycin.

Explain how this experiment supports the concept of evolution by natural selection. Your explanation should include the concepts of

- selective agent

- resistance

- reproduction

- offspring

25. Which statement describing a cause of extinction includes the other three?

(A) Members of the extinct species were unable to compete for food.

(B) Members of the extinct species were unable to conceal their presence by camouflage.

(C) Members of the extinct species lacked adaptations essential for survival.

(D) Members of the extinct species were too slow to escape from predators.

26. A population of mosquitoes is sprayed with a new insecticide. Most of the mosquitoes are killed, but a few survive. In the next generation, the spraying continues, but still more mosquitoes hatch that are resistant to the insecticide.

How could these results be explained according to the theory of evolution?

(F) The insecticide caused a mutation in the mosquitoes.

(G) The mosquitoes learned how to fight the insecticide.

(H) The insecticide caused the mosquitoes to develop an immune response, which was inherited.

(J) A few mosquitoes in the first population were resistant and transmitted this resistance to their offspring.

27. A European species of rabbit was released on a ranch in Victoria, Australia. The species thrived and reproduced rapidly. The rabbits overgrazed the land, reducing the food supply for the sheep.

In an effort to control the damage they were causing, some rabbits were captured and given a dose of the *Myxoma sp.* virus. Then they were released to spread the disease through the population. The first time this virus was used, it killed 99.8% of the rabbits. When the rabbits became a problem again, the virus was used a second time. This time, only 90% of the rabbits were killed.

When the rabbits became a problem a third time, the virus was used once again, and only 50% of the rabbits were killed. Today, this virus has little or no effect on this species of rabbit.

Describe what happened to the species of rabbit as a result of the use of this virus. In your answer, explain

- how this change involves the genetic makeup of rabbits in the population

- the role of variations in this rabbit population

- the way adaptation is involved in the process described in the passage

- how rabbits on the ranch in Australia demonstrated survival of the fittest in relation to the virus

28. The modern theory of evolution states that a basis for variation within a species is provided by

(F) mutations

(G) asexual reproduction

(H) cloning

(J) overproduction

29. Bones located in the wing of a bird and in the flipper of a whale are all similar in appearance, yet they have very different functions. This observation is evidence that they most likely

(A) developed in a common environment

(B) developed from a common ancestor

(C) have identical genetic makeup

(D) use identical methods to obtain food

30. Evolution is often represented as a branching tree similar to the one shown in the diagram below. The names shown represent different groups of organisms that are alive today; the lines represent their evolutionary histories.

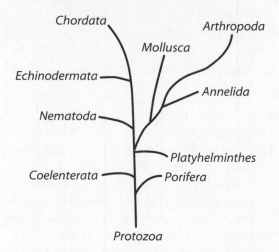

The statement that is best supported by the diagram is that

(F) Annelida and Arthropoda have an ancestor in common

(G) Echinodermata are more closely related to Mollusca than they are to Chordata

(H) Mollusca and Arthropoda probably evolved before Porifera

(J) Annelida and Arthropoda evolved from Echinodermata

31. Even though the American toad and the Fowler's toad are often found living in the same habitat, they do not breed with each other. Which conclusion can best be drawn from this information?

(A) The two types of toads do not interbreed because they are geographically isolated.

(B) The two types of toads do not interbreed because of differences in mating behavior.

(C) Adaptive mutations occurred more often during the evolution of the American toad.

(D) The Fowler's toad has a higher rate of survival than the American toad does.

Ecological Interactions

Our Earth is home to trillions of different organisms. None of these organisms can survive alone.

All organisms—including humans—must interact with both the living and nonliving things that surround them. This topic deals with these interactions.

7.1 Organisms and Their Environment

VOCABULARY			
abiotic	community	environment	population
biosphere	competition	habitat	predator
biotic	ecology	limiting factors	prey
carrying capacity	ecosystem		

As you read this book, you are surrounded by your environment, which includes this book and perhaps your chair, light streaming through the window, a dog barking outside, and a pretzel on the table. If you're in class, your environment may include other students squirming nearby, your teacher pacing the aisles, the drone of an airplane, the smell of the lunchroom, and the unseen mite picking skin flakes off your arm. In short, the **environment** is every living and nonliving thing that surrounds an organism. The study of how organisms interact with the living and nonliving things that surround them is known as **ecology**.

Parts of an Ecosystem

Ecosystem is a short way of saying "ecological system." Scientists use the term to describe any portion of the environment. An ecosystem is made up of all the living things, such as bacteria, plants, and animals that interact with one another. These interacting living things are termed **biotic** factors.

When scientists study ecosystems, they also study the nonliving things, such as soil, water, physical space, and energy that influence the organisms. Nonliving influences are termed **abiotic** factors.

A decaying log, a pond, a field of corn, and even a fish tank are ecosystems. In each of these ecosystems, organisms interact with both the biotic and abiotic parts of their environment. For example, frogs in a pond ecosystem may interact with insects, fish, hawks, and children chasing them with nets. They are also affected by abiotic factors, such as rainfall, the acidity of their pond, temperature, and the amount of light. Some biotic and abiotic parts of an ecosystem are shown in Figure 7-1 on the following page.

Because the world contains a wide variety of physical conditions, many different kinds of environments are available to organisms. Most species, however, have a specific environment that is their "home." That specific environment is known as the species' **habitat**. Familiar habitats include fields, forests, oceans, streams, and deserts.

All the organisms of a species that live in the same area make up a **population**. Ants in a single anthill would be one population. All the different populations are combined to form a **community**. Collectively, all of Earth's ecosystems make up the **biosphere**—the biologically inhabited portions of the planet. Earth's biosphere extends from the deepest ocean troughs to high above the surface of the planet. It includes all the water, land, and air in which organisms thrive. Throughout the biosphere, organisms interact and compete for vital resources, such as food, space, and shelter.

Figure 7-1. Parts of an ecosystem: The biotic part of the ecosystem (animals and plants) includes all the living things that make up the community. The abiotic part of the ecosystem (non-living things) includes factors such as water, soil, air, and light.

The fundamental concept of ecology is that all living organisms are interdependent, and they interact with one another and with the physical environment. These interactions result in a flow of energy and a cycling of materials essential for life. Figure 7-2 shows some of the organisms that interact in oceanic and terrestrial (land) ecosystems.

Environmental Limits on Population Size

In any ecosystem, the growth and survival of organisms depends on the physical conditions and on the resources available to the organism. If they had unlimited resources, living things could produce populations of infinite (unlimited) size. Within any ecosystem, however, resources, such as oxygen and carbon dioxide, water, nutrients, space, and sunlight, are finite (limited). This has a profound effect on the interactions among organisms: Because the resources are finite, organisms must compete with one another to survive.

Competition is the struggle for resources among organisms. Within any one species, competition keeps the size of the population in check. In established ecosystems, populations tend to increase or decrease depending on the resources that are available at the time. This variation in population size tends to follow a predictable cycle. Many populations, for example, vary with the seasons. Over time, however, the size of the population remains stable.

Factors in the environment that limit the size of populations are known as **limiting factors**. Some limiting factors are abiotic. For example, the amount of dissolved oxygen in a pond, may limit the kinds and numbers of fish that can live there. The amount of sunlight filtering through a forest may limit the number of green plants living on the forest floor.

Some other abiotic limiting factors include the intensity of light, the temperature range in the environment, minerals that are available in the water or soil, the type of rock or soil in the ecosystem, and the relative acidity (measured according to the pH scale).

Figure 7-2. Some ecosystems in Earth's biosphere: In each ecosystem, the organisms interact with one another and with their environment. The degree to which each abiotic factor is present determines the type of organisms that can live there.

Other limiting factors are biotic. An important biotic factor that limits population sizes is the relationship between **predators**, which kill and eat other organisms, and **prey**, which are killed for food. As predators kill and eat their prey, they limit the growth of the prey population. If too many prey animals are killed, predators begin to starve, and their population is reduced. With fewer predators, the size of the prey population begins to recover.

The number of organisms of any single species that an ecosystem can support is referred to as its **carrying capacity**. It is determined not only by the available energy, water, oxygen, and minerals (and the recycling of such minerals), but also by the interactions of its organisms.

For example, a field's carrying capacity for a population of foxes is affected not only by the climate, but also by the number and kinds of other populations present. If there are many mice for the foxes to eat, the fox population may boom. If there are many viruses affecting the health of the foxes, their population may crash. Figure 7-3

shows the population increase that normally occurs until the carrying capacity is reached.

Carrying Capacity for an Insect Population

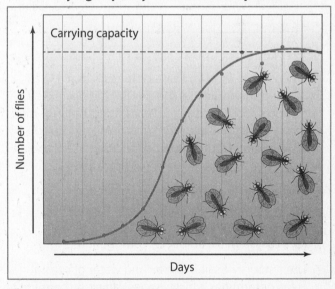

Figure 7-3. Carrying capacity: This population of insects increased until it neared its carrying capacity. Then the population became relatively stable.

7.1 Review

1. All of the Earth's water, land, and atmosphere within which life exists is known as (A) a population (B) an ecosystem (C) the biosphere (D) a biotic community

2. In the biosphere, what are some of the major abiotic factors that determine the distribution and types of plant communities? (F) temperature, sunlight, and rainfall (G) humidity, location, and humans (H) soil type, soil bacteria, and soil water (J) insects, carbon dioxide, and nitrogen in the air

3. The fact that an organism cannot live without interacting with its surroundings is a basic concept in the field of study known as (A) ecology (B) evolution (C) behavior (D) technology

4. When two different species live in the same area and use the same limited resources, which of the following will occur? (F) competition (G) succession (H) parasitism (J) industrialization

5. This graph shows the changes in two populations of herbivores in a grassy field.

Change in Populations Over Time

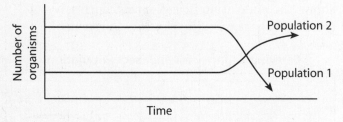

A possible reason for these changes is that (A) all of the plant populations in this habitat decreased (B) Population 2 competed more successfully for food than Population 1 did (C) Population 1 produced more offspring than Population 2 did (D) Population 1 consumed members of Population 2

6. Which term includes all of the interactions that occur between the organisms and the physical factors in a pond environment? (F) population (G) ecosystem (H) abiotic (J) competition

7. The amount of salt in the air and water of coastal areas determines which species can exist there. In these areas, salt functions as a (A) source of energy (B) biotic factor (C) food source (D) limiting factor

Base your answers to questions 8 and 9 on the two graphs shown below.

The first graph shows the number of days of snow cover from 1940 to 1960. The second graph shows the percentage of white mice in a population that was sampled during the same period.

Environmental Conditions and Mouse Population Data 1940-1960

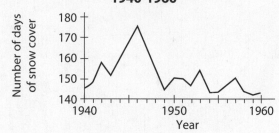

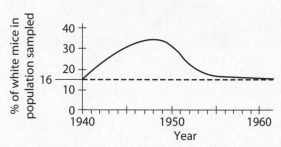

8. The appearance of the greatest percentage of white mice occurred (F) before the maximum number of days of snow cover (G) at the same time as the maximum number of days of snow cover (H) after the maximum number of days of snow cover (J) both before and after the maximum number of days of snow cover

9. Which statement is supported by the data in the graphs? (A) The percentage of brown mice was greatest during the years of longest snow cover. (B) The percentage of mice with white fur was greatest during the years of longest snow cover. (C) The actual number of white mice was greatest during the years of least snow cover. (D) The actual number of brown mice was greatest during the years of longest snow cover.

7.2 Population Interactions

There is a wide diversity of interacting species in most ecosystems. Most of the interactions occur as organisms obtain their food. Every population is linked, directly or indirectly, with all of the other populations in the ecosystem. Each population has one or more specific roles in the ecosystem. As a result, maintaining the ecosystem's diversity is essential to its stability.

Roles in the Ecosystem

The role that each species plays in the ecosystem is called its **ecological niche**. Only one species at a time can occupy a particular niche. If two species attempt to fill the same role in an ecosystem, competition results. Usually, one species will be more suited to the niche, which forces the other species to move on or face elimination. Eventually, only one species will occupy each niche.

Sometimes it appears as if different populations occupy the same niche. For example, deer and moose often live in the same area and seem to eat the same plants. A closer examination reveals that the deer and moose have different food preferences and only compete when food is very scarce. Similarly, several bird species may seem to nest and feed in the same tree.

In reality, it is more probable that the birds are nesting in different parts of the tree and eating different insects. For example, the northeastern United States is home to several species of warblers. Five of those species feed on the insects that live in spruce trees. As shown in Figure 7-4, each species feeds in a different part of the tree.

Competition for a particular ecological niche often occurs when a foreign species enters an area. The new species may be more successful than the native species, partly because the newcomer may not have any natural enemies to control its population. Humans frequently bring foreign species into an area, either on purpose or accidentally. One example is the zebra mussels that were brought to the Great Lakes on cargo ships. The zebra mussel has become a major problem in many states bordering the Great Lakes, and it is now feared that they may spread to middle Atlantic states as well.

Figure 7-4. Feeding patterns among warblers: Several warbler species feed in spruce trees, but they actually occupy different niches because each species feeds in a different part of the spruce tree.

Relationships in an Ecosystem

In every ecosystem, populations of different species are linked together in a complex web of interactions. Sometimes these relationships are competitive; occasionally they are cooperative. **Symbiotic relationships** involve organisms of two different species living in a close relationship that benefits at least one of them.

Symbiotic relationships are typically placed in one of three different categories: mutualism, commensalism, and parasitism. For example, termites have one-celled organisms in their intestinal tracts. These unicellular organisms help the termites digest their food. The tiny organisms gain a place to live and plenty of food, and the termites can make use of a food supply that they would not be able to digest without this cooperative relationship. Pollination of plants by insects is another example. The insect gets food such as nectar, and the insect helps the plant reproduce. This is an illustration of **mutualism**, a relationship in which both organisms benefit.

When a shark attacks and eats its prey, small pieces of the food drift downward. Smaller fish below the shark feed on these scraps. The small fish benefit, but the shark is unaffected. This is an illustration of **commensalism**, a relationship where one species benefits and the other is unaffected.

Ticks may live on a dog and also feed on its blood. This is an example of **parasitism**, a relationship in which one species benefits and the other is harmed. **Parasites** are organisms that attack other live organisms, called **host** organisms, but rarely kill them. Parasites, like ticks, may live on the body of their host, or they may live inside the host, as a tapeworm does.

FOOD CHAINS Among the most common relationships in any ecosystem are the predator-prey relationships. Food chains (see Figure 7.5) show the relationships between prey and predator. In simple terms, the **food chain** shows what eats what.

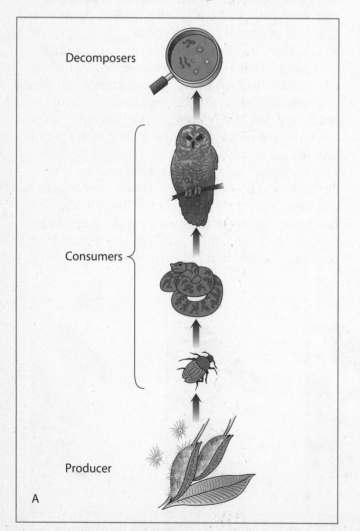

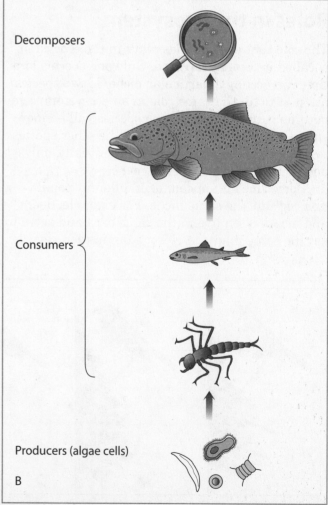

Figure 7-5. Typical food chains: In both a field ecosystem (A) and a pond ecosystem (B) bodies of all these organisms are consumed by the **decomposers**. The decomposers recycle materials that can then be reused by producers.

An organism's niche is defined by how it obtains food. For example, photosynthetic organisms make their own food and, in the process, store the sun's energy. They are known as **autotrophs** (self-feeders) or **producers**. They provide a source of food energy for almost all other living things.

The **heterotrophs** (other-feeders) cannot make their food directly, so they depend on obtaining food from other organisms. Heterotrophs that acquire food by eating other organisms are **consumers**. **Herbivores** are consumers that survive by eating plant tissues; **carnivores** are consumers that eat other animals, and **omnivores** are consumers that eat both plants and animals. **Decomposers** consume the wastes and dead bodies of all these organisms. As they break down wastes or dead organisms, decomposers recycle materials that can be reused by producers.

A feeding relationship between organisms that does not fit into the typical predator-prey category occurs when organisms feed on other organisms, but do not kill the organisms for food. **Scavengers**, such as vultures, are consumers that eat dead organisms. They are nature's "cleanup crew." Scavengers, however, are not decomposers. The dead bodies and wastes of scavengers still have to be broken down by decomposers.

Notice in Figure 7-5 that all food chains begin with autotrophs—the photosynthetic producers—and end with decomposers. The intermediate heterotrophs (the herbivores and carnivores that rely on others for food) are often, but not always, part of food chains. A food chain may be as simple as: grass ➔ decay bacteria.

Decomposers may be included at the end of a food chain, but it is important to remember that they actually consume and break down the chemical materials in all dead organisms and in the wastes of all living organisms.

FOOD WEBS Normally, each organism feeds on more than one kind of organism. Because organisms normally have more than one food source, food chain diagrams are oversimplified. **Food webs**, as shown in Figure 7-6, are diagrams that show the more complex feeding relationships among producers, consumers, and decomposers. The food web shows the many interconnected food chains that exist in the ecosystem. Because organisms have several food choices, ecosystems often remain stable even when one population shows a major decline in numbers. The organisms that normally feed on the declining population may have to rely more heavily on one of their other food choices until the declining population recovers.

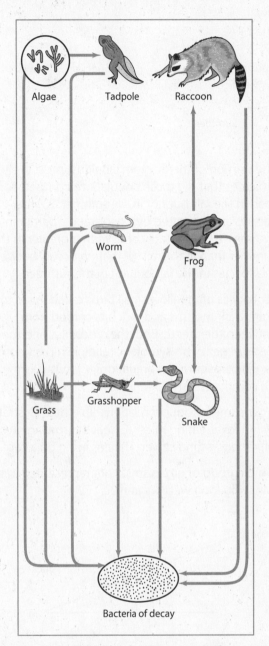

Figure 7-6. A simplified food web near a pond

 **7.2 Review**

1. An earthworm lives and reproduces in the soil. Through its feeding, excretion, and tunneling activities, the worm adds nutrients and allows air to enter the soil. Together, these statements describe the earthworm's (A) habitat (B) nutrition (C) niche (D) environment

2. The following diagram shows the feeding areas of two populations in the same ecosystem during the summer and fall. Both populations feed on oak trees.

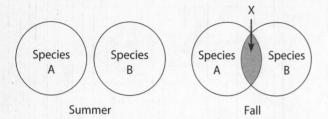

Summer   Fall

The portion of the diagram labeled X most likely indicates that (F) these populations compete for food in the fall, but not in the summer (G) the species are separated by a geographic barrier in the summer (H) the supply of oxygen is greater in the summer than in the fall (J) mating occurs between the species in the fall, but not in the summer

3. Crocodiles often allow small birds called ibises to enter their mouths and pick bits of food from between their teeth. Both the crocodiles and the ibises benefit. This symbiotic relationship is known as (A) parasitism (B) predation (C) mutualism (D) commensalism

4. A consumer-producer relationship is best illustrated by (F) foxes eating mice (G) leaves growing on trees (H) rabbits eating clover (J) fleas living on a cat

5. Which group of organisms is *not* represented in the following food web diagram?

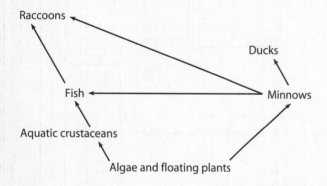

(A) consumers (B) carnivores (C) producers (D) decomposers

6. Which organisms are chiefly responsible for the recycling of dead matter? (F) parasites (G) viruses (H) decomposers (J) producers

7. In a natural community in Maryland, the producer organisms might include (A) bacteria, fungi, and viruses (B) deer, rabbits, and squirrels (C) grasses, maple trees, and weeds (D) trout, peas, and earthworms

8. Which sequence illustrates a generalized food chain in a natural community? (F) autotroph → herbivore → carnivore (G) autotroph → herbivore → autotroph (H) heterotroph → herbivore → carnivore (J) consumer → autotroph → carnivore

9. In a food chain consisting of photosynthetic organisms, herbivores, carnivores, and organisms of decay, the principal function of the photosynthetic organisms is to (A) capture energy from the environment (B) provide material for decay (C) prevent erosion of the topsoil (D) release energy from organic compounds

10. A characteristic shared by both predators and parasites is that they (F) feed on decomposing plant material (G) capture and kill animals for food (H) live inside their hosts (J) attack a living food source

11. As you drive down the highway, you may see crows feeding on dead animals. As a result of this nutritional pattern, crows may be classified as (A) scavengers (B) predators (C) herbivores (D) producers

12. In the following diagram of a food chain, what do the arrows indicate?

(F) the direction in which organisms move in the environment (G) the direction of energy flow through a series of organisms (H) the order of importance of the various organisms (J) the return of chemical substances to the environment

Base your answers to questions 13 through 15 on the following food chain.

Grass → grasshopper → spider → toad → snake

13. Which organism in this food chain can transform light energy into chemical bond energy? (A) spiders (B) aphids (C) grasses (D) snakes

14. Which population will most likely contain the smallest number of organisms? (F) spiders (G) aphids (H) grass (J) snakes

15. If many of the grasshoppers were killed off by the spraying of insecticide, what would most likely happen to the number of toads this ecosystem could support? (A) It would increase since there would be more spiders to eat. (B) It would decrease because there would be fewer spiders to eat. (C) It would stay the same because the grass would not be killed by the insecticide. (D) It would stay the same because the toads eat only spiders.

Base your answers to questions 16 and 17 on the diagram below.

16. Which organisms are components of the same food chain? (F) trees, mountain lion, snake, and hawk (G) trees, rabbit, deer, and shrubs (H) grasses, cricket, frog, and mouse (J) grasses, mouse, snake, and hawk

17. Although decomposers are not shown here, they are an essential part of any food web. Describe the role of decomposers in an ecosystem.

   • Identify an organism that acts as a decomposer.

   • Describe two ways decomposers benefit the ecosystem.

18. A large area of farmland is abandoned and within two years the area becomes a grassy field. Rabbits from nearby areas move to the field, find the conditions right for their needs, and begin to reproduce. Explain why this population of rabbits would not continue to increase indefinitely. In your response, discuss

   • the concept of carrying capacity
   • the role of predators

19. Many organisms live in a field ecosystem, including green plants, insects, birds, foxes and decomposer organisms. Some of the organisms may also be host to a number of parasites. Using examples from this field ecosystem, explain

   • the difference between a habitat and a niche

   • why a predator affects the population of its prey, but a parasite may not have the same effect on its host population

   • the role of the decomposers in this habitat

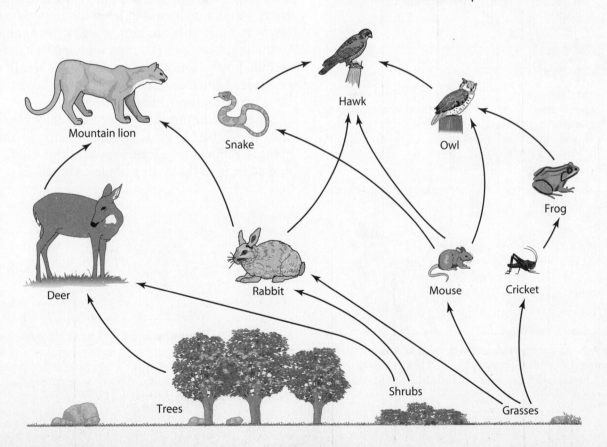

7.3 Energy Flow Through an Ecosystem

VOCABULARY			
biomass	decomposition	energy pyramid	trophic level
biomass pyramid			

Almost all organisms use the solar energy stored in food to power their life processes. That energy, however, does not remain in the organism forever.

Every second of every day, an animal that is not eating has less energy in its tissues than it had a few seconds before. This energy loss occurs because the organism is continually breaking the chemical bonds in food to use the energy to live. As it is released to make ATP and then used in the cells, much of the energy is converted to heat and lost to the environment. Only a small amount can actually be used by the cells. As a result, each next step in the food chain has less of the original solar energy available to it.

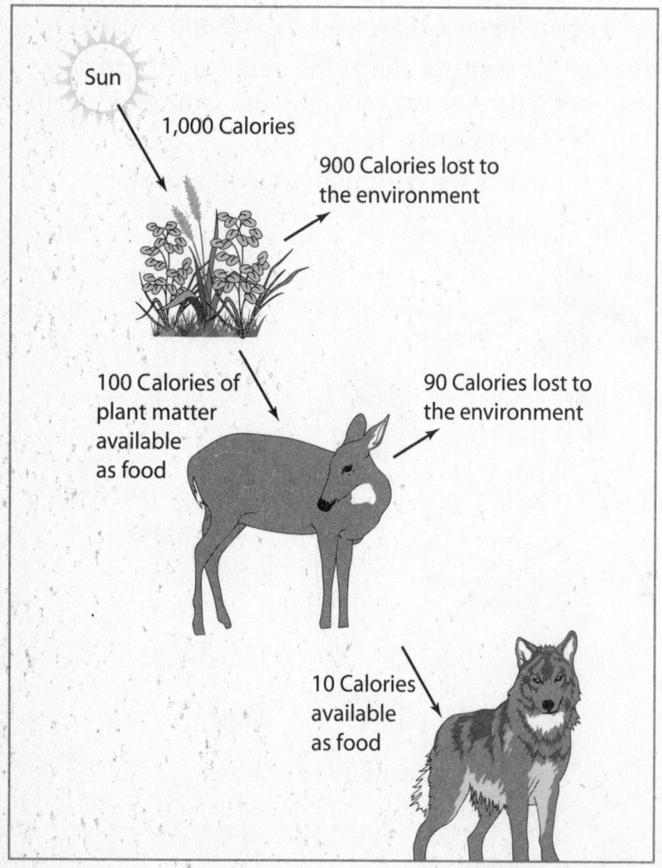

Figure 7-7 shows how the energy is lost. Only the energy stored in the body tissues of each organism is passed to the next consumer in the chain. Because of the energy loss described above, most of the original stored energy is lost in just a few steps of the food chain. For this reason, food chains are usually quite short.

An **energy pyramid**, shown in Figure 7-8, is a diagram that illustrates the transfer of energy through a food chain or web. Examples of organisms that could be found at each level are given on the sides of the pyramid.

Each block of the energy pyramid represents a trophic (feeding) level. The **trophic level** of an organism can be thought of as its feeding position. The size of the block represents the amount of energy that was obtained from the organisms below it. Only this amount of energy is available to the organisms in the next higher block or trophic level. Notice that each level is smaller because of the loss of heat energy as the organisms carry on their life activities.

A continual input of energy, typically from the sun, is required to start the process and to keep it going. Producer organisms capture this energy and store it in the chemical bonds of the food

Figure 7-7. As energy is transferred, much of it is lost to the environment. Notice that only a very small percentage of the calories taken in by a food organism is available to organisms at the next level.

Sun

1,000 Calories

900 Calories lost to the environment

100 Calories of plant matter available as food

90 Calories lost to the environment

10 Calories available as food

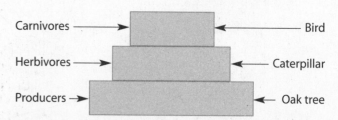

Carnivores — Bird

Herbivores — Caterpillar

Producers — Oak tree

Figure 7-8. An energy pyramid: Each block in the energy pyramid illustrates the amount of energy available for use by organisms at the next level above it. Energy for decomposers actually comes from organisms at all the levels, so they are not shown in this simplified pyramid.

molecules they make. The flow of energy that accompanies the transfer of the food shown in food chains and webs is essential to life on Earth. In spite of this constant drain of energy to the environment, life continues because the sun continues to provide energy.

The amount of living tissue that can be supported at each feeding level depends on the amount of energy available at that level. Therefore, the **biomass**, which is the total mass of the living organisms present in the ecosystem being studied, decreases at each higher trophic level.

In any community, the biomass of the producers is much more than the biomass of the herbivores feeding on them. For example, it takes more than 50 pounds of grass to keep 50 pounds of grasshoppers alive. Similarly, the biomass of the herbivores is always greater than the biomass of the carnivores that eat them. A **biomass pyramid** looks very similar to an energy pyramid.

Recycling and Reusing Materials

The parts of dead organisms that are not consumed during one of the other steps in the food chain are not wasted. Decomposers extract the last bit of energy contained in the dead organisms, as well as the energy in the waste products from living organisms, and use it to sustain their life processes. As they do so, they return the raw materials contained in the once-living matter to the soil. This process of breaking down waste products and dead organisms into their raw materials and returning those materials to the ecosystem is known as **decomposition**. Two examples of organisms that fill the role of decomposers are bacteria and fungi.

Because of the actions of decomposers, the atoms and molecules in living things cycle through both the nonliving and living parts of the biosphere. As they do, chemical elements that make up the bodies of living things, such as carbon, hydrogen, oxygen, and nitrogen, pass through food webs and are combined and recombined in different ways in different living organisms. For example, plants trap carbon dioxide and water molecules in energy-rich compounds (such as glucose and starch) during photosynthesis. These molecules

may be broken down and used by the organism when plants need energy to power their cell processes or are eaten by a consumer. During respiration, the molecules are released by the cells and returned to the environment.

Much of the cycling of materials in ecosystems is carried out by decomposers. Figure 7-9 shows some of the ways in which matter cycles throughout the ecosystem.

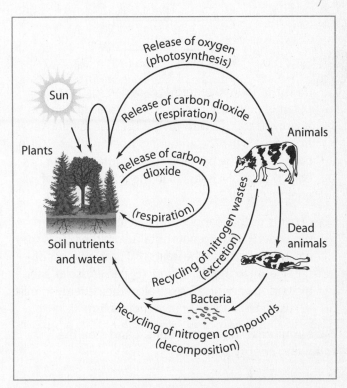

Figure 7-9. The recycling of materials in ecosystems: Dead organisms and wastes must be recycled in ecosystems so that their raw materials can be made available for reuse by producer organisms. The gas exchanges of photosynthesis and respiration, along with the action of decomposers, are crucial to the recycling process.

7.3 Review

1. Decomposition and decay of organic matter are accomplished by the action of (A) green plants (B) bacteria and fungi (C) viruses and algae (D) scavengers

2. Which statement about the pyramid of energy shown below is correct?

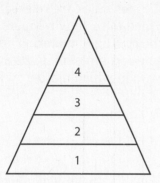

(F) The amount of energy needed to sustain the pyramid enters at level 4. (G) The total amount of energy decreases with each successive feeding level from 4 to 1. (H) The amount of energy is identical in each level of the pyramid. (J) The total amount of energy at level 4 is less than the total amount of energy at level 2.

3. Organisms that eat goats obtain less energy from the goats than the goats obtain from the plants they eat. This is because the goats (A) pass on most of the energy to their offspring (B) convert solar energy to food energy (C) store all of their energy in milk (D) use energy for their own metabolism

Base your answers to questions 4 and 5 on the following energy pyramid.

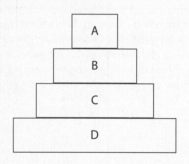

4. If birds eat insects that feed on corn, which level on this pyramid would birds occupy? (F) A (G) B (H) C (J) D

5. Which statement concerning the energy in the pyramid is correct? (A) The producer organisms contain the least amount of energy. (B) Stored energy decreases as it is passed from consumer to consumer. (C) Consumers contain more energy than producers. (D) Decomposers are the source of energy for this pyramid.

Base your answers to questions 6 through 9 on the activities described in the following paragraphs.

A tomato plant was placed under a sealed bell jar and exposed to light. Carbon dioxide containing radioactive carbon was introduced into the bell jar as shown in the following diagram. After an hour, the inlet valve was closed. Later, the entire plant was removed from the soil and cleaned by rinsing it in water. A Geiger counter indicated radioactivity in the roots. These roots were then dried and chopped into very small pieces. The chopped roots were sprinkled into an aquarium containing a very hungry goldfish that was *not* radioactive. Four days later, the fish was removed from the aquarium and a tissue section of the fish was tested with the Geiger counter. The counter indicated an above-normal level of radioactivity in the fish tissues.

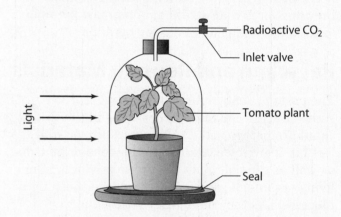

6. Which cycle is primarily being studied in this investigation? (F) oxygen (G) carbon (H) nitrogen (J) water

7. A control set-up for this investigation would be identical to the one described except for the replacement of the (A) tomato plant with a geranium plant (B) goldfish with a tadpole (C) radioactive carbon dioxide with atmospheric carbon dioxide (D) soil with distilled water

8. By which process was the radioactivity incorporated into the material that was transported to the roots? (F) growth (G) mitosis (H) photosynthesis (J) respiration

9. This investigation suggests that when plants are eaten by animals, some of the plant materials may be (A) changed to animal tissue (B) separated into smaller molecules before being digested (C) eliminated by the animal in a form that allows the plant to grow again (D) used in regulating the animal's digestive processes

10. Most green algae are able to obtain carbon dioxide from the environment and use it to synthesize organic compounds. This activity is an example of (F) cellular respiration (G) autotrophic nutrition (H) heterotrophic nutrition (J) heterotrophic respiration

11. A cycling of materials is represented in the following diagram.

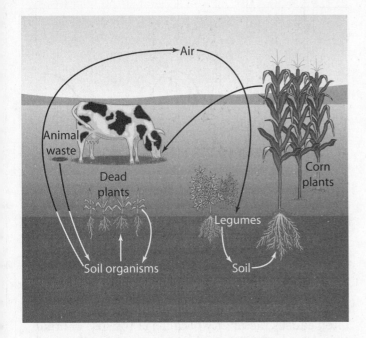

Which statement is supported by the events shown in the diagram? (A) Materials are cycled between living organisms only. (B) Materials are cycled between heterotrophic organisms only. (C) Materials are cycled between the living and nonliving components of the environment only. (D) Materials are cycled between autotrophic organisms only.

12. Imagine that you are stuck on a deserted island and will not be rescued for weeks. The only food you have available is two chickens and a bushel of corn. Because of environmental conditions, it is impossible for you to grow the corn. The only way to keep the chickens alive for more than a few days is to feed them the corn. You actually have three choices:

Choice A: You and the chickens eat the corn first, and then you eat the chickens.

Choice B: You eat the chickens first, and then eat the corn.

Choice C: You feed the corn to the chickens and eat the eggs. Later, you eat the chickens.

Explain why *Choice B* is the best choice. In your response

- discuss the concept of energy flow

- explain why the other two choices would provide you with less energy than choice B

Base your answers to questions 13 and 14 on the information below.

Analysis of a sample taken from a pond showed variety in both number and type of organisms present. The data collected are shown in the table below.

Pond Sampling Results

Type of Organisms	Number Present
bass	two
frogs	forty
phytoplankton	thousands
insect larvae	hundreds

13. If the frogs feed on insect larvae, what is the role of the frogs in this pond ecosystem? (A) herbivore (B) consumer (C) parasite (D) host

14. Which diagram best represents the organisms arranged as an energy pyramid?

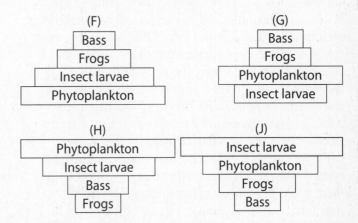

7.4 Diversity Benefits Species and Habitats

VOCABULARY

biodiversity

As a result of evolution, there is a great diversity of species on Earth. Almost every ecosystem is populated by many species, each occupying its own special niche. The interrelationships and interdependencies of these species help to keep ecosystems stable, and the diversity of species increases the chance that at least some organisms will survive in the face of large environmental changes.

Biodiversity is a measurement of the degree to which species vary within an ecosystem. There is a strong connection between biodiversity and the stability of an ecosystem. A natural forest, for example, contains many different species of trees. If disease or insects attack one population, nearby trees of another species are likely to survive.

The mix of species in the ecosystem also makes it difficult for the disease organisms to move quickly through this environment. Here, biodiversity serves as a barrier to the spread of disease or insect attack.

In contrast, on a tree farm where all of the trees are planted and are of a single species, the entire population could be seriously damaged by a single disease or insect attack.

The interactions between organisms may allow an ecosystem to remain stable for hundreds or thousands of years. In established, stable ecosystems, populations tend to increase and decrease in size in a predictable pattern. Over time, however, the size of the population remains relatively stable. For example, when the prey population increases, a large food supply causes the size of the predator population to rise. Because each predator requires many prey to meet its energy needs, the prey population rapidly decreases.

Soon, with the decline in a prey population, some of the predators begin to starve. When only a few predators remain alive, the prey population reproduces and greater numbers of prey survive. The cycle begins anew. Figure 7-10 illustrates the seasonal change in a rabbit population.

The loss of biodiversity in an ecosystem upsets its stability. Removing species from an environment

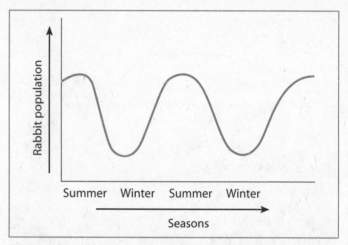

Figure 7-10. Rabbit populations: Rabbit populations may rise and fall over the course of a year, but from year to year they follow the same pattern if the environment is stable.

often causes instability because of the loss of organisms that were filling critical ecological niches.

Many species may be lost when natural disasters or human activities cause large-scale destruction to habitats. Clearing large areas of tropical rain forest, for example, has disrupted many ecosystems; some may never recover. Although some species may be able to return to a damaged ecosystem, others with critical roles may be totally lost. The interdependencies between populations in the original ecosystem may have been so great that if biodiversity is lost, the ecosystem may never be restored to its original state.

Species can also be lost when humans do not consider the environmental impact of their actions. For example, offering bounties for the removal of predatory mountain lions from some environments sounded like a good idea at one time, but it led to population explosions of deer herds.

Soon the deer exceeded the carrying capacity of the area. As a result, their overgrazing reduced the food supply so much that many deer starved. The overgrazing also led to soil erosion that caused permanent environmental damage. The negative effects begun by the removal of the mountain lions were evident for many years.

When humans clear land for agricultural purposes, the loss of biodiversity may also lead to an unstable environment. Disease and insect pests present major problems to farmers whose crops are genetically similar. For these farmers, any disruption threatens to affect the entire crop.

Farmers are constantly in search of ways to control insect pests and diseases in their crops, because they have created an environment that is always in danger of serious disruption. In natural ecosystems, the diversity of species provides no such concentration of one kind of food, making it far less likely that any single pest or disease will cause problems.

Biodiversity Benefits Humans

Biodiversity also represents one of the greatest resources known to humans. It ensures the availability of a rich variety of genetic material, some of which may prove valuable to humans. Though still largely untapped, the genetic diversity found in rain forests has provided humans with medicines, insecticides, and other useful resources. If we destroy ecosystems, we lose much of the biodiversity they hold. As diversity is lost, potentially valuable resources are lost with it.

 7.4 Review

1. Some data concerning bird species are shown in the chart below. Which statement is a valid inference based on information in the chart?

Number of Bird Species	Location
26	northern Alaska
153	southwest Texas
600	Costa Rica

(A) The different species in northern Alaska can interbreed. (B) There are conditions in Costa Rica that account for greater biodiversity there. (C) The different species in southwest Texas evolved from those in northern Alaska. (D) The greater number of species in Costa Rica is due to a greater number of predators there.

2. A greater stability of the biosphere would most likely result from (F) a decrease in finite resources (G) an increase in deforestation (H) an increase in biodiversity (J) a decrease in consumer populations

Base your answer to question 3 on the graph below.

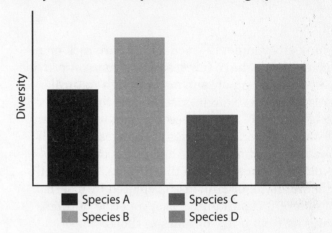

3. If the environment were to change dramatically or if a new plant disease were to be introduced, which plant species would be the most likely to have individuals that could survive the disease? (A) Species A (B) Species B (C) Species C (D) Species D

4. A forest community is made up of thousands of species of organisms and can exist practically unchanged for hundreds of years. This stability is due to the (F) diversity of organisms present (G) abundance of insects that feed on plants (H) changes in the climate of the area (J) lack of decomposers in the forest

5. Explain why it is important to preserve biodiversity.

- Compare the biodiversity of a vegetable farm with the biodiversity of an abandoned field.

- Explain why plant diseases are often less of a problem in an abandoned field ecosystem than in a field of vegetables of the same kind.

- Explain why medical researchers are concerned when the biodiversity of an ecosystem decreases.

7.5 Environments Change

Many environments, such as the bare rock on a mountaintop, have few resources that can provide homes for living organisms. Through natural processes, these environments will change over long periods of time to become habitats for many diverse species. The series of changes by which one habitat changes into another is called **ecological succession**. In this process, an existing community of organisms is replaced by a series of different communities over a period of time ranging from a few decades to thousands of years.

Pioneer organisms are the first to populate an area. As ecological succession progresses, each community causes modifications to its environment. The modifications result in changes that make it less suitable for the current community and more suitable for another community that eventually replaces it.

For example, as grasses grow in an area with very shallow soil, they add organic matter, making the soil deeper and more fertile. Shrubs are then able to live in this modified environment and will eventually produce enough shade to eliminate the grasses growing below them.

Over a period of many years, these gradual changes may result in the formation of a stable forest community that can last for hundreds or even thousands of years. In dry or cold climates, succession may not advance to the forest stage, but the final stage will be a stable ecosystem that can last for many years. The stable, unchanging **climax community** that eventually develops is a self-perpetuating community with animal and plant species that remain in balance with one another for an extended period of time.

Climatic changes, natural disasters, and the activities of humans and other animals, can disrupt ecological succession at any stage. These changes may be rapid, perhaps due to a forest fire or flood, or may occur over a period of years, as when a long-term drought or climate change occurs. The altered environments will again undergo a slow series of successional changes that may eventually result in a climax community.

There are two commonly observed patterns of succession. A community of mostly bare rock will gradually accumulate soil, leading to a progression of vegetation types from grasses to shrubs, and eventually a forest. This process is seen in Figure 7-11.

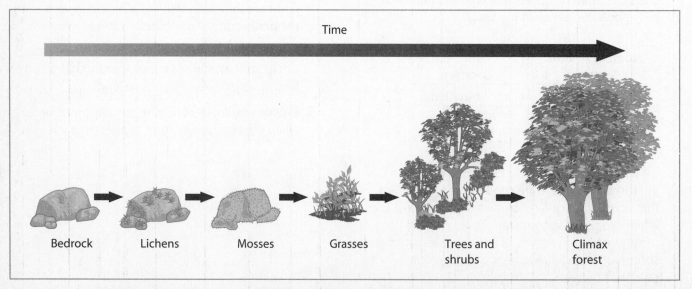

Time

Bedrock → Lichens → Mosses → Grasses → Trees and shrubs → Climax forest

Figure 7-11. Succession from bare rock to a forest: The original bedrock is covered with soil as plants grow, die, and decay. As the depth of the soil increases, it can support the root systems of larger plants until there is enough to support a climax forest.

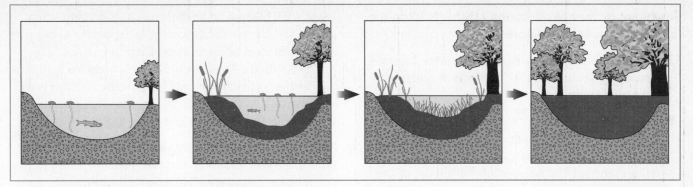

Figure 7-12. Succession from a lake to a forest

Another commonly observed example of ecological succession is the change from a lake community to a forest. The lake will gradually accumulate sediments from erosion and the buildup of organic debris from plants and dead organisms. As the lake fills in, it becomes shallower. After many years, it may become a swamp. The filling-in continues, and eventually a mature forest may result. Successional changes from lake to forest are shown in Figure 7-12.

 **7.5 Review**

1. When a stable forest community is destroyed by fire, the community usually is (A) not restored (B) restored in a series of successive changes (C) restored only if humans reforest the area (D) changed into a permanent grassland

2. In a pond, which change would most likely lead to land succession? (F) a decrease in the amount of particles suspended in the water of the pond (G) an increase in the speed of the water currents in the pond (H) a decrease in the number and diversity of organisms inhabiting the shallow water of the pond (J) an increase in the amount of sediment, fallen leaves, and tree limbs accumulating on the bottom of the pond

3. When Mount St. Helens erupted in 1980, a portion of the surrounding area was covered by lava, which buried all of the vegetation. Four months later, *Anaphalis margaritacea* plants were found growing out of lava rock crevices. The beginning of plant regrowth in this area is a part of the process known as (A) species preservation (B) natural selection (C) biotic competition (D) ecological succession

4. Lichens on bare rock and weeds growing in a burned-over area are known as pioneer organisms because they (F) are the last to grow in a given area (G) exhibit mutualism with other species (H) initiate the nitrogen cycle (J) start ecological succession

5. Which statement best describes the climax stage of an ecological succession? (A) It will be populated only by plants. (B) It persists until there are drastic changes in the environment. (C) It represents the initial phase of evolution. (D) It will change rapidly from season to season.

Base your answers to question 6 on the information provided below.

If you travel inland from the shores of Lake Michigan, which was once much larger than it is today, you would travel through the following areas:

1. the present sandy beach

2. grasses

3. a cottonwood forest

4. a pine forest

5. an oak forest

6. a beech-maple forest (where the shoreline was once located)

6. How is this pattern of vegetation associated with ecological succession?

- Describe why only grasses can grow near the sandy beach.

- Explain why grasses are not found in the cottonwood forest.

- Describe the type of vegetation that was present in the area of the pine forest before it became a pine forest.

Base your answers to questions 7 through 10 on the following sequence of diagrams.

7. This sequence of diagrams best illustrates (A) succession (B) evolution (C) the effects of acid rain (D) a food chain

8. The natural increase in the amount of vegetation from 1840 to 1930 is related to the (F) decreasing water depth (G) increasing amount of sunlight (H) presence of bottom-feeding fish (J) use of the pond for fishing

9. If a fire burned off all of the vegetation in the area today, which would most likely happen? (A) the area would soon become a pond similar to the one in 1840 (B) the forest would quickly grow back (C) in a few years the area would begin to be covered with grasses and shrubs (D) the area would become a swamp and remain that way for thousands of years

10. If no human intervention or natural disaster occurs, by the year 2050 this area will most likely be a (F) lake (G) swamp (H) desert (J) forest

1840

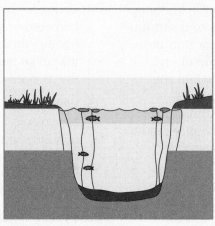

1870

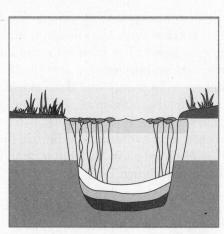

1900

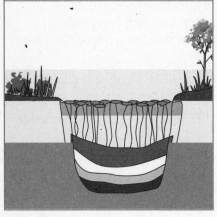

1930

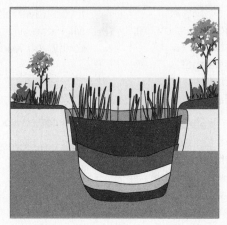

1960

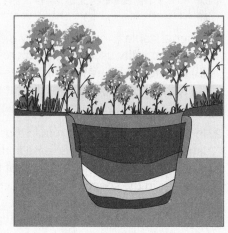

1990

1. The members of an animal community are usually similar in
   (A) size
   (B) structure
   (C) food requirements
   (D) environmental requirements

2. Which is a biotic factor that affects the size of a population in a specific ecosystem?
   (F) the average temperature of the ecosystem
   (G) the number and kinds of soil minerals in the ecosystem
   (H) the number and kinds of predators in the ecosystem
   (J) the concentration of oxygen in an ecosystem

3. Overpopulation of deer in a certain area will most likely lead to
   (A) a decrease in the number of predators of the deer
   (B) an increase in the number of autotrophs available for food
   (C) a decrease in the incidence of disease
   (D) an increase in competition between the deer

4. A farmer abandons one of his fields, and over the years he notices that one field community is replaced by another community. This replacement represents part of
   (F) a food chain
   (G) an abiotic community
   (H) an energy pyramid
   (J) an ecological succession

5. An ecosystem, such as an aquarium, is self-sustaining if it involves the interaction between organisms, a flow of energy, and the presence of
   (A) an equal number of plants and animals
   (B) more animals than plants
   (C) material cycles
   (D) organisms undergoing succession

6. In order to be self-sustaining, an ecosystem must contain
   (F) a large number of organisms
   (G) a warm, moist environment
   (H) a constant source of energy
   (J) organisms that occupy all of the niches

Base your answers to questions 7 through 9 on the information and graph below.

The graph illustrates a comparison between pH conditions and species survival rates in certain lakes in the Adirondack region of the northeastern U.S.

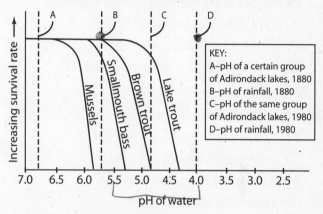

The Effect of pH on Survival Rates of Selected Species in Certain Adirondack Lakes

KEY:
A–pH of a certain group of Adirondack lakes, 1880
B–pH of rainfall, 1880
C–pH of the same group of Adirondack lakes, 1980
D–pH of rainfall, 1980

–*National Geographic* (adapted)

7. Which species can tolerate the highest level of acidity in its water environment?
   (A) mussels
   (B) small mouth bass
   (C) brown trout
   (D) lake trout

8. In the years between 1880 and 1980, which species would most likely have been eliminated *first* because of the gradual acidification of Adirondack lakes?
   (F) mussels
   (G) small mouth bass
   (H) brown trout
   (J) lake trout

9. What was the total change in pH in the rainwater from 1880 to 1980?
   (A) 1.3
   (B) 1.7
   (C) 5.3
   (D) 9.7

10. Which types of organisms must be present in an ecosystem if the ecosystem is to be maintained?

   (F) producers and carnivores

   (G) producers and decomposers

   (H) carnivores and decomposers

   (J) herbivores and carnivores

11. Although three different bird species all inhabit the same type of tree in an area, competition between the birds rarely occurs. The most likely explanation for this lack of competition is that these birds

   (A) have different ecological niches

   (B) eat the same food

   (C) have a limited supply of food

   (D) are unable to interbreed

12. Producer organisms function to

   (F) store more energy than they use

   (G) use more energy than they store

   (H) store energy but not use it

   (J) use energy but not store it

13. Which foods are derived from organisms that occupy the trophic level that contains the greatest amount of energy in an energy pyramid?

   (A) bread and tomatoes

   (B) shrimp and rice

   (C) hamburger and French fries

   (D) chicken and lettuce

14. Which statement describes symbiotic relationships?

   (F) Two species live in close association in an ecosystem.

   (G) Abiotic factors interact in an ecosystem.

   (H) Decomposers respond to abiotic changes in the ecosystem.

   (J) Ecosystem feeding levels show changes in energy.

15. Which pair of terms would most likely apply to the same organism?

   (A) heterotroph and herbivore

   (B) heterotroph and autotroph

   (C) autotroph and parasite

   (D) producer and predator

16. Which ecological principle is best illustrated by the following diagram?

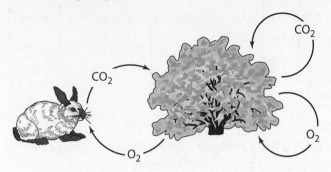

   (F) In an ecosystem, material is cycled among the organisms and the environment.

   (G) In an ecosystem, the number of producers and consumers is equal.

   (H) Competition within a species results in natural selection.

   (J) An ecosystem requires a constant source of energy.

Base your answers to questions 17 and 18 on the following diagram of a food web.

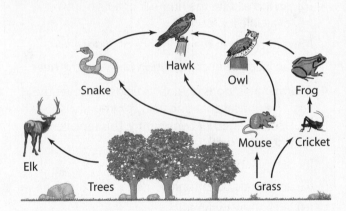

17. Which organisms are most likely to be competitors?

   (A) mouse and frog

   (B) cricket and owl

   (C) cricket and frog

   (D) owl and hawk

18. Which organism would most likely be adversely affected by a continuous decrease in the population of mice?

   (F) grass

   (G) crickets

   (H) elk

   (J) hawks

19. In the following food chain, which are the most abundant organisms?

corn plants ➔ mice ➔ garter snakes ➔ hawks

(A) corn plants

(B) garter snakes

(C) mice

(D) hawks

Base your answers to questions 20 through 23 on the following graphs showing data on some environmental factors affecting a large lake.

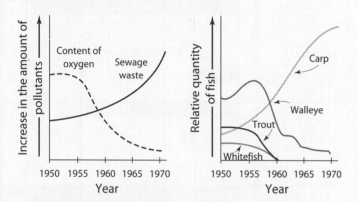

20. Which relationship can be correctly inferred from the data present?

(F) As sewage waste increases, the oxygen content decreases.

(G) As sewage waste increases, the oxygen content increases.

(H) As oxygen content decreases, the carp population decreases.

(J) As oxygen level decreases, the trout population increases.

21. The greatest change in the lake's whitefish population occurred in the years between

(A) 1950 and 1955

(B) 1955 and 1960

(C) 1960 and 1965

(D) 1965 and 1970

22. Which fish species appears to withstand the greatest degree of oxygen depletion? (F) trout (G) walleye (H) carp (J) whitefish

23. Using the graph as a reference, explain the impact of increased sewage levels on the biodiversity of the lake ecosystem.

• Describe how the biodiversity of the lake changed between 1950 and 1970.

• Explain why the sewage affected the kinds of fish present in the lake.

Base your answer to question 24 on the following information and data table.

A field study was conducted to observe a deer population in a given region over time. The deer were counted at different intervals over a period of 40 years. During this entire time, no deer hunting was allowed.

From 1905 through 1920, hunters were encouraged to kill mountain lions and other predators of deer. After 1920 it was nearly impossible to find any predators of deer. Reports of predators were very rare in the area between 1924 and 1940. A summary of the data is presented in the table.

Deer Population Changes 1900–1940

Year	Deer Population (thousands)	Status of Predators	Status of Deer Hunting
1900	3.0	Killing of deer predators was encouraged	No deer hunting allowed
1910	9.5		
1920	65.0		
1924	100.0	Deer predators hardly ever seen	
1926	40.0		
1930	25.0		
1940	6.0		

24. Analyze the data provided in the table.

• Describe the trend shown by the deer population over this 40 year period.

• Suggest one likely reason for the change in the deer population from 1900 through 1924.

• Suggest how carrying capacity may be associated with the change in the deer population from 1924 through 1940.

Base your answers to questions 25 through 28 on the information provided.

For 25 years, hay was cut from the same 10 acres on a farm. During these years, shrews, grasshoppers, spiders, rabbits, and mice were seen in this hayfield. After the farmer retired, he no longer cut the hay, and the field was left unattended.

25. Which description best matches the events in the former hayfield over the next few decades?

(A) The plant species will change, but the animal species will remain the same.

(B) The animal species will change, but the plant species will remain the same.

(C) Neither the plant species nor the animal species will change.

(D) Both the plant species and the animal species will change.

26. The grasshoppers, spiders, shrews, and other organisms, along with the soil minerals, amount of rainfall, and other factors, constitute

(F) an ecosystem

(G) a species

(H) a biosphere

(J) a food web

27. Just before he retired, the farmer determined the population size of several of the field species during the months of May, July, and August. The results are recorded in the table.

Field Species	Number of Organisms		
	May	**July**	**August**
Grasshoppers	1,000	5,000	1,500
Birds	250	100	100
Grasses	7,000	20,000	6,000
Spiders	75	200	500

Draw a food chain that represents the most likely feeding relationships among four of the organisms (grasshopper, birds, grasses, and spiders) that live in the field.

28. Which graph best represents the relative population size of the field species for May?

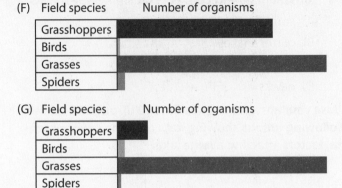

(F)

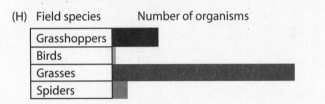

(G)

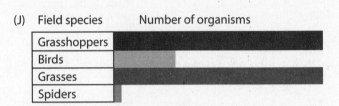

(H)

(J) Field species   Number of organisms

29. The acacia tree is protected from other insects by a certain species of ant. The ants, in turn, feed on a sweet secretion produced by the tree. This type of nutritional relationship is known as

(A) decomposition

(B) parasitism

(C) mutualism

(D) commensalism

Base your answers to questions 30 and 31 on the information below.

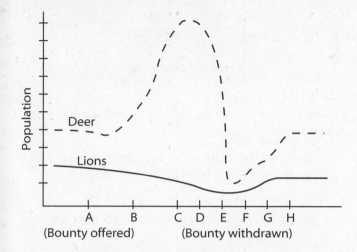

The graph shows the relative populations of mountain lions and deer in a certain geographic area that is generally favorable to both animals. At the time indicated by point A, hunters were offered a bounty payment for each mountain lion killed. Later, at the time indicated by point E, these bounties were withdrawn and hunting mountain lions was discouraged.

30. Which explanation best accounts for the fact that, according to the graph, the deer population is always higher than the mountain lion population?

(F) The geographic location is more favorable for deer than for mountain lions.

(G) Hunters are likely to kill more mountain lions than deer.

(H) The organism serving as the food supply is normally more numerous than its predator.

(J) Mountain lions usually produce more offspring than deer.

31. The graph is an illustration of the principle that

(A) predators serve an important purpose in a balanced ecosystem

(B) human intervention has little permanent impact on the survival of animal species

(C) deer need the protection of humans in order to survive the attacks of their natural enemies

(D) mountain lions do not pose the greatest danger to deer in their struggle for survival

32. When the food relationships in a habitat are illustrated by means of a diagram, the result is always a complicated web-like pattern. This is due to the fact that

(F) many consumers are adapted to use more than one food source

(G) producer organisms always outnumber the consumer organisms

(H) matter is lost in an ecosystem as it moves from producers to consumers

(J) both producers and consumers require oxygen for metabolic processes

33. Although three different butterfly species all inhabit the same flower garden in an area, competition between the butterflies rarely occurs. The most likely explanation for this lack of competition is that the butterflies

(A) occupy different niches

(B) have a limited supply of food

(C) share food with each other

(D) are able to interbreed

Base your answers to questions 34 and 35 on the information below.

Lichens are composed of two organisms, a fungus that cannot make its own food and algae that contain chlorophyll. Lichens may live on the bark of trees or even on bare rock. They secrete acids that tend to break down the rock they live on, helping to produce soil. As soil accumulates, having formed from the broken rock and dead lichens, other organisms, such as plants, may begin to grow.

34. The ability of lichens to alter their environment, enabling other organisms to grow and take their places in that environment, is one step in the process of

(F) biological evolution

(G) ecological succession

(H) maintenance of cellular communication

(J) differentiation in complex organisms

35. What is the role of the algae component of a lichen in an ecosystem?

(A) decomposer

(B) parasite

(C) herbivore

(D) producer

36. Some people claim that certain carnivores should be destroyed because they kill beneficial animals. Explain why these carnivores should be protected. Your answer should include information concerning

- prey population growth

- extinction

- importance of carnivores in an ecosystem

- examples of predator-prey relationships

37. Zebra mussels have caused several major changes in the ecosystem of many rivers around the Great Lakes. Native to Eurasia, zebra mussels were accidentally imported to the Great Lakes in ships during the late 1980s and first appeared in some nearby rivers in 1990. In recent years there have been concerns raised about these organisms spreading down from the headwaters of the Susquehanna River to the Chesapeake Bay area.

 In some parts of the currently affected rivers, zebra mussels have depleted the levels of dissolved oxygen to the point where many native organisms either die or move to other waters. In addition, large amounts of phytoplankton (small photosynthetic organisms) are consumed by the zebra mussels. Before the introduction of zebra mussels, one typical food chain in these rivers was:

phytoplankton ➝ freshwater clams ➝ other consumers

Describe some long-term changes in these river ecosystems that could be caused by zebra mussels.

- State how the population of each of *two* different species (other than the zebra mussels) found in these river ecosystems would be expected to change, and explain why.

- Identify *one* gas normally present in these ecosystems and explain how a change in its concentration due to the effects of zebra mussels would affect organisms other than the zebra mussels.

- State how the death of many of the native organisms could affect the rate of decay and the amount of material being recycled.

- Explain why the size of the zebra mussel population would decrease after an initial increase.

38. The diagram represents an energy pyramid.

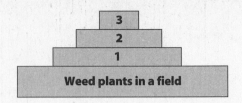

Explain what an energy pyramid represents about an ecosystem.

- Describe the relationship between the organisms at different levels of an energy pyramid.

- Identify three organisms, in order from 1 to 3, that could occupy the three numbered trophic levels of this pyramid.

- Explain why the blocks decrease in size from bottom to top.

- Explain why the base of an energy pyramid always represents producer organisms.

39. Which statement best describes energy transfer in a food web?

(A) Energy is transferred to consumers, which convert it to nitrogen and use it to make amino acids.

(B) Energy from producers is converted into oxygen and transferred to consumers.

(C) Energy from the sun is stored in green plants and transferred to consumers.

(D) Energy is transferred to consumers, which use it to produce food.

Human Influences on Global Ecosystems

All living things affect the environment around them. Porcupines chew the bark from trees; squirrels sometimes break twigs as they leap from branch to branch. Generally, the changes to the environment are small. Humans, however, have made impressive technological achievements in the past few hundred years. As a result, we are now making significant changes in Earth's diverse environments.

As the human population grows and our need for the resources to sustain our technology expands, the possibility that we will harm Earth's ecosystems increases. Our decisions about how to use—or misuse—Earth's resources will have a profound impact on all the organisms that depend on those resources.

8.1 Understanding the Biosphere

VOCABULARY			
energy flow	nonrenewable resource	pollution	renewable resource

The Need to Understand Our Environment

Human activities can create ecological problems that must be avoided or corrected. If we are to find solutions to those problems, we must encourage everyone to become environmentally literate. That means people need to understand the causes and effects of environmental problems as well as the possible solutions that could lead to environmental stability. Because environmental issues often concern many countries, resolving environmental issues frequently requires global awareness, cooperation, and action.

Like all living things, humans are part of Earth's natural ecosystems. We depend on our ecosystem to supply the food we eat, the water we drink, and the air we breathe. As long as our ecosystem functions normally, those essential resources will be available.

We can continue to depend on the plants in the ecosystem to provide food and oxygen and to recycle the carbon dioxide we exhale. We will also be able to rely upon our ecosystem to maintain the quality of our water.

Limited Resources

Earth has a finite supply of resources. Some of Earth's resources, such as our food supply and solar energy, are renewable. Given sufficient time, **renewable resources** can be replaced within a generation or two. Other resources, such as fossil fuels and minerals, are nonrenewable resources. Once they're used, they cannot be replaced. Decisions we make today and tomorrow will determine whether we increase our consumption of Earth's limited resources.

One way to reduce our use of resources is to control the growth rate of our population. An ever-increasing human population accelerates the use of Earth's limited resources. Making the right decisions about these issues will affect you as well as the future generations of all the organisms that share the biosphere.

RENEWABLE RESOURCES Although many resources are renewable, they must be used carefully. Increased consumption can stress the natural processes that renew some resources. As a result, the resource might be unable to renew itself. For example, the fish we eat are a

Table 8-1. How Individuals Can Preserve Resources		
The 3 R's	**Action**	**Example**
Reduce	Avoid using the resource.	Use energy efficiently; walk, bike, or car-pool instead of driving.
Reuse	Use the same product over and over, instead of throwing it away after one use.	Use dishes rather than paper plates. Instead of discarding your paper lunch bag, take it home and use it again.
Recycle	Don't throw the product in the trash. Instead, discard it in such a way that it can be used to make another product.	Paper, metal, plastic, and glass are all easily recycled.

renewable resource. Even if many fish are captured, over time the fish populations can reproduce and recover their losses. Today, however, commercial fishing can remove so many fish so quickly that specific populations may not have time to recover. In some cases, the reduction can be so severe that the fish population may fail to reproduce. At that point, the fish would no longer be a renewable resource.

NONRENEWABLE RESOURCES Our increasing consumption of resources is becoming a serious problem. Most metals, such as the aluminum we use for packaging, and other minerals, such as the silicon we use for computer chips, are **nonrenewable resources**. These resources cannot be replaced naturally within a few generations. Fossil fuels, such as the gas that runs our cars and the coal that powers many factories, are also nonrenewable resources. Using too many nonrenewable resources will cause their depletion (serious reduction) within a relatively short time.

PRESERVING OUR RESOURCES Individuals can help maintain our supply of both renewable and nonrenewable resources by practicing the three R's: reducing, reusing, and recycling. Suggestions are included in Table 8-1.

Natural Processes in Ecosystems

Several natural processes that occur in ecosystems affect the life and health of humans as well as all the other organisms that rely on the ecosystem. Some activities of humans affect these processes, and most of the changes are likely to be damaging to ecosystems.

For example, if **pollution**—a harmful change in the chemical makeup of the soil, water, or air—spreads to a particular habitat, some of the species that live in that habitat will suffer. The stability of the ecosystem and the variety of species that live in it might be threatened.

MAINTAINING ATMOSPHERIC QUALITY Throughout the biosphere, animals and plants take in oxygen during respiration and release carbon dioxide. Plants and algae use carbon dioxide during photosynthesis and release oxygen. Through the biotic processes of respiration and photosynthesis, the levels of carbon dioxide and oxygen in the atmosphere are kept in the range that is suitable for life.

Abiotic factors also help maintain the quality of the atmosphere. For example, as rain falls, it cleans the air of particles and soluble gases. The rainfall also helps maintain humidity in the atmosphere.

SOIL FORMATION Soils form when weathering breaks down rocks and when organic materials from decaying plants and animals accumulate. Such soils support the growth of many producer organisms and serve as a habitat for decomposers.

The root systems of plants hold the soil in place. If the vegetation that covers the ground is removed, the soil can be washed away by rain or blown away by wind. Soil erosion sometimes occurs during a drought when many plants die, leaving bare soil.

THE WATER CYCLE Water continuously evaporates from the surface of the land and bodies of water. Water also evaporates from the leaves of

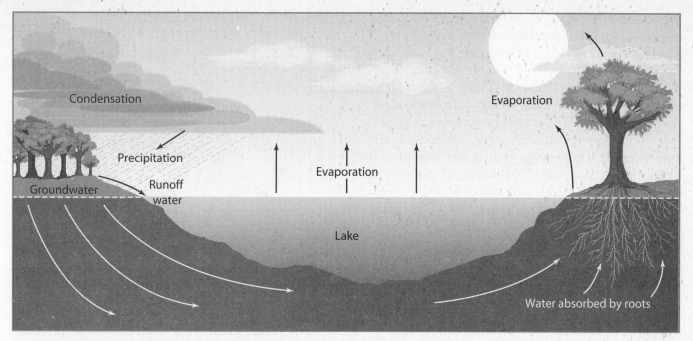

Figure 8-1. The water cycle: Water cycles between the atmosphere and land. The processes of evaporation, transpiration by plants, and precipitation are involved in the cycling of water.

plants during transpiration. The water vapor rises into the atmosphere and collects as clouds that can move long distances. Eventually, the vapor condenses as precipitation, which is distributed over many areas of Earth. The water collects as runoff or groundwater, or it evaporates, which continues the cycle. The complete process, which is known as the water cycle, is shown in Figure 8-1. This process allows many ecosystems to maintain a supply of fresh water, which is available to all organisms.

WASTE REMOVAL AND THE RECYCLING OF NUTRIENTS

Plants that live in the soil use the soil's minerals as they grow. The nutrients are transported from one organism to another through the food chains in the ecosystem. Those that are not released into the atmosphere eventually end up in the dead bodies and wastes of organisms. Decomposers break down these wastes and dead bodies, removing the nutrients in the process. The nutrients are then restored to the soil where plants, continuing the cycle, can use them.

Without this natural recycling, much of the abiotic materials needed by living organisms would remain "locked up" in the bodies of dead organisms. Minerals and other nutrients would not be available for new organisms. In tropical forests, where heavy rains are frequent, decomposition and the recycling process must take place rapidly. Otherwise, the frequent rains strip the land of minerals before new plants can absorb and use them. In areas where the Amazon rain forest has been cleared and burned for planting, many nutrients have been washed away, leaving the soil unfertile.

Humans sometimes make use of this natural recycling process when they mix decaying lawn and garden wastes to make compost, which is a natural fertilizer and soil conditioner. Adding compost to the soil recycles wastes naturally and reduces the need for chemical fertilizers. It also reduces the amount of waste material in landfills and eliminates the need to burn yard waste, which pollutes our atmosphere.

THE FLOW OF ENERGY

Food chains, food webs, and energy pyramids illustrate the **energy flow** through ecosystems. (For a review, refer back to Figures 7-7 and 7-8 in the previous topic.) Each organism has a role in the process and contributes to the overall stability of the ecosystem. As a result, losing all or most of the members of any species of an ecosystem could upset the stability of the whole.

Unlike nutrients, energy is passed through the environment, but it is *not* recycled. Instead, at each feeding level in an energy pyramid, organisms lose large amounts of energy (as heat) to the environment. This energy cannot be recaptured by living things. Because of this constant energy loss, ecosystems need a constant source of new energy. That energy source is usually the sun.

People and the Environment

Because humans are part of Earth's ecosystems, they affect the way ecosystems function. They also are affected by changes in the ecosystem. Once the ecosystem is damaged, people may suffer from that damage just like any other species.

Population Growth

Most species in new environments can have a period of rapid population growth. The population increase levels off as it approaches the ecosystem's carrying capacity, which is the number of individuals the environment can support.

For example, as rabbits move into a field, their population may boom. Eventually, the food supply dwindles, and the scarcity of food leads to a reduction in the population of rabbits. Those that do not get enough to eat may become too weak to escape predators or recover from diseases. Some may even die of starvation. The population growth levels off when the number of rabbits is balanced by the availability of food and the presence of limiting factors, such as predators. The relationship between population and the carrying capacity of an environment is shown in Figure 8-2.

Earth can only support a certain number of people. Our planet has a carrying capacity for humans just as it does for other species. The more people there are, the more resources they need. These resources come from the environment. More people also produce more waste, which must be disposed of or recycled. Overcrowding and lack of food become problems when populations are very large.

Population Growth Curve

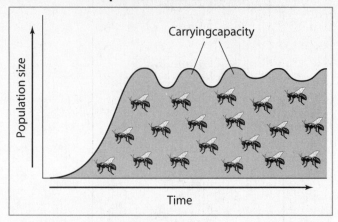

Figure 8-2. **A population growth curve:** In a new environment, the population usually increases quickly, but it stabilizes when it reaches the carrying capacity of that environment.

For thousands of years, the human population grew slowly. Then, about 300 years ago, our food supply began to increase, and improvements in health care and hygiene led to dramatic increases in our population. At present, the population "curve" points steeply upward. To many population scientists, the sharp increase suggests that the human population is growing at a dangerously fast rate. Compare Figure 8-3, the growth curve for the human population, with Figure 8-2, the growth curve typical for animals in an ecosystem.

If the human population continues to grow at the rate shown in Figure 8-3, Earth's carrying capacity could be reached soon. That result could be catastrophic. With no controls, the human

Human Population Growth Curve

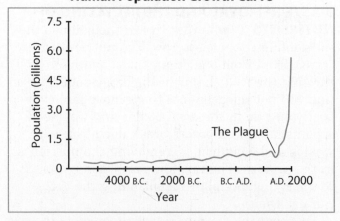

Figure 8-3. **Growth curve for the human population worldwide:** The current rapid upward trend is a cause for concern.

population might even overshoot Earth's carrying capacity for our species. There might not be enough food, water, space, and oxygen for everyone. The resulting deaths from famine, disease, or wars over resources could reduce the human population to a small fraction of its present level. Finding ways to slow our population growth so that the growth rate levels off before Earth's carrying capacity is reached could save future generations from suffering the consequences of unlimited population growth.

8.1 Review

1. Which of the following is a renewable resource? (A) wood (B) oil (C) iron (D) coal

2. The best way to ensure that there will be enough aluminum for all future needs is to (F) dig more mines and process more aluminum ore (G) buy more aluminum from other countries and save our own (H) recycle and reuse aluminum (J) increase space exploration and search for new sources of aluminum

3. The natural limiting factor that will most likely prevent further human population growth in many parts of the world is (A) habitat destruction (B) political intervention (C) food supply (D) social intervention

4. Which of these human activities is quite often responsible for the other three human activities? (F) increasing demand on limited food production (G) rapid increase of loss of farmland due to soil erosion (H) rapid increase of human population (J) increasing levels of air pollution

5. Which situation has had the most *negative* effect on the ecosystems of Earth? (A) use of air pollution controls (B) use of natural predators to control insect pests (C) recycling glass, plastic, and metals (D) increasing human population

6. Which human activity would be *least* likely to disrupt the stability of an ecosystem? (F) disposing of wastes in the ocean (G) using fossil fuels (H) increasing the human population (J) recycling bottles and cans

7. Which statement illustrates how human activities can most directly change the dynamic equilibrium of an ecosystem? (A) A hurricane causes a stream to overflow its banks. (B) Increased wind increases water evaporation from a plant. (C) Water pollution causes a decrease in fish populations in a river. (D) The ozone layer helps prevent harmful radiation from reaching the surface of Earth.

8. Some factories have a negative impact on Earth's ecosystems because they (F) have high energy demands that require the use of fossil fuels and nuclear fuels (G) use agricultural technology that decreases soil erosion (H) decrease the need for finite resources (J) limit the amount of emissions produced each year

Base your answers to questions 9 through 12 on the diagram, which represents the growth rate of a mouse population introduced into an abandoned field ecosystem.

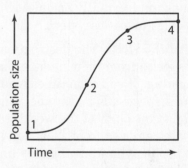

9. At what points is food most likely a limiting factor in the rate of mouse population growth? (A) 1 and 2 (B) 2 and 3 (C) 3 and 4 (D) 2 and 4

10. At what point is the rate of population growth the greatest? (F) 1 (G) 2 (H) 3 (J) 4

11. At what point would the mouse population be the greatest in the ecosystem? (A) 1 (B) 2 (C) 3 (D) 4

12. Compare the growth rate of the mouse population in the abandoned field to the growth rate of the human population. In your comparison be sure to identify

• how it is similar

• how it is the same

8.2 Human Activities and Their Effects

Some human activities that destroy habitats and degrade ecosystems do far more than damage individual organisms. They also destroy diversity in the environment. For example, when humans use land to build a parking lot, the organisms that lived on that land are likely to die. Other organisms that ate the plants, burrowed through the ground, or nested in the nearby trees are also affected. There will be fewer resources available for a variety of species.

Many deliberate human activities, such as clearing land to plant a single crop, can change the equilibrium in an ecosystem. So can some accidents, such as inadvertently or unknowingly adding a species to an ecosystem.

DIRECT HARVESTING The destruction or removal of species from their habitats is known as direct harvesting. It can sometimes lead to the extinction of a species. For example, some species that live in distant parts of the world (rain forests or deserts) are removed from their native habitats and sold to people who want them as unusual pets, ornaments, or house or garden plants. That cute monkey or beautiful parrot in the pet shop may not have been born in captivity. Instead, it may have been captured in the wild and shipped here. Many animals die in the process.

Other organisms are killed to collect a specific body part. For example, baby harbor seals are killed for their pelts, and elephants are killed for the ivory in their tusks, which people carve into jewelry or other trinkets. Direct harvesting can threaten the existence of the entire population of a species.

Because of overharvesting, such large numbers of some species of plants and animals have been taken from their native habitats that those species are now endangered. For example, so many whales have been slaughtered that some species are now in danger of extinction.

In the past, humans have caused the extinction of several species. For example, in the early 1800s, billions of passenger pigeons lived in North America. (See Figure 8-4.) Each year, hunters shot millions until the population was greatly reduced. By the time people realized that the species was endangered, it was too late to save it. The last passenger pigeon died in a zoo in Cincinnati, Ohio, in 1914.

Today, some endangered species are protected by law. However, because there may be a demand for products made from endangered species, poaching (illegally capturing or killing an organism) continues to be a problem.

Figure 8-4. The passenger pigeon: The passenger pigeon, once present in huge numbers, is now extinct because of uncontrolled hunting.

LAND USE As human populations grow, we use more resources to make the things we need or want, such as clothes, homes, refrigerators, radios, and cars. We also need more space for places to live. More land is needed to grow food, to build roads and factories, and even to provide parks and recreational areas. As human populations and needs increase, our use of land decreases the space and resources available for other species.

HABITAT DESTRUCTION Many people think that when a habitat is destroyed, the organisms simply find a new home. However, because other parts of the ecosystem are already occupied, displaced animals seldom find a new place to live. Habitat destruction occurs when people take over

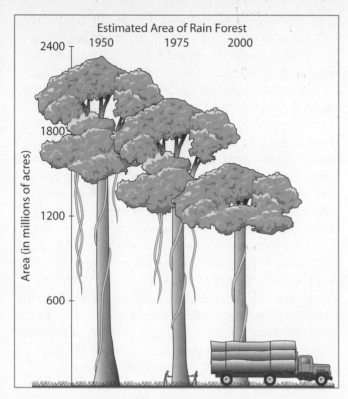

Estimated Area of Rain Forest

Figure 8-5. Habitat destruction: The destruction of rain forests, an example of deforestation, eliminates many ecosystems.

Deforestation, or the destruction of forests resulting from human activity, is a land use decision that causes widespread habitat destruction. People clear the forest by burning or cutting down the trees. Deforestation can provide people with land for farming and places to live. It also provides resources to use in building or manufacturing. Because of deforestation, the area covered by the world's rain forests is only about half as large as the area covered 150 years ago. (See Figure 8-5.) The wetlands, fields, and forests of Maryland are also threatened by development.

BIODIVERSITY An ecosystem in which a wide variety of different species live together is said to have biodiversity. A decrease in biodiversity occurs when species are lost. This lost biodiversity can affect the health of whole ecosystems and food webs. It can even affect the proportion of gases in the atmosphere. Our future ability to find new medicines for treating diseases or to discover new sources of genes that could be genetically engineered into more productive and pest-resistant crops is threatened when biodiversity is lost.

Habitat destruction, such as deforestation, can lead to loss of biodiversity, but it is not the only way that human activities threaten biodiversity. For example, a farmer might plow under a meadow that is home to many species. Then the farmer might plant a single crop, such as corn or wheat, on many continuous acres of land. This practice greatly reduces the biodiversity of the area. (See Figure 8-6.) In addition, it creates an ideal

land for their own use. It is an important way that species can become endangered: They simply have nowhere to live! As habitats are destroyed, whole ecosystems can be damaged and entire species may become extinct. For example, pandas are endangered today because humans have greatly reduced the size of their habitat.

Figure 8-6. Loss of biodiversity: The corn in this field provides habitats for only a few species. The meadow that once grew here was home for hundreds of species of flowers, shrubs, trees, insects, birds, and other small animals.

environment for insects that feed on that crop. To control the insects, the farmer may need to use pesticides, which could harm other organisms living in the same or nearby environments.

IMPORTED SPECIES Biodiversity is often reduced when people import and release a species from one environment into another. The release may be inadvertent or intentional. For example, before 1859, there were no rabbits in Australia. Then two dozen rabbits were released in Australia. By 1953, more than a billion rabbits occupied 1.2 million square miles of the continent. These rabbits ate massive amounts of vegetation ordinarily available to the native species.

Many species become pests when they are added to a new environment. Because the new organisms are not part of an existing food web in the area, they often have no natural enemies in their new environment and rapidly overpopulate the area. They then crowd out, feed on, or otherwise eliminate native species. Two examples are Japanese beetles and gypsy moths, which were accidentally released in the United States. (See Figure 8-7.) Now they are serious pests in the eastern U.S.

Figure 8-7. Imported species: During the larval stage, the gypsy moth consumes vast quantities of leaves. The adult moth lays hundreds of eggs, continuing the problem.

Once an imported species becomes a pest, it is very difficult to control. If another species is imported to control it, the second species may choose to feed on native organisms instead, adding another problem. Using pesticides or poisons can kill other organisms in addition to the imported one. Sometimes scientists find a disease organism that affects only the imported species. The rabbits that overran Australia were eventually controlled by a disease organism. However, there is always a risk that the species may become resistant to the disease and overpopulate again.

Because imported species are such a problem, many states and countries have laws to restrict the transport of fruits or vegetables. The goal of these laws is to avoid introducing diseases or insects that might damage local crops. Some countries require the quarantine of certain animals and plants, which keeps them in isolation until officials are sure they are free of any pests that could escape into the new environment.

Scientists are working to find safer methods of pest control. One safe method is setting traps that use chemical scents to attract insects. With this method, no other species are harmed and the population of the pest species can be reduced to a safe level. Breeding and releasing native predators of a pest species also has been used sometimes successfully and without harm to other species.

8.2 Review

1. Ladybugs were introduced as predators into an agricultural area of the United States to reduce the number of aphids feeding on grain crops. This action is an example of (A) preservation of endangered species (B) conservation of natural resources (C) protection of watershed areas (D) use of a nonchemical means of insect control

2. An example of a human activity that has had a positive effect on the environment is the (F) disruption of natural habitats through deforestation (G) capture and sale of rare South American birds (H) use of reforestation to control erosion in the mountains (J) hunting of endangered species of animals

3. The trees in a forest help reduce flood damage chiefly because their (A) branches store water in the form of sap (B) leaves absorb moisture from the air (C) root systems hold the soil in place (D) stems serve to store food

4. The creation of wildlife refuges and the enforcement of game laws are conservation measures that promote increased (F) use of chemicals to control pests (G) preservation of species (H) use of natural controls to limit pest populations (J) exploitation of wildlife species

5. A method of agriculture in which one crop is grown on many acres of land has in some cases created serious insect problems. This is primarily because the method (A) increases soil erosion (B) provides concentrated areas of one kind of food for insects (C) increases the effectiveness of insecticides used over long periods of time (D) involves the growing of crops in former desert areas

6. The least ecologically damaging method for controlling the mosquitoes that spread the diseases malaria and encephalitis is by (F) draining the swamps where mosquitoes breed (G) spraying swamps with chemical pesticides (H) spreading oil over swamps (J) introducing local fish species to the swamps where mosquitoes breed

7. Which human activity would most likely result in the addition of an organism to the endangered species list? (A) the use of cover crops to prevent soil erosion (B) the use of pollution controls by industry (C) the use of erosion prevention measures by road construction crews (D) habitat destruction by shopping mall developers

8. Which of the following human activities would be the most likely to prevent certain species from becoming extinct? (F) pass laws to place all endangered species in zoos (G) increase the hunting of predators (H) increase wildlife management and habitat protection (J) mate organisms from different species to create new and stronger organisms

9. Refer to the chart below, which illustrates some methods of pest control.

Methods of Insect Pest Control

Insect pests can be repelled or attracted with sex hormones.
Insect populations can be controlled by releasing males sterilized with X-rays.
New plant varieties that are resistant to insect pests can be produced and grown.
Insect pests can be controlled by introducing their natural enemies.

One likely effect of using these methods of pest control will be to (A) prevent the extinction of endangered species (B) increase water pollution (C) reduce pesticide contamination of the environment (D) harm the atmosphere

10. Human activities continue to place strains on the environment. One of these strains is the loss of biodiversity. Explain what this problem is and describe some ways humans are involved in both the problem and the possible solutions. In your answer be sure to

- state the meaning of the term *biodiversity*

- state one *negative* effect on humans if biodiversity continues to be lost

- suggest one practice that could be used to preserve biodiversity in Maryland

11. When land is cleared for agriculture or home construction, small isolated sections of the original habitat may remain. How might this reduction in habitat size and the isolation of small sections of habitat lead to species endangerment?

12. A tropical rain forest in the country of Belize contains over 100 kinds of trees and thousands of species of mammals, birds, and insects. Dozens of species living there have not yet been classified and studied. The rain forest could be a commercial source of food, as well as a source of medicinal and household products. However, most of this forested area is not accessible because of a lack of roads and, therefore, little commercial use has been made of this region. The building of highways into and through this rain forest has been proposed.

Discuss some aspects of carrying out this proposal to build highways.

- State *one* possible impact on biodiversity and *one* reason for this impact.

- State *one* possible reason for an increase in the number of some producers as a result of road building.

- Identify *one* type of consumer whose population would most likely increase as a direct result of an increase in a producer population.

- State *one* possible action the road builders could take to minimize human impact on the ecology of this region.

8.3 Dealing With the Impact of Technology

VOCABULARY			
acid rain	greenhouse effect	nuclear fuel	smog
fossil fuel	industrialization	ozone layer	trade-off
global warming			

Humans modify ecosystems through population growth, consumption, and technology. As human populations grow, they take up more space, consume more resources, and produce more waste.

The expansion of technology (using scientific knowledge and technical processes to meet human needs) also increases the quantity of resources that people use. All of these activities lead to changes in ecosystems, including the way they function. The equilibrium of ecosystems can be upset by human actions.

Industrialization

Industrialization is the development of an economy in which machines produce many of the products people use. These products may add to the quality of life, but their manufacture can also harm the environment. In addition to contributing to pollution of the air and water, industrialization increases the demand for energy, water, and other resources, including fossil and nuclear fuels.

The higher energy demands in an industrialized society mean that more power plants must be built. Additional power plants—especially those that burn coal—add to the pollution of our air and water. **Nuclear fuel** is an energy source that results from splitting atoms. Nuclear power plants do not pollute the air or water with toxic chemicals, but they can cause thermal pollution of waterways. Also, the disposal of radioactive nuclear wastes presents a huge environmental problem.

Another problem with increased industrialization is that most factories use a lot of water. Large wells drilled for factories sometimes dry up the nearby smaller wells that individuals use to supply their homes. In some cases, withdrawing large quantities of water allows the ground to collapse, forming sinkholes. In dry climates, reducing the supply of groundwater can have serious consequences for native plants and the consumers that depend on them for food.

Just as conservation can help preserve our resources, it can also help to limit the negative impact of industrialization. We can *reduce* our demand for energy and manufactured goods that we don't really need. We can *reuse* manufactured products rather than discard them, and we can *recycle* as many products as possible, conserving both energy and resources in the process.

Water Pollution

Water pollution occurs when wastes end up in rivers, lakes, and oceans. These wastes include sewage, wastes from homes and factories, and animal wastes from farms. This addition of pollutants to natural environments can change conditions in ecosystems. For example, sewage and animal wastes can act as fertilizer, increasing the growth of plants, algae, and bacteria in aquatic systems.

Plants consume oxygen all the time, day and night. However, photosynthesis, the primary source of oxygen, stops at night because it requires light. As a result, oxygen production also stops. Then, oxygen levels drop and many organisms suffocate. When these organisms die, oxygen-using decomposers begin their decay activity, which further decreases the oxygen supply. Eventually, all the organisms in this oxygen-reduced ecosystem may be lost. Figure 8-8 shows several ways in which water pollution can affect a natural habitat.

TOXIC WASTES Many wastes dumped into waterways from cities, farms, or industries can be toxic (poisonous) to the organisms that use or live in the water. Chemical fertilizers and weed and insect killers can be washed off farmlands into streams

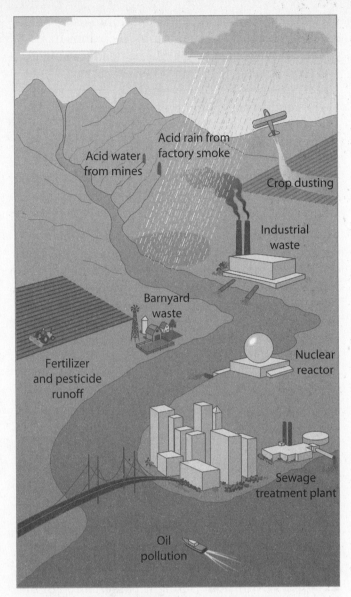

Figure 8-8. Water pollution: Water pollution, which can damage an ecosystem, comes from many sources.

Labels in figure:
Acid rain from factory smoke
Acid water from mines
Crop dusting
Industrial waste
Barnyard waste
Nuclear reactor
Fertilizer and pesticide runoff
Sewage treatment plant
Oil pollution

herbivores, the toxins are stored in the herbivores' fatty tissues. There it stays until the herbivores are eaten by the next consumers in the food chain. At each level of the chain, larger and larger amounts of toxic material collect in the fatty tissue. Organisms at or near the top of the food chain are most likely to accumulate enough of these chemicals in their bodies to cause them harm.

For example, farmers used to spray the pesticide DDT on their crops. Rain would then wash some of the DDT off the land and into streams and rivers. In the water, the DDT moved up through the food chain. Soon, fish-eating birds at the top of the food chain produced eggs with very thin shells. The shells were so thin that they broke easily, which killed the next generation of birds before it even hatched.

THERMAL POLLUTION Some power plants and industries use water to cool their machines or materials. The warmed water is then released into a river or lake, and the water temperature in the river or lake rises. Because warm water cannot hold as much dissolved oxygen as cold water, the oxygen level in the river or lake drops as the water temperature rises. Some species may suffocate as a result of such thermal pollution, while others may be forced to try to find a new home.

The solution to most of these problems is to find better ways to deal with wastes and to reduce the need for power. Sewage can be treated before it is discharged into waterways. Toxic wastes can be separated from other materials and either recycled or stored safely. People could conserve energy by using less power. Methods could be developed for cooling industrial processes that would reduce their damage to the environment.

Air Pollution

Just as wastes dumped into rivers and oceans cause water pollution, harmful substances released into the air cause air pollution. Early in the industrial age, people thought that burned wastes just disappeared into the atmosphere and that they didn't have to worry any more about the wastes. We now know this is not true. Most of the pollutants released into the atmosphere eventually wind up in the water cycle and return to the water or land. Like water pollution, air pollution can damage habitats and harm the organisms that

or rivers. The chemicals can collect in the cells of organisms living in the water and along the shore. These toxic materials then move through the food chain and eventually damage or kill many kinds of organisms.

Although the level of toxic substances in the water might be low, scientists have learned that the concentration of a toxin increases as it moves through the food chain. For example, small quantities of toxic substances are absorbed into the cells of algae and other producers living in the water. When those producers are eaten by small

live in them. Figure 8-9 shows how air pollution can affect a natural habitat.

Figure 8-9. Air pollution: Trees can be damaged or killed by polluted air.

BURNING FOSSIL FUELS Fuels such as the coal and gas that formed from the remains of organisms that lived millions of years ago are known as **fossil fuels**. Factories, cars, and most electrical power-generating plants burn fossil fuels. When fossil fuels are burned, carbon dioxide and other gases—some containing sulfur and/or nitrogen—are added to the air.

Acid Precipitation Sulfur and nitrogen compounds that are produced when fossil fuels burn can combine with moisture in the atmosphere. When this moisture falls to Earth, it has a low pH level and is much more acidic than normal precipitation. This precipitation is called **acid rain** (or acid snow).

Some acid precipitation can be as acidic as lemon juice. When highly acidic rain or snow touches plants, it may damage them and disrupt the way they function. The damaged plants may be more susceptible to attacks by fungi or insects.

Acid precipitation can also fall into lakes and streams or run off the land into the water. In lakes, the lower pH levels can be deadly to algae, the eggs of some fish, and other organisms. Producer organisms, such as algae, are killed by these conditions. Without algae suspended in it, the water looks crystal clear and pure. However, this visible change means that the food chains in the ecosystem have been disrupted, and populations of fish and other organisms have died. Some lakes become so acidic that nothing can live in them.

Smog Other air pollutants are produced by automobile exhaust and by industrial processes. Some of these pollutants can be toxic when inhaled. This kind of pollution becomes more serious when weather conditions trap the gases in an area for hours or even days. **Smog** is a kind of air pollution that results when certain pollutants react with sunlight. It looks like a gray or brown haze and contains many airborne pollutants. People with respiratory diseases are especially sensitive to air pollution and may be in danger when air pollution is intense.

Global Atmospheric Changes

Some pollutants in the air harm living things directly, as with the trees in Figure 8-9. Others can cause worldwide atmospheric changes that threaten many habitats and the organisms that live in them.

GLOBAL WARMING Sunlight passes through the gases in the atmosphere to reach Earth. But some of these atmospheric gases, called greenhouse gases, also trap and absorb the infrared radiation that bounces off Earth's warmed surface. For thousands of years, this process—called the **greenhouse effect**—has kept Earth warm. In recent years, however, the amount of greenhouse gases in the atmosphere has increased.

As Figure 8-10 shows, the increased amount of greenhouse gases in Earth's atmosphere traps some of the heat that would normally radiate into space. The result is that Earth's average temperature is rising. This increase in temperature, called **global warming**, could lead to changes in climate patterns and even to the melting of the ice caps at the North and South Poles. Most of the recent increase in greenhouse gases has been caused by burning fuel for transportation and industry.

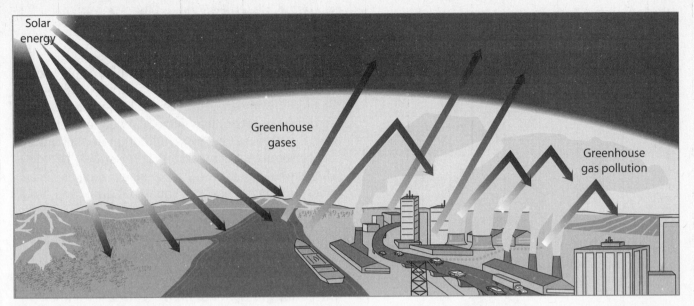

Figure 8-10. Global warming: Pollution caused by human activity is increasing the amount of greenhouse gases in the atmosphere. This increase can intensify the greenhouse effect, causing global warming.

Carbon dioxide, a major greenhouse gas, is released when fossil fuels are burned. (See Figure 8-11.) If the greenhouse effect causes climate change, the world's food supply may deteriorate. Another possible effect is that polar ice caps could melt, leading to a rise in sea level and flooding in many coastal habitats.

Finding and using energy sources that do not add carbon dioxide to the atmosphere is one way to prevent further global warming. Because trees remove large quantities of carbon dioxide during photosynthesis and store it in their tissues as carbon compounds, growing more long-lived trees also could help solve the problem.

OZONE DEPLETION Ozone depletion is another atmospheric problem that humans must solve. Like global warming, ozone depletion is a worldwide problem, and international cooperation is needed to find an effective long-term solution.

The release of certain industrial gases into the atmosphere has caused substantial damage to the **ozone layer**, the layer of ozone gas in the upper atmosphere that protects Earth from some of the sun's radiation. (See Figure 8-12 on the next page.) The thinning of the ozone layer allows above-normal amounts of ultraviolet radiation from the sun to reach Earth's surface.

Ultraviolet radiation can cause genetic mutations and can kill cells that are exposed to it. An increase in ultraviolet radiation at Earth's surface could result in more cases of skin cancer. It could also destroy many of the producer organisms in the oceans. This would disrupt food chains and reduce the amount of oxygen released by the producers.

The main cause of ozone depletion is the release of gases called chlorofluorocarbons, or CFCs, into the atmosphere. CFCs have been used as coolants in refrigerators and air conditioners, as propellants in aerosol cans, and in the

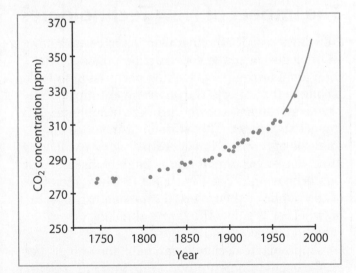

Figure 8-11. Carbon dioxide in the atmosphere from 1750 to 2000: The amount of carbon dioxide in the atmosphere has increased greatly since the beginning of the Industrial Revolution. The dots are data from ice core samples; the solid line represents direct measurements.

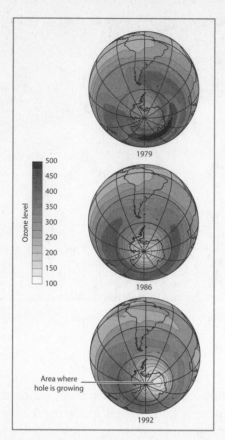

Figure 8-12. **The "hole" in the ozone layer:** These satellite maps show how much the "hole" in the ozone layer above the South Pole grew in just over a decade.

manufacture of plastic foam. (See Figure 8-13.) Some steps have been taken to reduce the release of these gases. Researchers have found alternatives to the products that cause the most damage, and international agreements have been made to reduce emissions of the harmful gases.

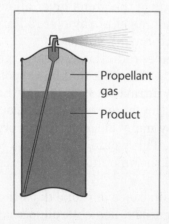

Figure 8-13. **CFCs:** Aerosol cans no longer use ozone destroying CFCs as propellants. Safer alternatives have been found.

Individual Choices and Societal Actions

Many people hope technology will help solve some of our environmental problems. In fact, technology has led to some improvements. For example, advances in technology have allowed farmers to greatly increase the crop yield of an acre of land. Larger crop yields mean a greater supply of food. However, some kinds of technology, such as pesticides and fertilizers, can cause pollution and have other harmful effects on the environment.

If technology cannot solve all our environmental problems, people will need to take some difficult steps to save our ecosystem. For some problems, solutions are now available, but they can affect our quality of life. For example, we know how to reduce the air and water pollution caused by factories, power-generating plants, and automobiles, but the solutions are expensive and would make the products we buy cost more. We also know how to conserve energy, but many people are unwilling to give up their large cars, brightly-lit neighborhoods, and air-conditioned comfort and to turn off their radios, computers, and televisions.

For each environmental problem, people must learn to assess the risk to the ecosystem. For each solution, they must learn to analyze the costs and benefits. Then they must determine which **trade-off**, or compromise, is acceptable and which is simply too dangerous to the welfare of future generations.

The Impact of New Technologies

New laws restrict the introduction of certain new technologies or major construction projects. The individual or company seeking permission to make a change that affects the environment must prepare a statement known as an environmental impact statement. This statement includes an analysis of how the project or technology will affect the environment and is usually discussed at public hearings. (See Figure 8-14.) Then, members of the public or their elected representatives vote on whether to allow the new technology or construction project to go forward.

Appropriate decisions can be made only if the public is environmentally literate and has a clear understanding of the issues. If an incorrect decision is made, it may be impossible to undo the damage that might result.

Figure 8-14. Public hearings: Discussions can be held to consider environmental issues.

Figure 8-15. Recycling: Decisions about recycling are made by individuals and their communities.

Today's Decisions Affect the Next Generation

The decisions we make today can have a huge impact on our environment. Those decisions, right or wrong, will affect the people living today, as well as future generations.

The loss of some species may seem unimportant. However, the loss of that single species might have a huge impact on the ecology of an area. If the loss of species continues, large-scale destruction of natural environments will result with serious consequences for the future. For example, the destruction of large forests or the loss of algae in ocean waters does not only affect the organisms that live in those ecosystems now. Those losses may also compromise Earth's ability to produce enough oxygen and remove enough carbon dioxide to maintain an atmosphere that meets the needs of all of its inhabitants, including humans.

Many important decisions about the environment are made by states and nations. Individuals make a surprising number of important decisions each day. For example, individuals decide whether to burn their garden waste or turn it into compost, whether to toss the soda can into the trash or recycle it, whether to grab a fresh sheet of paper or write a note on an old envelope. (See Figure 8-15.)

Much of the impact of our technology and population growth on Earth's ecosystems has been detrimental. If our environmental problems are not recognized and solved, the long-term damage will be irreversible and severe. On the other hand, cooperation by individuals and nations can help maintain the stability of the ecosystems upon which all life depends. Making people aware of how people can succeed when they work together may be the most promising approach to solving these problems.

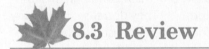

8.3 Review

1. Plants help maintain the quality of the atmosphere by (A) storing carbon dioxide (B) opening holes in the ozone layer (C) causing global warming (D) storing oxygen

2. Greenhouse gases in the atmosphere (F) keep Earth warm (G) are released mostly from greenhouses (H) are valuable as fuels (J) reduce holes in the ozone layer

3. Which human activity has probably contributed *most* to lake acidification in the northeastern region of the United States? (A) passage of environmental protection laws (B) reforestation projects in areas that have been logged (C) production of chemical air pollutants by industry (D) use of biological insect controls to eliminate pests

4. The number of industries along Maryland's rivers is increasing. What is the most likely consequence of increased industrialization? (F) a decrease in the amount of water needed by industry (G) a decrease in the amount of water pollution (H) an increase in the destruction of natural ecosystems (J) an increase in the amount of water available for recreational use

Base your answers to questions 5 through 7 on the following technical passage.

Polychlorinated biphenyls (PCBs) are microcontaminants that are found in some waters. Microcontaminants do not change the appearance, smell, or taste of the water, yet they affect parts of the surrounding ecosystem. After PCBs get into water, they are absorbed by some algae. As a result, the PCBs are concentrated within the algae. Then fish, which feed on the algae, concentrate the PCBs many more times. The PCBs are thousands of times more concentrated in the fish than they are in the water in which the fish live. At this level of contamination, the survival of some species in the food web is threatened. The health of other species, including humans who may consume predator fish such as salmon, is also threatened.

5. In which of the following are PCBs usually most concentrated? (A) dissolved oxygen (B) water (C) algae (D) fish species

6. Which is a harmful effect of microcontaminants on an aquatic ecosystem? (F) They decrease the density of the water. (G) They give water used for human consumption an unpleasant taste. (H) They accumulate in some organisms, making them toxic to other organisms. (J) They make water appear cloudy.

7. The producer organisms described in the passage are (A) fish (B) humans (C) algae (D) PCBs

8. Base your answer to this question on the information and graph below.

Reducing toxic chemicals released into the environment often requires laws. When making decisions about whether or not to support the passing of such laws, individuals must weigh the benefits against the potential risks if the law is not passed. The amounts of toxic chemicals released into the environment of a northern state over a ten-year period are shown in the graph below.

Releases of Toxic Chemicals, 1988 to 1997

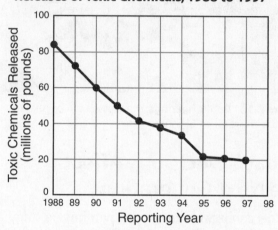

Describe the benefits and risks of supporting laws to reduce the volume of toxic chemicals released in your state.

- Identify one possible *negative* effect of passing a law to reduce the release of toxic chemicals.

- Suggest a possible explanation for why the amount of toxic chemicals released remained relatively constant between 1995 and 1997.

- Identify one other type of environmental problem that has been reduced by passing laws.

9. Without the constant recycling of water in ecosystems, organisms would be negatively affected. Human activities often interfere with the water cycle.

- Identify what part of the water cycle is directly affected by the burning of fossil fuels, such as coal and oil. Explain your answer.

- Explain how the runoff from farmland and golf courses might be dangerous to organisms living in ponds, rivers, or streams.

- Explain why there are frequent water shortages in parts of Maryland, even though the water supply is nearly constant.

10. Base your answer to this question on the technical passage below.

Amphibians have long been considered an indicator of the health of life on Earth. Scientists are concerned because amphibian populations have been declining worldwide since the 1980s. In fact, in the past decade, twenty species of amphibians have gone extinct and many others have become endangered. Scientists have linked this decline in amphibians to changes in global climate.

Warmer weather during the last three decades has resulted in the destruction of many of the eggs produced by the Western toad. Warmer weather has also led to a decrease in rain and snow in the Cascade Mountain Range in Oregon, reducing the water level in lakes and ponds that serve as the reproductive sites for the Western toad. As a result, the eggs are exposed to more ultraviolet light. This makes the eggs more susceptible to a water mold that kills the embryos by the hundreds of thousands.

According to the passage, global warming is responsible for the decline of amphibian populations. Explain what is causing global warming to occur and describe its potential global impact.

- Explain what the term *global warming* means.

- Identify a human activity that is thought to be a major contributor to global warming and provide an explanation of how it may contribute to the problem.

- Describe two ways that the decline in amphibian populations could disrupt the stability of the ecosystems they inhabit.

11. Base your answer to this question on the information and data table below.

Trout and black bass are freshwater fish that normally require at least 8 parts per million (ppm) of dissolved oxygen (O_2) in the water for survival. Other freshwater fish, such as carp, may be able to live in water that has an O_2 level of 5 ppm. No freshwater fish are able to survive when the O_2 level in water is 2 ppm or less.

Temperature affects the ability of oxygen to dissolve in water. Some factories or power plants are built along rivers so that they can use the water to cool their equipment. They then release the water (which is sometimes as much as 8°C warmer) back into the same river.

The Rocky River presently has an average summer temperature of about 25°C and contains trout, bass, and carp. A proposal has been made to build a new power plant on the banks of the Rocky River. Some people are concerned that this will negatively affect the river ecosystem. The table below shows the amount of oxygen (in ppm) that will dissolve in fresh water at different temperatures.

Relationship Between Dissolved Oxygen and Temperature

Temperature (°C)	Fresh Water Oxygen Content (ppm)
1	14.24
10	11.29
15	10.10
20	9.11
25	8.27
30	7.56

Determine whether a new power plant built on the banks of the Rocky River will have a negative environmental impact on the Rocky River ecosystem downstream from the plant.

- Describe the relationship between temperature change and the oxygen content of fresh water. Support your answer using specific information from the data table.

- Explain how the water released from the power plant would be expected to affect each of the three fish species known to be present in the river.

1. Today's lifestyles have led to increased demands for disposable products. The packaging of these products has caused environmental problems most directly associated with

    (A) food web contamination

    (B) atmospheric depletion

    (C) solid waste disposal

    (D) the use of nuclear fuels

2. Some modern agricultural methods have created serious insect problems, primarily because these methods

    (F) increase soil loss

    (G) provide concentrated areas of food for insects

    (H) aid in the absorption of water

    (J) grow crops in areas where formerly only insects could live

3. The decline and extinction of many predatory animal species is most probably the result of

    (A) an overabundance of prey species

    (B) the introduction of a new species of animal into an area

    (C) the disruption of natural food chains

    (D) the decreased use of chemical pesticides

4. Modern methods of agriculture have contributed to the problem of soil depletion because many of these methods

    (F) require smaller amounts of mineral and fertilizer application

    (G) interfere with the natural cycling of elements

    (H) use many varieties of cloned plants

    (J) depend on the practice of planting and harvesting

5. Which attempt by humans to solve an ecological problem has actually had the most negative effect?

    (A) seeking better means of birth control in the human population

    (B) applying scientific farming techniques to oceans

    (C) producing stronger and more effective pesticides

    (D) developing new techniques for the disposal of sewage and industrial and chemical wastes

6. Japanese beetles, a major insect pest in the United States, do relatively little damage in Japan because they

    (F) are kept in check by natural enemies

    (G) are kept in check by effective pesticide sprays

    (H) hibernate during the winter months

    (J) have gradually adapted to the environment

7. Gypsy moths were accidentally introduced into North America. The most probable reason these insects have become serious pests in North America is that they

    (A) were bred by research scientists and are resistant to all pesticides

    (B) are protected by environmental laws and feed on other insect species

    (C) have few natural enemies and reproduce successfully

    (D) are affected by natural controls and feed on plants

8. The survival of many plants and animals has been aided most by

    (F) increases in the height of industrial smokestacks to spread air pollutants away from the immediate vicinity of combustion

    (G) reduction in the number of restrictive pollution control laws

    (H) heavy use of pesticides to kill all of the insect pests that compete with humans for food sources

    (J) development of research aimed toward the preservation of endangered species

9. DDT is an insecticide that accumulates in the fatty tissues of animals and is transferred through food chains. Its concentration increases at each link of a food chain.

    Which organism in a food chain is most likely to accumulate the highest concentration of DDT?

    (A) rabbit (a herbivore)

    (B) corn (a producer)

    (C) field mouse (a consumer)

    (D) owl (a predator)

10. What is the most likely cause of the change in life expectancy shown in the graph?

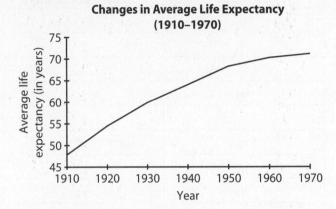

Changes in Average Life Expectancy (1910–1970)

(F) poor land-use management that has affected the quality of the topsoil

(G) technological oversights that have had an impact on air quality

(H) a decrease in natural checks on the population, such as disease

(J) widespread use of pesticides, such as DDT, in water supplies

11. A desired outcome derived from an understanding of the principles of ecology would be

(A) the elimination of most predatory species

(B) an increase in world human population

(C) a decrease in disruptions of existing wildlife habitats

(D) an increase in the amount of industrialization

12. Humans are responsible for some of the negative changes that occur in nature because they (F) have controlled the use of many pesticides and other environmentally damaging chemicals (G) have passed laws to preserve the environment (H) are able to preserve scarce resources (J) are able to modify their physical environment to provide for human needs

13. Deforestation and global warming are two environmental issues that are linked. Explain how they are linked. In your answer

• explain what is meant by the term *deforestation*

• explain what is meant by the term *global warming*

• describe the connection between the two

14. Humans have the ability to modify nearly any environment on Earth, but in the process they may have a negative impact on the species living there. This has happened on a number of occasions.

Select one instance in which humans chose to modify an environment and the activity led to a negative impact on the species living there. Describe

• the particular change that was made

• the reason the change was made

• a specific negative impact on the original ecosystems that occurred as a result

Base your answers to questions 15 and 16 on the following information and graph.

A species of fly found in the southern U.S. is a destructive parasite of livestock. The graph shows the results of an experiment in which one population of these flies was treated with pesticides and another group of equal size was treated with ionizing radiation, which made the male flies sterile.

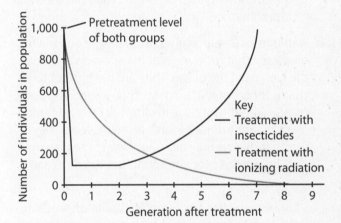

15. At what point after treatment will the group treated with pesticide probably reach its pretreatment population?

(A) first generation

(B) seventh generation

(C) third generation

(D) eighth generation

16. At what point after treatment will the sterility method be more successful against these flies than the pesticide method?

(F) immediately

(G) second generation

(H) third generation

(J) sixth generation

17. Cattail plants that grow in freshwater swamps in Maryland are being replaced by an imported species of plant called purple loosestrife. The two species have very similar environmental needs. Since cattails and loosestrife occupy the same niche, it is predicted that eventually only one of the two species will exist in Maryland freshwater swamps.

   Some people suggest using chemical herbicides to control the spread of the loosestrife. Others suggest a biological control such as a beetle that feeds only on loosestrife plants.

- Provide one reason why loosestrife will probably out-compete the cattails and be more successful in that niche.

- Explain why loosestrife plants replacing the native cattails would potentially cause a decrease in many swamp wildlife populations and perhaps even lead to the elimination of some species from Maryland.

- Explain why the biological control is expected to have less environmental impact than the chemical control method.

18. Plankton is the name given to the algae and microscopic life that grow in great numbers on and near the surface of the ocean. They are the basis of food chains for oceanic life. Scientists have become concerned with the increase in ultraviolet (UV) radiation reaching the surface of Earth in recent years. They fear that UV rays may negatively affect the plankton.

   Discuss this problem and its impact on ocean ecosystems.

- Explain why the amount of UV radiation reaching the surface may be on the increase, especially near the North and South Poles.

- Describe the effect any large-scale plankton destruction will have on larger species living in these same areas of the ocean.

- Describe how a negative impact on ocean food webs may have an eventual impact on humans who are a part of the terrestrial food web.

Base your answers to questions 19 and 20 on the information in the paragraph provided.

A single protist (a one-celled organism) was placed in a large test tube containing nutrient broth. The tube was kept at room temperature for 24 hours. Samples from the tube were observed periodically during the 24 hours, using the low power objective of a compound light microscope. The data are summarized in the table.

Age and Number of Protists in Culture

Age of the Population in Hours	Number of Protists in the Population
0	1
6	2
8	3
10	4
13	8
16	16
18	32
20	64
22	128
24	256

19. Which graph best represents the data given in the table?

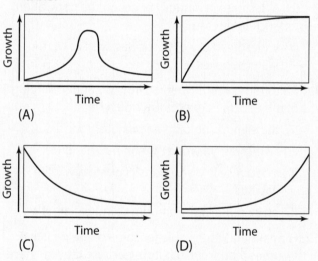

(A)   (B)

(C)   (D)

20. Which graph most resembles the present growth of the human population?

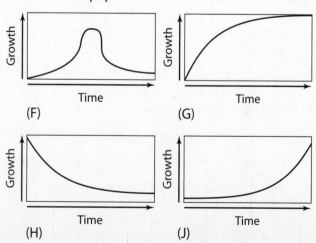

(F)   (G)

(H)   (J)

21. Select one of the following ecological problems.

Ecological Problems
Acid rain
Increased amounts of nitrogen and phosphorus in a lake
Loss of biodiversity

For the ecological problem that you selected, briefly describe the problem and state one way to reduce it.

- Identify the ecological problem you selected.

- Explain how humans have caused the problem you selected.

- Describe one specific effect that the problem you selected will have on the ecosystem.

- Describe one specific action humans could take to reduce the problem you selected.

Base your answers to questions 22 through 25 on the following technical passage.

The gypsy moth, *Porthetria dispar,* is a defoliator (an agent that removes leaves) of both deciduous trees and conifers in Maryland. The gypsy moth undergoes complete metamorphosis from egg to larva (caterpillar) to pupa to adult moth. The gypsy moth larvae cause the most damage to trees. The heaviest defoliations occur in oak forests because these trees are highly favored as food plants by all larval stages. The adult moths do not feed; their only function is to reproduce.

The male moth is a fairly strong daytime flier and tends to fly upwind in a zigzag pattern. The female is so heavily laden with eggs that she is unable to fly. Egg laying occurs soon after the moths mate, usually within a day or so after the female reaches the adult stage. Moths die soon after egg laying is completed.

The best means of controlling gypsy moths in the forests of Maryland is through the development and use of biological methods of pest control. The most important of these are *Ooencytrus kuwanae,* a tiny wasp that parasitizes the upper layers of eggs in a cluster and is normally effective on about three-fourths of the eggs, and *Calosoma sycophanta,* a ground beetle that preys on both gypsy moth larvae and pupae.

An important natural agent that causes gypsy moth populations to collapse is a viral disease that affects the larvae. Affected caterpillars are seen hanging from trees. The virus is always present in gypsy moth colonies in a dormant form and becomes activated when outside stress is applied. The viral disease, starvation, stress-induced diseases, and parasitism may cause a population to collapse after a forest has undergone two or three years of defoliation.

22. Which method is the best way to eliminate gypsy moth populations from Maryland?

(F) Spray oak, beech, and maple trees with a pesticide.

(G) Apply pesticides to the trunks of spruce, fir, and pine trees.

(H) Introduce a species of ground beetle that preys upon gypsy moth larvae.

(J) Apply a phosphate fertilizer to the soil to prevent larval attack against conifer and deciduous root systems.

23. Which factor is *not* likely to cause a population of gypsy moths to decline after two or three years of heavy defoliation?

(A) parasitism

(B) starvation

(C) viral disease

(D) climate-resistant eggs

24. Which statement concerning the gypsy moth is true?

(F) Adult gypsy moths die shortly after they finish laying eggs.

(G) Adult gypsy moths heavily defoliate oak forests in Maryland.

(H) Gypsy moth larvae can survive the cold winters in Maryland.

(J) The male gypsy moth is not a very good daytime flier.

25. Identify which diagram represents the stage of development of the gypsy moth in which it destroys the most deciduous trees and conifers in Maryland.

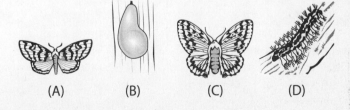

(A)   (B)   (C)   (D)

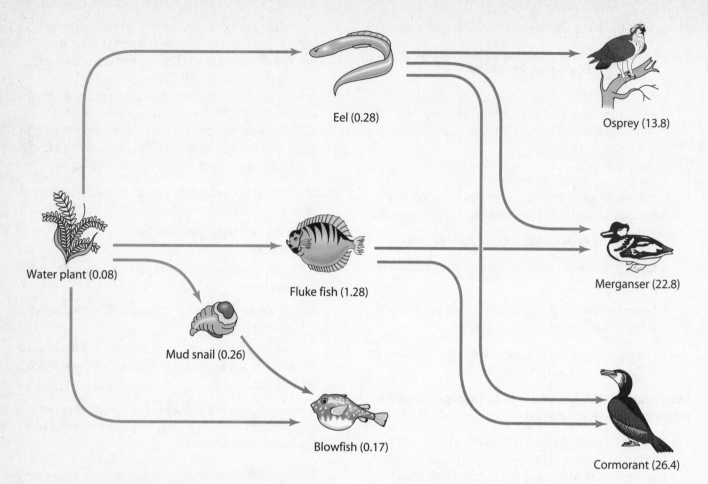

Eel (0.28)

Osprey (13.8)

Water plant (0.08)

Fluke fish (1.28)

Merganser (22.8)

Mud snail (0.26)

Blowfish (0.17)

Cormorant (26.4)

26. Global warming is generally considered a negative aspect of human involvement with the ecosystem.

- Explain how solving this problem will require increasing global awareness and cooperation.

- Identify two trade-offs that may have to be considered in decisions regarding what to do about the problem.

27. Base your answer on the above diagram, which represents part of a food web in a Maryland ecosystem.

The numbers show the concentration of the insecticide DDT in parts per million (ppm) in the body tissues of the various organisms. Explain

- why the water plant contains the pesticide DDT

- why the amounts of DDT in the three bird species are so much higher than in the other organisms of this food web

Laboratory Skills and Procedures

Science is about observing things, asking questions, proposing solutions, and testing those proposals. These activities often involve using specialized pieces of equipment and gathering data. Knowledge of which pieces of equipment to use for specific tasks and how to properly and safely use the equipment is very important.

When you perform experiments in biology class, they must be safe, as well as challenging and interesting. Certain safety hazards exist in the laboratory. You should know about them and the precautions you should take to reduce the risk of an accident.

9.1 Tools for Measurement

VOCABULARY			
balance	graduated cylinder	metric ruler	triple-beam balance
electronic balance	mass	scientific notation	volume

During laboratory investigations, you are often required to make measurements of length, mass, and volume. You need to know the proper pieces of equipment to select and the appropriate procedures and units to use.

MEASURING LENGTH Typically, a **metric ruler** is used to determine the length of an object. To measure length in the laboratory, you will generally use either centimeters (cm) or millimeters (mm). You should know how to convert millimeters to centimeters and vice versa.

The metric ruler shown in Figure 9-1 is calibrated—or scaled—in centimeters. The lines indicated by the numbers 1, 2, 3, and so on each represent a distance of 1 centimeter. The smaller divisions each equal 1 millimeter (10 mm = 1 cm).

It is not necessary to begin measuring at the zero point of the ruler, but if you do not, be sure to calculate the actual length using the numbers at each end of the object being measured. Notice that a line equal to 5 cm is shown above the ruler in Figure 9-1. The 5 cm line shown begins at 3.5 cm and extends to 8.5 cm, making it 5 cm in length.

Metric rulers vary, with some having the zero point at the very edge of the ruler and others having it a short distance in from the edge. Be sure you do not use the edge of a ruler to begin your measurement if the zero point is not at the edge.

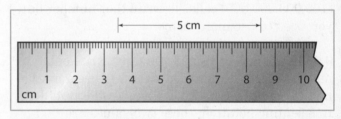

Figure 9-1. Metric ruler: The tool used for measuring length in centimeters and millimeters

Micrometers (μm), are very tiny units that are used to measure objects through the microscope. One thousand micrometers equal one millimeter.

Figure 9-2 shows a metric ruler as seen under the low-power objective of a microscope. The distance across the field of view is approximately 3.2 millimeters, or 3,200 micrometers (since 1.0 mm = 1,000 μm).

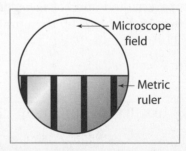

Figure 9-2. Microscope field with metric ruler

If the cells observed on the slide in Figure 9-3 are being viewed through the same low-power objective, the field of view is still 3.2 millimeters. The approximate length of each cell is therefore about 1 millimeter or 1,000 micrometers, since about 3 cells fit across the diameter (the widest part) of the field.

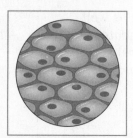

Figure 9-3. **Microscope field with cells**

Scientific Notation

When making measurements, some of the numbers you use are very large, others are very small. For example, the human brain has about 100 billion (100,000,000,000) cells. To write that number out, you need to use many zeros.

The average radius of a hydrogen atom is 0.00000000005 m. Again, you must write out many zeros. It is more convenient to use a mathematical abbreviation known as **scientific notation**. In scientific notation, these two values are 1.0×10^{11} m and 5.0×10^{-11} m, respectively.

The following examples show how the process works.

- If the superscripted number is *positive*, such as in 1.0×10^{11}, *multiply* 1.0 by the number 10 a total of 11 times:

$$1.0 \times 10^{11} = 1.0 \times 10 \times 10 \times 10 \times 10 \times 10 \times$$
$$10 \times 10 \times 10 \times 10 \times 10 \times 10$$

The result will be the number 1 followed by 11 zeros.

- If the superscripted number is *negative*, such as in 5.0×10^{-11}, *divide* by the number 10 a total of 11 times:

$$5.0 \times 10^{-11} =$$

$$\frac{5.0}{(10 \times 10 \times 10 \times 10 \times 10 \times 10 \times 10 \times 10 \times 10 \times 10 \times 10)}$$

The result will be a decimal point followed by 10 zeros and the number 5, *for a total of 11 numbers* after the decimal point.

Table 9-1 provides some more examples.

Table 9-1. **Examples of Scientific Notation**	
Actual Number	**Number in Scientific Notation**
4,380	4.38×10^3
0.0000045	4.5×10^{-6}
34,560,000	3.456×10^7
0.007	7×10^{-3}

Under an international agreement reached in 1960, scientists throughout the world use the International System of Units, abbreviated as SI, for measurement. It is based on the metric system. Table 9-2 on the next page shows some SI units and their equivalents. Notice the pattern of change when reading down the first two columns of this table.

MEASURING VOLUME A **graduated cylinder** is often used to measure a liquid's **volume**, or the space it occupies. Liters and milliliters are typically used to indicate volume in the metric system, while quarts and ounces are used in the English system. Graduated cylinders are calibrated in milliliters (mL). You should know how to convert milliliters to liters and vice versa.

Water and many other fluids form a meniscus (curved surface) when placed in the narrow tube of a graduated cylinder. To correctly read the volume of the liquid, place the cylinder on a flat surface. Then read from the bottom of the meniscus at eye level. The volume of liquid in the graduated cylinder in Figure 9-4 is 13 mL.

MEASURING TEMPERATURE In the biology laboratory, temperature is often measured in degrees Celsius. The freezing point of water is 0°C; the boiling point is 100°C. Human body temperature is 37°C, which is the temperature indicated on the thermometer in Figure 9-5.

Table 9-2. Scientific Notation Using SI Units

Number	Factor	Prefix	Example
1 billion	$1{,}000{,}000{,}000 = 10^9$	giga	1 gigameter (Gm) = 10^9 m
1 million	$1{,}000{,}000 = 10^6$	mega	1 megameter (Mm) = 10^6 m
1 thousand	$1{,}000 = 10^3$	kilo	1 kilogram (kg) = 10^3 g
1 hundred	$100 = 10^2$	hecto	1 hectogram (hg) = 100 g
ten	$10 = 10^1$	deka	1 dekaliter (daL) = 10 L
1 tenth	$0.1 = 10^{-1}$	deci	1 decimeter (dm) = 0.1 m
1 hundredth	$0.01 = 10^{-2}$	centi	1 centimeter (cm) = 0.01 m
1 thousandth	$0.001 = 10^{-3}$	milli	1 milliliter (mL) = 0.001 L
1 millionth	$0.000\ 001 = 10^{-6}$	micro	1 micrometer (μm) = 10^{-6} m
1 billionth	$0.000\ 000\ 001 = 10^{-9}$	nano	1 nanometer (nm) = 10^{-9} m

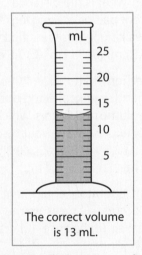

Figure 9-4. Graduated cylinder: You can find the volume of a liquid using a graduated cylinder.

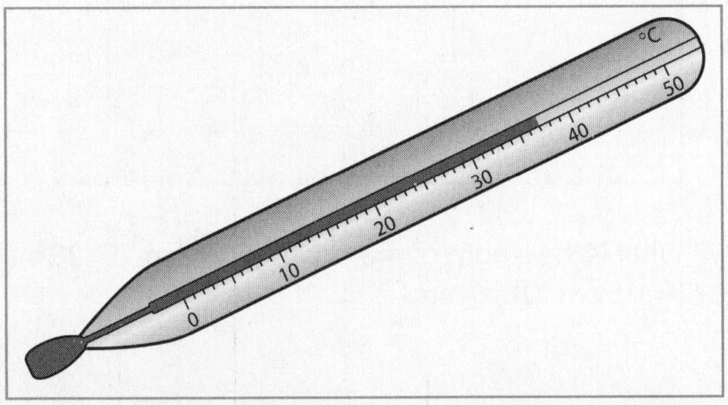

The correct volume is 13 mL.

MEASURING MASS In the biology laboratory, mass—the quantity of matter in something—is often measured with a **balance**, which is a tool that works by comparing an object of unknown mass with an object of known mass. The triple-beam balance or an electronic balance is typically found in a high school laboratory.

A **triple-beam balance** (see Figure 9-6) has a single pan and three bars (beams) that are calibrated in grams. One beam, the 500-gram beam, is divided into five 100-gram units. Another beam is divided into ten units of 10 grams totaling 100 grams. The front beam is divided into 10 major units of 1 gram each. Each of these divisions is further divided into 0.1-gram units.

Figure 9-5. Thermometer: This Celsius thermometer shows human body temperature.

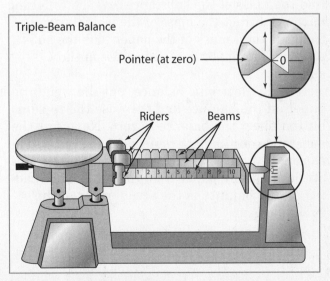

Figure 9-6. Triple-beam balance

Before using a balance, make sure that the pan is empty and that the pointer and all of the riders (devices that are moved along the beams) are on zero.

To determine the mass of an object, it is first placed on the pan. Then, starting with the 500-gram beam, the masses on the beams are adjusted until the pointer is again pointing to zero. The mass of the object is equal to the sum of the readings on the three beams.

An **electronic balance** measures mass automatically. To use an electronic balance, first turn it on and wait until it shows a zero mass. (This may require using the re-zero button shown in Figure 9-7.) Place the object with the unknown mass on the pan. Read the mass.

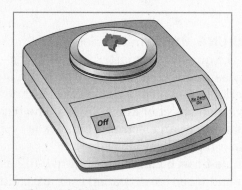

Figure 9-7. Electronic balance

Never place a substance directly on a balance pan. Instead, protect the balance with a weighing paper or dish. With a triple-beam balance, first find the mass of the weighing paper. Then find the mass of the substance *and* the weighing paper. Subtract the mass of the weighing paper from the total mass of the paper plus the substance. The remainder is the mass of the substance.

For an electronic balance, put the weighing paper on the balance and then use the re-zero button to set the balance to zero. Next, put the substance on the paper and read the mass. The re-zero button automatically subtracts the mass of the weighing paper from the total. The reading on the balance is the actual mass of the substance.

9.1 Review

1. The crab shown in the following illustration has four pairs of walking legs and one pair of pincer legs. The crab is shown in its normal walking position.

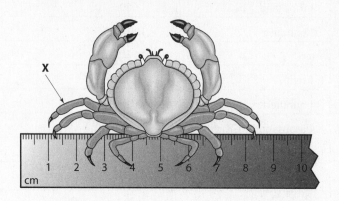

In this position, what is the distance between the ends of the front pair of walking legs? (One of the front pair of walking legs is identified with an "X" above.) (A) 8.5 cm (B) 85 cm (C) 7.5 cm (D) 75 cm

2. Use the conversion: 1 liter (L) = 1,000 milliliter (mL). A sample of pond water collected during an investigation has a volume of 2.5 liters. Which measurement correctly expresses the volume of the sample in milliliters? (F) 2.5×10^{-3} mL (G) 2.5×10^{3} mL (H) 25×10^{-4} mL (J) 25×10^{4} mL

3. Which piece of laboratory equipment would be used to most accurately measure the volume of a liquid? (A) beaker (B) balance (C) test tube (D) graduated cylinder

4. A student measured a larva using a metric ruler, as represented in the following diagram.

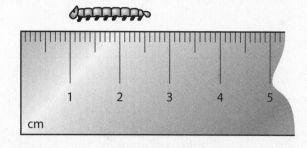

What is the length of the larva? (F) 26 cm (G) 26 mm (H) 16 cm (J) 16 mm

5. The following diagram shows a triple-beam balance with a mass on the pan. With the riders in the positions indicated, what is the mass of the object on the pan of the balance? (A) 9 grams (B) 200 grams (C) 249 grams (D) 942 grams

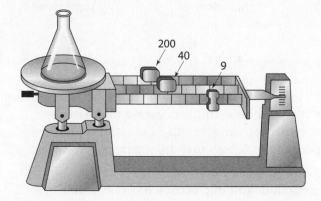

6. Which of the following diagrams shows a correct measurement?

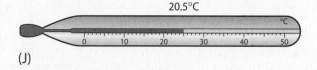

(F)

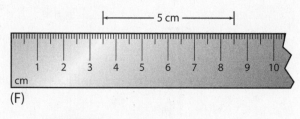

(G)   (H)

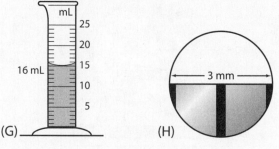

(J)

7. Which of the following graduated cylinders contains a volume of liquid closest to 15 mL?

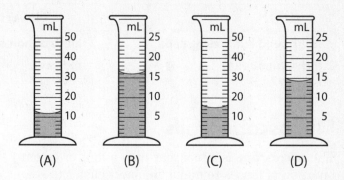

(A)   (B)   (C)   (D)

8. The distance from Earth to the Sun is 150,000,000,000 m. Which measurement correctly expresses the distance? (F) 1.5×10^{11} m (G) 15×10^{-3} mm (H) 150×10^3 mm (J) 1.5×10^{10} m

9. The following diagram shows a wasp positioned next to a centimeter ruler.

What is the approximate length of one of this wasp's wings? (A) 10 mm (B) 1.4 cm (C) 3.5 cm (D) 35 mm

10. Name the piece of laboratory equipment you would use to accurately measure 10 grams of glucose.

11. Draw a meniscus to represent a water level of 6 mL on the diagram of a graduated cylinder.

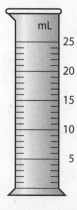

9.2 Tools for Observation and Analysis

Microscope Skills

The **microscope** is a tool that uses a lens or a combination of lenses to make an object easier to see. It allows for the examination of objects too small to be seen with the unaided eye. Microscopes also permit the close observation of fine details. For example, without a microscope you can see the legs and wings of a fly, but with a microscope you can also see the hairs covering the fly's body, the pads and claw-like structures on its feet, and the framework of its wings. This is possible for two reasons. A microscope magnifies the specimen and also allows you to distinguish between objects that are close together. Magnification is the ability of a microscope to make an object appear larger.

TYPES OF MICROSCOPES There are many different types of microscopes. The two most commonly found in a high school laboratory are the compound light microscope and the stereoscope. The primary difference between the two is whether light reflects off the specimen or passes through it.

STEREOSCOPES With a stereoscope (see Figure 9-8), light is reflected off the specimen. A **stereoscope**, sometimes called a dissecting microscope, has two oculars, or eyepiece lenses, and one

or more objectives—the other lenses of the microscope. The amount of magnification is low, but the image is three-dimensional and is not reversed as it would be with a compound microscope. Stereoscopes are often used to observe parts of specimens such as insects, worms, or flowers.

COMPOUND MICROSCOPES The typical **compound light microscope** has one ocular (eyepiece) lens, at least one objective lens, and a light source. Light passes through the object being examined, through the objective lens, and then through the eyepiece (see Figure 9-9).

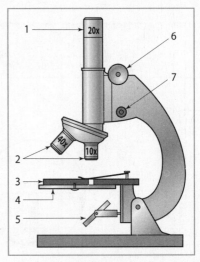

Figure 9-9. A compound microscope: Each part is labeled with a number. The names and functions of the parts are given in Table 9-3.

The image you see is magnified by both lenses—the ocular lens and the objective lens. The total magnification is calculated by multiplying the magnification of the ocular by the magnification of the objective. For example, if you use a microscope that has a 10× eyepiece and a 40× objective, the magnification of a specimen would be 400×.

Eyepiece	×	Objective	=	Total Magnification
10×	×	40×	=	400×

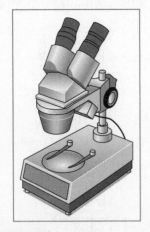

Figure 9-8. A stereoscope

Table 9-3. Names and Functions of Parts of a Compound Microscope

Microscope Part	Function
1 Eyepiece or Ocular Lens	• lens nearest the eye; used to "look through" • usually magnifies 10×
2 Objective Lenses	• lenses located closest to specimen • usually 2 or 3 • commonly magnify at 4×, 10×, and 40×
3 Stage	• flat surface (platform) on which the slide is placed • stage clips hold the slide in place
4 Diaphragm	• located under the stage • controls the amount of light passing up through the specimen
5 Light Source	• might be a mirror or a light bulb • provides light that passes up through the specimen and makes it visible
6 Coarse Adjustment	• used to focus only under low power (up to 100×) • never used when the high-power objective is in place for viewing • usually the larger knob; causes a large amount of movement of the lenses
7 Fine Adjustment	• the only focus you should use with high power • used to sharpen the image under low power • also used to see different layers of a specimen • usually the smaller of the focus knobs; causes a small amount of movement of the lenses

Microscope lenses may get dirty from contact with fingers, specimens, stains, and so on. Do not use paper towels or your shirt to clean them! Use only lens paper to clean the lenses of a microscope. Lens paper will not scratch the soft glass of the lens.

TECHNIQUES FOR USING MICROSCOPES

Because of how microscope lenses work, there are a number of things you need to remember when viewing objects through a compound light microscope.

• The image will be upside-down and backwards, as shown in Figure 9-10.

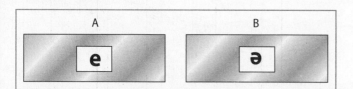

Figure 9-10. Microscope view: The letter "e" as seen on a slide (A) and as seen through the microscope (B). (Only the change in position of the letter is shown, not the magnification.)

• You must move the slide in the direction that is opposite the way that the organism appears to be moving. In other words, if the organism appears headed toward the upper right side of your field of view, you must move the slide down and to the left to keep it in view. See Figure 9-11.

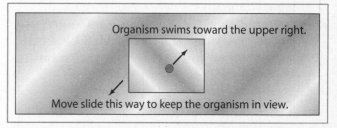

Figure 9-11. **Moving the slide to follow a moving object**

• The field becomes darker as you increase the magnification. You will need to increase the amount of light passing through the specimen as you go from low power to high power. The diaphragm, located under the stage, can be used to do this.

- Since the field becomes smaller under high power, center the object you are viewing before switching to a higher power. Otherwise the object may be outside of the field of view.

FOCUSING When observing specimens through the compound light microscope, first use the low-power objective. Do this even if higher magnification is needed to make your observations.

1. First, place the slide on the stage of your microscope. Position the slide so that the specimen is over the opening in the stage. Anchor the slide with the stage clips.

2. Move the coarse adjustment so that the low-power objective is as close to the slide as you can get it without touching the slide. Some microscopes have a built-in "stop" that prevents you from getting the objective lens too close to the slide. You should look at the objective and the slide while doing this. Never lower the objective while looking through the eyepiece.

3. Look through the eyepiece with both eyes open and turn the coarse adjustment so that the low-power objective and slide move apart. The specimen should come into view.

4. Next, turn the fine adjustment to bring the specimen into sharp focus.

5. To focus the specimen under higher magnification after locating it under low power, move the slide so that what you are interested in seeing is located in the center of your field of view. Remember that as you increase the magnification, the object appears larger, but you see less of it. The field of view becomes smaller when you switch from low power to a higher power. See Figure 9-12.

6. Watch from the side of the microscope and slowly turn the high-power objective into place. Be sure that the high-power objective is not going to touch the slide. High-power objectives are longer than low-power objectives and can easily hit the slide—be careful.

7. If the objective is not going to hit the slide, click it into position. As you look through the eyepiece, the specimen should be visible. Use the fine adjustment to sharpen the focus. Remember never to use the coarse adjustment when using the high-power objective. You could damage the microscope lens and break the slide.

PREPARING WET-MOUNT SLIDES Only specimens that are small and thin can be seen through a compound light microscope. However, thin slices may quickly dry and shrivel. To avoid this, a temporary wet-mount slide can be prepared by using the following steps:

1. Using a pipette (eye dropper), add a small drop of water to the center of a clean glass slide.

2. Place the object to be viewed in the water. (It should be lying flat rather than folded over.)

3. Use forceps to position a coverslip, as shown in Figure 9-13. Using forceps will keep you from getting fingerprints on the coverslip. Fingerprints could interfere with your ability to view the image clearly.

4. Lower the coverslip slowly. This technique will prevent the formation of air bubbles under the coverslip.

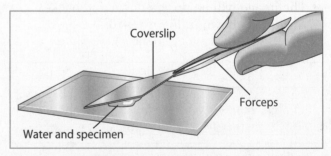

Figure 9-13. **Preparing a wet-mount slide**

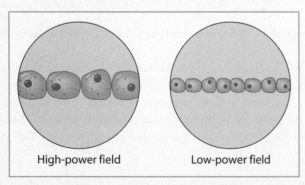

High-power field   Low-power field

Figure 9-12. **Specimen under low and high power:** Note that the high power field is narrower (only 4 cells can be seen), but the cells appear larger and more detail is visible.

STAINING SPECIMENS When you examine cells and cell parts through a microscope, they often appear to be transparent. You need to adjust the light and the focus so that you can see differences in thickness and density. Although adjusting the amount of light passing through the specimen may help, stains are often used to create greater contrast. Different types of cells and cell parts vary in their ability to soak up various stains. For example, certain cell parts turn darker in the presence of iodine stain, while others do not.

To add a stain such as methylene blue to a wet-mount slide, place a drop of the stain beside one edge of the coverslip. Next, touch a small piece of paper towel to the opposite edge of the coverslip. The towel absorbs water and draws the stain across the slide under the coverslip. This technique allows you to keep the slide on the stage of the microscope. You do not need to prepare a new slide. (See Figure 9-14.)

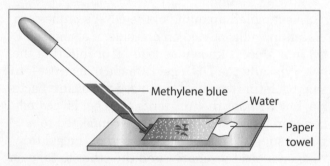

Figure 9-14. Staining a wet-mount slide

IDENTIFYING AND COMPARING CELL PARTS

It is important to remember that cells have specific structures that perform specific jobs. (See Figures 9-15 through 9-17.) Many of these structures are visible through a compound light microscope. Some of the parts include

- **Nucleus**—usually observed as a rounded, dense, dark-staining structure. It can be located anywhere in the cell, not just in the middle.
- **Cytoplasm**—typically fills the cell. It appears to be clear in some cells and very grainy in others. Cell organelles, which may or may not be visible, are suspended in the cytoplasm.
- **Cell membrane**—found surrounding the cytoplasm. It is the outer boundary of animal cells and is located between the cell wall and the cytoplasm in plants and some other organisms.
- **Cell wall**—located on the outside of the cell membrane in plant cells. The nonliving cell wall is a supportive structure. Many bacteria form a different type of protective cell wall.

- **Chloroplasts**—green, oval structures found in the cytoplasm of some plant cells and photosynthetic one-celled organisms.
- **Vacuoles**—often seen as clear areas in the cytoplasm. Plant cells contain very large fluid-filled vacuoles that occupy much of the inside of the cell. Some single-celled organisms may contain specialized vacuoles for digestion and for regulating water balance.
- **Chromosomes**—most easily observed in cells undergoing mitosis or meiosis. They are usually dark-staining and threadlike.

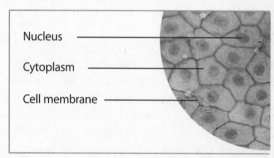

Figure 9-15. Animal cells: As seen through a compound light microscope

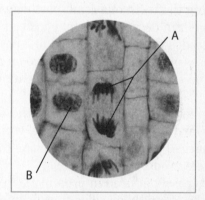

Figure 9-16. Plant cells undergoing mitotic cell division: *A* indicates chromosomes, and *B* indicates a nucleus before the cell undergoes mitotic cell division.

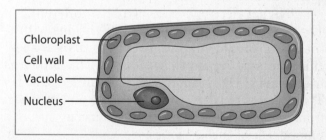

Figure 9-17. Typical plant cell: Structures that can be seen through a microscope

Additional Laboratory Techniques

There are many techniques that are useful in the biology laboratory. Some of the most common are electrophoresis, chromatography, and the application of stains and indicators. Dichotomous keys are especially useful for field research.

ELECTROPHORESIS Gel electrophoresis is a very powerful tool and is widely used by scientists in many disciplines—not just biologists. It allows scientists to separate mixtures of large molecules according to size. DNA and protein are the two types of molecules most often separated by gel electrophoresis.

When setting up a protein gel, a sample of biological material is prepared by breaking open the cells that contain the proteins being studied. Next, the proteins are treated with both chemicals and heat. One of the chemicals coats the protein molecules and gives them a negative charge. Then, very small amounts of the prepared sample are placed in wells at the top of a special gel positioned in a gel electrophoresis apparatus.

The wells are similar to the holes you would get by pressing the teeth of a comb part way into a block of gelatin dessert. The gel is placed between two electrodes that are connected to a power supply. This causes one end of the gel to take on a positive charge and the other to take on a negative charge.

Positively charged molecules in the sample move toward the negative electrode, while negatively charged protein molecules move toward the positive electrode.

The type of gel used in protein electrophoresis is made up of long molecules that form a tangled mesh. Smaller molecules are able to work their way through the gel more quickly than larger molecules. Therefore, molecules are separated by both their size and electrical charge. See Figure 9-18.

DNA gel electrophoresis is a little different. The analysis of an individual's DNA begins with the use of special enzymes to cut the DNA at specific points in the sequence of bases. This produces fragments of DNA that are of different lengths. These pieces of DNA will vary in size and number from one individual to another because of the uniqueness of each genetic code.

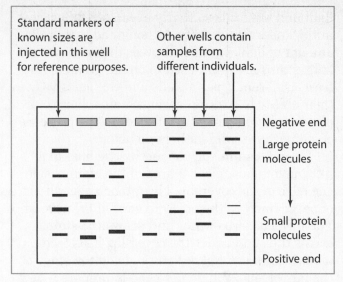

Figure 9-18. Protein gel electrophoresis: Protein gels are typically run vertically.

Next, small amounts of the DNA samples are placed in wells located on one side of a semisolid gel in a process known as loading or injecting the gel. Typically the DNA gel is made of agarose—the same gelatin-like substance used to culture bacteria, but without the nutrients. The gel is located between two electrodes that are connected to a power supply. This causes one end of the gel to take on a positive charge and the other to take on a negative charge when the current is turned on. The negatively charged DNA fragments move toward the positive electrode.

As with the protein gel, the smaller the fragment, the more rapidly it moves through the gel. Small pieces of DNA will travel farther and be located farther from the well where they were initially placed. (See Figure 9-19.) This allows the DNA fragments to form a distinct pattern that becomes visible through staining or a variety of other techniques.

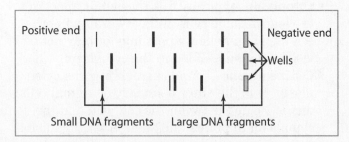

Figure 9-19. DNA gel electrophoresis: DNA gels are typically run horizontally.

The information provided by both DNA and protein gels looks very much like a bar code. The patterns formed from different protein samples or the DNA of different individuals can provide information about relatedness.

DNA has been used to determine who the father of a child actually is in paternity cases or who the parents are in instances where a couple suspects that the child given to them in the hospital is not their child.

DNA has also been used to determine guilt or innocence during criminal investigations. The source of blood, semen, or skin can be identified with this technique. DNA left at a crime scene can be compared to a suspect's DNA to determine whether the suspect was at the crime scene.

In the case of endangered species, scientists can use DNA electrophoresis to learn which groups are being devastated by poachers, since skins from members of the same group will have similar DNA patterns. Gel electrophoresis can also be used to determine whether the alleles responsible for specific genetic disorders, such as sickle cell disease, are present.

CHROMATOGRAPHY Like gel electrophoresis, chromatography is a technique used for separating mixtures of molecules. In one type of chromatography commonly used in the biology laboratory, the mixture being separated is placed on a paper to which it sticks. For example, chlorophyll extract from plant leaves is placed on filter paper or special chromatography paper.

First, a small dot of the concentrated chlorophyll extract is placed near one end of a strip of the paper. Then, the end of the paper nearest the dot of extract is placed in a solvent. In the case of chlorophyll, the solvent could be alcohol. The solvent cannot touch the dot when it is initially set up, or the chlorophyll would simply wash away into the solvent.

As the solvent soaks into the paper and moves upward, substances in the mixture that do not stick tightly to the paper will be picked up by the solvent and moved along quickly. Substances that are held more tightly to the paper and less attracted to the solvent will also be picked up but will move along more slowly. This results in the forma-

tion of bands of the different substances on the chromatography paper.

If the substances in the mixture are colorless, they can be viewed by combining them with reactive chemicals that will give them color. The chlorophyll extract consists of several plant pigments that are very colorful and easy to distinguish.

In summary, the rate at which a substance moves along the paper in a given solvent can be used to separate it from other substances. By comparing the distances moved with those of known substances in the same solvent, the unknowns can be identified. See Figure 9-20.

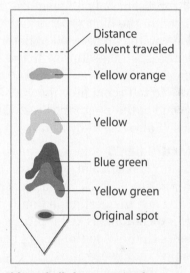

Figure 9-20. Chlorophyll chromatography

STAINS AND INDICATORS **Stains** can be used to make cell structures more visible. In fact, chromosomes were so named for the fact that they are easily stained ("chromo" is a prefix that means "color").

Commonly used stains are iodine and methylene blue. Iodine darkens certain cell structures. It is especially useful when examining plant cells through the microscope. Methylene blue stains structures in the nucleus. It is useful when observing many types of cells.

An **indicator** is a substance that changes color when it contacts certain chemicals. The examples

Table 9-4. Indicators Used in the Biology Laboratory	
Indicator	**What the Indicator Tests**
pH paper	A piece of pH paper is dipped in the solution to be tested. Its color is then matched to a color scale. Specific colors indicate whether the solution is acidic (pH values from 0 to 6), neutral (pH 7), or basic (pH values from 8 to 14).
Lugol's iodine solution	A color change from golden brown to blue-black indicates the presence of starch in the tested solution.

in Table 9-4 represent only a few of the indicators commonly used in the biology laboratory.

Other indicators can be used to determine how much sugar there is in a solution or the amount of carbon dioxide present. Swimming pool owners use indicators to tell them how much chlorine is in the water. Some of the pregnancy test kits that pharmacies sell also use indicators.

DICHOTOMOUS KEYS A key is used to sort, name, or classify a particular organism. By working through a series of steps, organisms are eliminated until the one in question is finally identified. Each step of a **dichotomous key** typically consists of two statements that divide the things being identified or classified into two groups. Each statement is followed by a direction that indicates either what step to go to next or the name of the organism.

To make your own dichotomous key, you would need to start out with two statements that divide the organisms being classified into two groups. Each statement would be followed with a direction about the next step to take. At the next step, you again divide the organisms into two groups that are again followed by directions about the next step to go to or the identity of the organism or object. For example, this is how you might construct a key to classify the following objects: bicycle, car, jet, and motorcycle.

1a Requires petroleum fuel . . . . go to Step 2
1b Requires only muscle power . . . . bicycle

2a Has wings and flies . . . . jet
2b Has no wings and does not fly . . . . go to Step 3

3a Has two wheels . . . . motorcycle
3b Has more than two wheels . . . . car

Pretend that you do not know a motorcycle from a bicycle from a jet or from a car. All you could do is examine each one of the objects, make observations, and determine how they work. Once you did that, you would be ready to place names on each of the four items. Notice that if you did not work through the key step by step, it would be very easy to misname an object.

If you thought about a bicycle as having two wheels and scanned down the list with no attention to the steps, you could easily mistake the bicycle for a motorcycle. You would spot step 3a, which says, "Has two wheels" and say to yourself, "That's the bicycle." You would miss the fact that the object in step 3a must run on petroleum fuel. Always start at the beginning of a key.

Observing Plant and Animal Specimens

Classroom experiences involving plants and animals range from observation to dissection. Opportunities to observe plants and animals require careful handling and consideration for the organism. The abuse of any live organism for any purpose is intolerable.

DISSECTION AND PRESERVED SPECIMENS
The dissection of plant and animal specimens provides a framework upon which to organize biological knowledge. Dissection and examination of preserved specimens provides a way to

- observe similarities and differences that exist among species
- understand the relationship between biological form and function
- expose and identify the internal structures of organisms

To dissect a specimen correctly, you need

- the knowledge of what equipment to use and how to use it properly
- a work area that is clean and well organized both before and after the activity

Equipment commonly used during dissection activities is described in Table 9-5.

Table 9-5. Dissection Equipment

Equipment	How the Equipment Is Used
Dissecting pan	Resembles a cake pan but has a wax or a rubber-like substance at the bottom. The specimen is placed on the waxy surface.
Dissecting pins	Large pins with a "T" shape used to anchor the specimen during the dissection.
Scalpel	A sharp instrument used to slice open the specimen so that the internal parts can be observed.
Scissors	Used for cutting open the specimen and to remove parts. May have two sharp points or one blunt end and one sharp point.
Probe/Teasing needle/ Dissecting needle	Used to move structures around while they are still intact. The probe can be used to lift some organs so that others located below them are observable. The probe or dissecting needle is also used to point out different structures when showing specific features to someone else. Another function is to "tease" or gently tear apart structures such as muscle tissue.
Tweezers/Forceps	Used to lift out small parts, to move structures, and to pry parts open.
Safety goggles	Wrap-around, shatter-proof glasses used to protect eyes from accidental splashes of preservative when dissecting and in other lab situations.

9.2 Review

Base your answers to questions 1 through 3 on the following diagram and information.

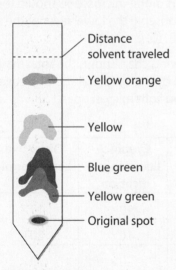

Distance solvent traveled

Yellow orange

Yellow

Blue green

Yellow green

Original spot

Several drops of concentrated green pigment extract obtained from spinach leaves were placed near the bottom of a strip of highly absorbent paper. When the extract dried, the paper was suspended in a test tube containing solvent so that only the tip of the paper was in the solvent. As the solvent was absorbed and drawn through the paper, the various pigments within the extract became visible, as shown in the diagram.

1. A valid conclusion that can be drawn from this information is that spinach leaves (A) contain only chlorophyll (B) contain pigments in addition to chlorophyll (C) contain more orange pigment than yellow pigment (D) are yellow-orange rather than green

2. The technique used to separate the parts of the extract in the diagram is known as (F) staining (G) dissection (H) chromatography (J) electrophoresis

3. In which organelle would most of these pigments be found? (A) nucleus (B) mitochondrion (C) ribosome (D) chloroplast

4. When stained with certain dyes, cell structures known as nucleoproteins appear black. These dyes would most likely be used to (F) identify specific nucleoproteins within cells (G) stain all types of cell organelles (H) determine the chemical composition of nucleoproteins (J) indicate the presence of nucleoproteins

5. When viewed with a compound light microscope, which letter would best illustrate the way in which the microscope inverts and reverses the image? (A) A (B) W (C) R (D) D

6. To test for the presence of glucose, a student added the same amount of Benedict's solution to each of four test tubes. To determine whether glucose is present, Benedict's must be mixed in the unknown solution and heated for several minutes.

Test tubes 1 and 2 contained different unknown solutions. Test tubes 3 and 4 contained known solutions. The chart below shows the color results obtained after the solutions were heated in the four test tubes in a hot water bath.

The student could correctly conclude that (F) all of the tubes contained glucose (G) tubes 1 and 2 contained glucose (H) tube 1 did not contain glucose, but tube 2 did (J) tube 2 did not contain glucose, but tube 1 did

Testing Results

Tube	Contents	Color After Heating
1	Unknown solution #1 + Benedict's solution	Royal blue
2	Unknown solution #2 + Benedict's solution	Red orange
3	Water + Benedict's solution	Royal blue
4	Glucose + water + Benedict's solution	Red orange

7. A student viewing a specimen under the low-power objective of a compound light microscope switched to high power and noticed that the field of view darkened considerably.

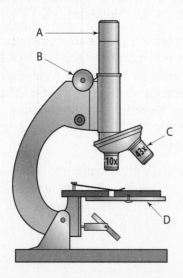

Which part identified on this microscope would the student adjust to brighten the field of view? (A) A (B) B (C) C (D) D

8. While focusing a microscope on high power, a student crushed the coverslip. The student probably (F) shut the light off (G) turned up the light intensity (H) rotated the eyepiece (J) used the coarse adjustment

9. A student studied the upper layer of cells of a tissue sample on a slide, using the high-power objective of the compound microscope shown.

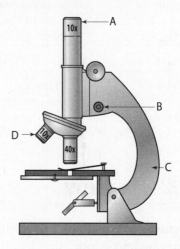

Which part of the microscope should the student adjust to observe the lower layer of the sample? (A) A (B) B (C) C (D) D

10. The following chart shows the total magnification produced by the eyepiece and objective lenses in compound light microscopes.

Microscope	Eyepiece Lens Magnification	Objective Lens Magnification	Total Magnification
1	10×	10×	100×
2	10×	20×	200×
3	20×	20×	400×
4	20×	40×	?

What is the total magnification of microscope 4? (F) 60× (G) 20× (H) 600× (J) 800×

11. The following diagram represents part of the process of

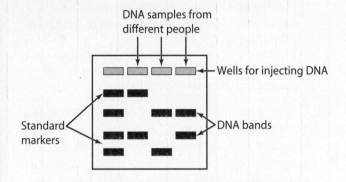

DNA samples from different people

← Wells for injecting DNA

Standard markers

DNA bands

(A) gel electrophoresis (B) genetic engineering
(C) homeostatic control (D) cell culturing

12. For what purpose would the equipment in the following illustration most likely be used? (F) dissecting an earthworm (G) removing cell organelles (H) identifying and classifying a single-celled organism (J) observing mitosis on prepared slides

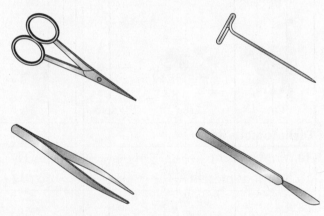

13. The diagram represents the field of view of a compound light microscope. Three single-celled organisms are located across the diameter of the field.

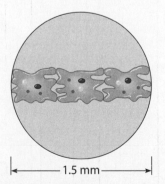

|← 1.5 mm →|

Knowing that 1 mm = 1,000 micrometers, what is the approximate length of each single-celled organism? (A) 250 micrometers (B) 500 micrometers (C) 1,000 micrometers (D) 1,500 micrometers

14. A student views some cheek cells under low power. Before switching to high power, the student should (F) adjust the eyepiece (G) center the image being viewed (H) remove the slide from the stage (J) remove the coverslip from the slide

15. A student sees the following image when observing the letter "f" with the low-power objective lens of a microscope.

Which of the four following diagrams most closely resembles the image the student will see after switching to high power?

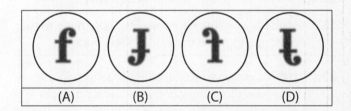

(A)   (B)   (C)   (D)

16. When preparing a wet-mount slide of onion cells, a student put a drop of Lugol's iodine stain on the slide. Lugol's iodine stain was added to (F) prevent the formation of air bubbles (G) make cell structures more visible (H) increase the magnification (J) increase the rate of photosynthesis in the cells

17. Bromthymol blue turns yellow in the presence of carbon dioxide. This characteristic makes it possible for bromthymol blue to function as (A) a measure of volume (B) an indicator (C) a catalyst (D) an energy source

Base your answers to questions 18 through 21 on the photograph below.

The photograph shows onion root-tip tissue viewed under the high-power objective of a compound light microscope.

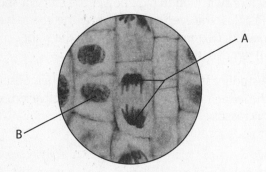

18. The photograph illustrates stages in the process of (F) meiosis in root tips (G) mitotic cell division in plants (H) water conduction in onions (J) chlorophyll production in chloroplasts

19. Identify the structures indicated by arrow A.

20. Identify the structure indicated by arrow B.

21. Describe one adjustment that could be made to the microscope to make the field of view brighter.

22. A student observed a one-celled organism in the field of view of a compound light microscope, as shown in the diagram below. On the diagram, draw an arrow to indicate the direction in which the organism would seem to move if the student moved the slide on the stage to the left and down.

23. A student is viewing a single-celled organism with the low-power objective of a compound light microscope. What adjustments would the student need to make to see the organism more clearly and in more detail, and how would the view change? Describe

• an adjustment the student would need to make to see the organism more clearly without increasing the magnification

• how the student could increase the magnification of the organism

• how the size of the organism in comparison to the diameter of the field would change at increased magnification

• how the brightness of the field of view would change and how to correct for this

24. The eyepiece of a compound light microscope has a magnification of 10×, and the low-power objective and high-power objective lenses have magnifications of 10× and 30×, respectively. If the diameter of the low-power field measures 1,500 micrometers, the diameter of the high power field will measure either 4,500 micrometers or 500 micrometers. Select the correct diameter and explain your answer.

25. The dichotomous key begun below should allow users to classify the organisms illustrated. Complete the key using only information shown in the illustration.

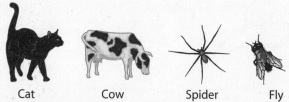

| Cat | Cow | Spider | Fly |

Dichotomous Key
1a. Wings present ···························· Fly
1b. No wings present ···················· go to 2

9.3 Laboratory Safety

VOCABULARY		
hot water bath	MSDS	toxicity

Laboratory investigations are, for some students, the most exciting part of a biology course. However, they sometimes involve potentially dangerous activities and materials. As a result, careful attention to safety procedures is critical.

Using Safety Equipment

You should know how to properly use the safety equipment located in your biology laboratory. It is critical to be aware of the location in your laboratory of each of the following

- fire extinguisher
- safety shower
- eye wash station
- fire blanket
- emergency gas shutoff

Use the safety equipment provided for you. Goggles should be worn whenever a lab calls for the use of chemicals, preserved specimens, or dissection. If indicated by your teacher, you should also wear a safety apron when using chemicals. Some activities, such as those involving chemicals or live or preserved organisms, also require the use of special gloves. A good way to know the potential dangers associated with a chemical is to check the Material Safety Data Sheet (**MSDS**) for the chemical. These fact sheets give you information about the kinds of gloves to wear, **toxicity** of the chemical (how poisonous it is), first aid procedures, and other safety data.

Safety in the Laboratory

Read all of the directions for an investigation before you start to work. If you are unsure about any part of the lab procedure, check with your teacher. As a general rule, do not perform activities without permission; do only what the instructions and your teacher direct you to do. Some safety rules to follow at all times are

- Do *not* eat or drink in the laboratory.
- When you are heating a test tube, always slant it so that the open end of the tube points away

from you and others. Never heat a closed container, such as a test tube that has been closed with a stopper.

- Never inhale or taste any of the chemicals you are using in a laboratory. This includes the specimens you are dissecting.
- If you spill a chemical or get any on your skin, wash it off immediately. Also, report the incident to your teacher.
- Tell your teacher about any personal injury no matter how minor it may seem.
- Tie back long hair and keep loose clothing away from laboratory equipment, chemicals, and sources of heat and fire.
- Never expose flammable liquids to an open flame. Use a **hot water bath**, such as a large beaker of water heated on a hot plate, if you need to heat flammable liquids such as alcohol. See Figure 9-21 for a typical hot water bath.

Figure 9-21. **Hot water bath:** A hot water bath is used to heat test tubes that contain a flammable liquid such as alcohol.

- Know what equipment to use when handling hot glassware. Do not use bare fingers to pick up hot test tubes or beakers. Use test tube holders and beaker tongs.
- Do not use glassware that has cracks or large chips. Tell your teacher about the damage and get a replacement.
- Do not pour chemicals back into stock bottles or exchange stoppers on the stock bottles.

- Use laboratory apparatus only as it is intended to be used. For example, do not stir a solution using a thermometer, plastic ruler, or your pen.

- Do not use electrical equipment around water. If electrical cords seem to have exposed wires or if you get a shock handling electrical equipment, notify your teacher immediately. Do not attempt to disconnect the equipment yourself.

Cleaning Your Work Area

It is important to work in an area that is clean and uncluttered, with no safety hazards present. It is also important to leave the area clean after you are finished working there for the safety of others who may use the area later. Some basic rules to follow are

- Turn off the gas and water after you are done with them. Disconnect any electrical devices.

- Clean your work area by returning materials to their appropriate places, washing glassware according to your teacher's instructions, and wiping off the lab surface.

- Dispose of chemicals according to the instructions provided by your teacher.

- Wash your hands thoroughly!

9.3 Review

1. A student performing an experiment noticed that a beaker containing water being heated had a small crack in it. It was not leaking. What should the student do? (A) Stop heating the beaker and try to fix the crack. (B) Stop heating the beaker and report the crack to the teacher. (C) Stop heating the beaker and immediately take the beaker to the teacher. (D) Continue heating as long as the liquid does not start to leak out of the crack.

2. An *unsafe* procedure for heating a nutrient solution in a flask would be to (F) heat the solution briefly at a low temperature on a hot plate (G) stopper the flask tightly to prevent evaporation of the solution as it is heated (H) use a microwave to heat the solution a few seconds at a time (J) stir the solution while it is heating

3. When they are not being used during a laboratory investigation, electrical devices should be (A) put away (B) turned off (C) unplugged (D) covered

4. The following diagram shows a student conducting a laboratory experiment.

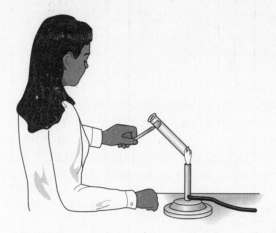

The student is not following at least two important safety procedures. Identify what she is doing wrong.

- Identify two specific safety errors she is making, as shown in the diagram.

- Describe why the safety errors you identified are unsafe.

- Describe what she should do to correct the two errors you identified.

5. A student is heating a test tube containing an indicator solution and glucose. The student is wearing safety goggles and a laboratory apron. Describe another safety procedure that this student should be following.

6. Some students did a lab to test the vitamin C content of several fruits. They squeezed the juice from some of the fruits and cut others up and placed them in a blender to obtain a juice sample. Juice for each fruit was kept in a labeled beaker. A Bunsen burner was used to heat some of the juice samples. Pipettes were used to transfer the juices to test tubes and an indicator was added for analysis.

   During the laboratory cleanup, one student drank some of the juice left in one beaker. Proper safety procedures are important while working in the laboratory. Discuss

- the role of the indicator in this investigation

- why drinking the leftover juice was an unsafe procedure

- what safety precautions should be taken while heating the juice samples

- *another* safety procedure that the students should observe when doing this investigation

1. Gel electrophoresis is a technique used to

   (A) cut DNA into pieces of various sizes

   (B) separate DNA fragments by charge and size

   (C) move DNA fragments from one species to another

   (D) make copies of chromosomes

2. Use the conversion: 1 millimeter (mm) = 1,000 micrometers (μm).

   A leaf cell measures 8 micrometers in length. Which of these correctly expresses the length in millimeters?

   (F) 8×10^{-3} mm

   (G) 8×10^3 mm

   (H) 5×10^{-6} mm

   (J) 8×10^6 mm

3. Which statement describes two unsafe laboratory practices represented in the following diagram?

   (A) The flame is too high, and the test tube is unstoppered.

   (B) The opening of the test tube is pointed toward the student, and the student is not wearing goggles.

   (C) The test tube is unstoppered, and the student is not wearing goggles.

   (D) The beaker has water in it, and the flame is under the tripod.

4. A student who is not wearing safety goggles gets some unknown chemical in his eye. What is the most appropriate action he should take?

   (F) Put on safety goggles immediately.

   (G) Ask his lab partner to see if his eye looks OK.

   (H) Go to the eye wash station and use it to rinse his eye thoroughly.

   (J) Rub the eye gently and see if it hurts or stings.

5. With only the materials list supplied below and common laboratory equipment, design an investigation that would show how a change in pH would affect the activity of enzyme X.

   Materials
   Enzyme X
   Sugar solution
   Indicators
   Substances of various pH values:
       vinegar (acidic)
       water (neutral)
       baking soda (basic)

   Your design should include

   • a detailed procedure

   • a description of what laboratory equipment is used for each step in the procedure

   • two safety precautions that should be used during the investigation

6. Read the conversion shown below.

   1 liter (L) = 1,000 milliliters (mL)

   During a field investigation, several samples of water from the ocean were collected and brought back to the classroom. Students measured a total volume of 350 milliliters. Which of these correctly expresses the volume of the sample in liters?

   (F) 3.5×10^{-1}

   (G) 3.5×10^1

   (H) 35×10^{-3}

   (J) 35×10^3

7. Pieces of pH paper were used to test the contents of three test tubes. The results are shown in the diagram below.

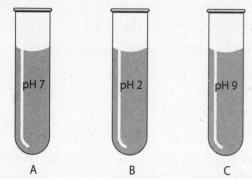

A   B   C

Which statement about the tubes is correct?

(A) Tube A contains a base and tube B is neutral.

(B) Tube B contains an acid and tube C contains a base.

(C) Tube A is neutral and tube C contains an acid.

(D) Tube A contains an acid and tube B contains a base.

8. Several students want to test the effect of temperature on the action of pepsin, a protein-digesting enzyme present in stomach fluid. After checking several references, they decided to place 20 milliliters of stomach fluid and 10 grams of protein in each of five test tubes. They want to keep the tubes at different temperatures and then, after 24 hours, test the contents of each tube to determine the amount of protein that has been digested.

To perform this investigation, the students must have access to several laboratory tools. Identify what tools are necessary and describe how each should be used. Be sure to include

- the name of the tool that should be used measure 20 milliliters of stomach fluid and the procedure to follow to get an accurate measurement

- the name of the tool that should be used measure 10 grams of protein and the procedure to follow to get an accurate measurement

- the name of the tool that should be used to measure the temperature of the 5 test tubes and how to avoid contamination of the samples during the process

- at least 2 safety rules that should be followed and an explanation of why each is important during this investigation

9. Below is a drawing of a hypothetical electrophoresis gel. Included on the gel are some bands for several different individuals.

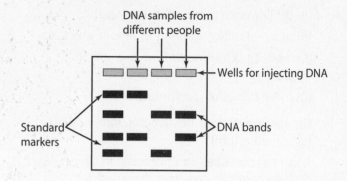

- Describe where the smallest fragments of DNA would be located on the gel in the illustration.

- Discuss two practical applications of information that can be obtained through this process.

10. The following diagram shows a student heating some test tubes with chemicals in them during a laboratory activity.

Explain

- why the student was correct in *not* using stoppers in the tubes

- one safety precaution the student is *not* following

- how the student should safely remove the tubes from the beaker once they have been heated

Appendix A: Strategies for Answering Test Questions

This appendix provides strategies to help you answer various types of questions on the Maryland High School Assessment in Biology. Strategies are provided for answering selected response (SR) and brief constructed response (BCR) items. There are also tips for questions based on diagrams, data tables, and graphs. For each type of question, practice questions are provided to show you how to apply the strategies.

A.1: Strategies for Selected Response Questions

Selected response questions account for more than 50 percent of the questions on the Maryland High School Assessment in Biology. Both Session 1 and Session 2 contain selected response questions. Therefore, it is important to be good at deciphering them. Here are a few helpful strategies. Keep in mind that for any one question, not all strategies will need to be used. The numbers are provided for reference, not to specify an order, except for Strategies 1 and 2.

1. Always read the entire question, but wait to read the choices.

2. Carefully examine any data tables, diagrams, or photographs associated with the question.

3. Underline key words and phrases in the question that signal what you should be looking for in the answer. This will make you read the question more carefully. This strategy applies mostly to questions with a long introduction.

4. Try to think of an answer to the question before looking at the choices given. If you think you know the answer, write it on a separate piece of paper before reading the choices. Next, read all of the choices and compare them to your answer before making a decision. Do not select the first answer that seems correct. If your answer matches one of the choices, and you are quite sure of your response, you are probably correct. Even if your answer matches one of the choices, carefully consider all of the answers, because the obvious choice is not always the correct one. If there are no exact matches, re-read the question and look for the choice that is most similar to your answer.

5. Eliminate any choices that you know are incorrect. Each choice that you can eliminate increases your chances of selecting the correct answer.

6. If the question makes no sense after reading through it several times, leave it for later. Complete the rest of the exam and then return to the questions you are not sure of. Something you read on other parts of the exam may give you some ideas about how to answer these questions. If you are still unsure, go with your best guess. There is no penalty for guessing. Answers left blank will be counted as wrong. If you employ your best test-taking strategies, you just may select the correct answer.

Practice Questions

1. Most of the oxygen that enters the atmosphere comes from the process of
(A) respiration (B) photosynthesis (C) excretion (D) digestion

EXPLANATION OF ANSWER Use strategy 5. Eliminating choices 3 and 4 may be easy, but think about the other two choices carefully before choosing your final answer. Be sure that you are not confusing respiration with photosynthesis. The correct answer is choice (B), photosynthesis.

2. Cellular respiration in humans occurs in (F) red blood cells only (G) the cells of the lungs only (H) the cells of the digestive system only (J) all the cells of the body

EXPLANATION OF ANSWER Use strategy 4. Note that the question is asking where cell respiration occurs in humans. Your answer before reading the choices should be that respiration occurs in all of the cells of the body or that respiration occurs in the mitochondria. All of the choices are different types of cells. Think about what cell respiration is and why cells respire. Lung cells and red blood cells help obtain and carry oxygen, but cell respiration is a process that releases energy in *all* cells. Therefore, the correct answer is choice (J), all the cells of the body.

3. A number of white potato plants are grown by placing pieces of one potato in the ground. This method of reproduction is most similar to (A) sexual reproduction (B) cloning (C) genetic engineering (D) zygote formation

EXPLANATION OF ANSWER Use strategy 5. You should be able to eliminate choices (A) and (D) since both are related to the same form of reproduction. The fusion of sex cells results in the formation of a zygote. Since there can be only one correct answer, these will not work. Genetic engineering refers to the manipulation of genes leading to the development of new combinations of traits and new varieties of organisms. Since only one parent (potato) is involved, the genetic make-up of the new potato plants will be the same as that of the original plant. Therefore, cutting up a potato and planting the pieces is most like choice (B), cloning. This is a form of asexual reproduction in which all offspring are genetic copies.

4. Overexposure of animals to X-rays is dangerous because X-rays are known to damage DNA. A direct result of this damage is cells with (F) unusually thick cell membranes (G) no organelles located in the cytoplasm (H) abnormally large chloroplasts (J) changes in chromosome structure

EXPLANATION OF ANSWER Use strategy 3. As you read this question, underline key words: Overexposure of <u>animals</u> to <u>X-rays</u> is dangerous because X-rays are known to <u>damage DNA.</u> A <u>direct result</u> of this damage is cells with (J) changes in chromosome structure. You should know that chromosomes are composed of DNA molecules and that X-rays can cause mutations, which are changes in DNA and/or chromosome structure. Choices (F), (G), and (H) can be eliminated, since even if they could occur, they would not be a <u>direct result</u> of the <u>DNA</u> being <u>damaged.</u>

A.2: General Strategies for Brief Constructed Response Questions

Some questions require a constructed response. Some of these questions on the Maryland High School Assessment in Biology require you to write a paragraph or more. The following general strategies will help you write constructed responses.

1. Always read through the entire question.

2. Underline key words and phrases in the question that signal what you should be looking for in the answer. This will make you read the question more carefully.

3. Write a brief outline, or at least a few notes to yourself, about what should be included in the answer.

4. Pay attention to key words that indicate how to answer the question. Several of these key words are very common. For example, you might be asked to discuss, describe, explain, define, compare, contrast, or design. The table on the next page lists key words and directions for your answers.

5. When you write your answer, don't be so general that you are not saying anything. Be very specific. You should use the correct terms and clearly explain the processes and relationships. Be sure to provide details, such as the names of processes, names of structures, and, if appropriate, how they are related.

Using Key Words to Direct Your Answers

Key Word	What Direction Your Answers Should Take
Analyze	• Break the idea, concept, or situation into parts, and explain how they relate. • Carefully explain relationships, such as cause and effect.
Compare	• Relate two or more topics with an emphasis on how they are alike. • State the similarities between two or more examples.
Contrast	• Relate two or more topics with an emphasis on how they are different. • State the differences between two or more examples.
Define	• State the exact meaning of topic or word. • Explain what something is or what it means.
Describe	• Illustrate the subject using words. • Provide a thorough account of the topic. • Give complete answers.
Discuss	• Make observations about the topic or situation using facts. • Thoroughly write about various aspects of the topic or situation.
Design	• Plan an experiment or component of an experiment. • Map out your proposal, being sure to provide information about all of the required parts.
Explain	• Clarify the topic of the question by spelling it out completely. • Make the topic understandable. • Provide reasons for the outcome.
State	• Express in words. • Explain or describe using at least one fact, term, or relationship.

6. If a question has two or three parts, answer each part in a separate paragraph. This will make it easy for the person scoring your paper to find all of the information. When writing your answer, don't shortchange one part of the question by spending too much time on another part.

7. Be sure that you write sentences. A sentence should always have a subject and a verb and a good answer should not start with the word *because*. Note that you will not lose points for incorrect grammar, spelling, punctuation, or poor penmanship. However, such errors could impair your ability to make your answer clear to the person scoring your paper. If that person cannot understand what you are trying to say, you will not receive the maximum number of points.

A.3: Specific Strategies for Brief Constructed Response Questions

A Brief Constructed Response (BCR) question on the Maryland High School Assessment in Biology is a type of short essay that requires the synthesis of at least two sets of information. The essay should take you about 8 minutes to write and will be scored using the Maryland Science Rubric. When developing your answer to a BCR question, keep the following helpful strategies in mind.

- Read the question carefully and determine the general topic. Analyze the question.

- Go back through the question and underline important ideas. Be sure you understand what each part of the question is asking you.

- On a piece of scrap paper, answer the following.

  (1) What is the main concept/idea behind the question?

  (2) What scientific terms/vocabulary are important and should be used when answering the question?

  (3) What data and other information from class activities and laboratory exercises should you use when answering the question? Support your answer with scientific data/details.

- Write out your answer. Refer back to what you recorded for (1) to (3) above to be sure you have included all of the important information.

- Proofread your response. Be sure it is clear to anyone reading it.

- If necessary, make revisions to your answer.

Practice Question

5. In the past, a specific antibiotic was effective in killing certain species of bacteria. Now, most members of this bacterial species are resistant to this antibiotic. Explain how this species of bacteria has become resistant. You answer must include the concepts of

- overproduction
- variation
- natural selection
- adaptation to the environment

EXPLANATION OF ANSWER Break the question into parts. What is it really asking? Be sure to use scientific terms that are appropriate to the concept. If possible, connect your response to a laboratory activity or reading. Be sure to include facts that are relevent to the situation and assemble your ideas into an explanation that answers all parts of the question. This question asks you to explain how bacteria evolves to become resistant to an antibiotic.

You should break the question down into segments. Use a bulleted list as a guide. You might try something like this.

- Overproduction—In terms of evolution, you should discuss how organisms produce many more offspring than can possibly survive. Many species of bacteria reproduce very rapidly. (In a short amount of time, thousands of bacteria are produced.)

- Variation—Within a species, there are always variations. Some organisms are larger or smaller, faster or slower, or produce or lack a particular enzyme. Within the species discussed in this question, some bacteria possess a variation that makes them resistant to the antibiotic. They survive, while others do not possess this variation and are killed by the antibiotic.

- Natural selection—Environmental factors select for some traits and against others. An insect with the appropriate shape and coloration blends into its surroundings. It is not visible to predators and therefore survives. Bacteria with the variation for antibiotic resistance survive when a person takes the antibiotic. Those without the variation are *selected against* and are killed by the antibiotic.

- Adaptation to the environment—The bacteria that survive the antibiotic are well adapted to the environment. The presence of the antibiotic in the environment is not a problem for them. These bacteria go on to reproduce more bacteria that posses the resistance variation. Those that do not possess the variation do not survive and therefore do not produce offspring. Soon there are many more antibiotic-resistant bacteria than nonresistant ones.

The major concepts should then be put together to form a single, logical answer that might look like this:

> Bacteria reproduce rapidly, so more bacteria were produced than can possibly survive (over-production). Because of genetic differences (variation), some bacteria had genes making them resistant to the antibiotic and so were better adapted to an environment containing the antibiotic. They were the ones most likely to survive and produce the next generation (natural selection). Over several generations, a greater percentage of the population was resistant (adaptation to the environment).

A.4: Strategies for Questions Based on Diagrams

Both Selected Response and Brief Constructed Response questions frequently include diagrams or pictures. Usually the diagrams provide information needed to answer the question. The diagrams may be realistic or they may be schematic. Schematic drawings show the relationships among parts and sometimes the sequence of events that occur in a system.

Practice Questions

Base your answer to questions 6 and 7 on the following diagram. The diagram illustrates one possible scheme of evolution among various groups of organisms.

- **First, study the diagram.** Ask yourself what the diagram is about and what it shows you. Read the title or description provided, if there is one.

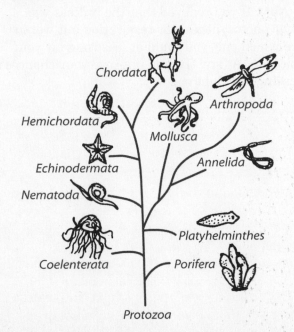

You are told that the diagram represents a possible sequence of events in the evolution of a number of organisms. Based on the illustration, you see that Protozoa are the common ancestor of all the other animals shown. It also indicates that Porifera, Platyhelminthes, Nematoda, and Coelenterata existed before Echinodermata, Hemichordata, Chordata, Arthropoda, Annelida, and Mollusca. The diagram also shows that Platyhelminthes and Nematoda are very closely related, as are Arthropoda, Annelida, and Mollusca. You need to know that the closer the point of branching, the more closely related the organisms. The farther apart the point of branching, the more distant the relationship is considered to be.

- **Second, read the question.**

6. Which inference does the diagram best support?

For this type of question, it is difficult to try to anticipate what the correct answer might be. Carefully read each of the choices, one at a time, and see if they make sense by looking back at the diagram. As you do this, eliminate any choices you can.

- (F) Members of the animal kingdom are more complex than members of the plant kingdom.

- (G) Members of the animal kingdom and members of the plant kingdom share common ancestry.

- (H) Chordates are more closely related to arthropods than to echinoderms.

- (J) Members of the group Echinodermata and the group Annelida share common ancestry.

EXPLANATION OF ANSWER There is no information provided about plants by the diagram; you can eliminate choices (A) and (B).

According to the diagram, chordates are more closely related to Echinodermata than they are to Arthropoda—the opposite of what choice (C) states—because Echinodermata branches off the same line that chordates are on. Arthropod ancestors branched before that.

The correct answer is (D), Members of the group Echinodermata and the group Annelida share common ancestry. All of the animals on this diagram share a common ancestor—Protozoa.

7. Which two groups of organisms in the diagram are shown to be the most closely related?

Before reading the choices, consider how you could tell which organisms are closely related—by two organisms being close on one branch. Apply this knowledge to eliminate wrong choices. Do not select the first answer that seems correct.

(A) Porifera and Echinodermata

(B) Chordata and Platyhelminthes

(C) Mollusca and Annelida

(D) Arthropoda and Coelenterata

EXPLANATION OF ANSWER Choices (F), (G), and (J) have separate branches and are widely separated, so these choices can be eliminated. Mollusca and Annelida are the only two groups that share a common side branch on the diagram.

Therefore, the correct answer is (H), Mollusca and Annelida.

For the next question, number 8:

• **First, study the diagram for question 8.** Ask yourself what the diagram is about and what it shows you. It shows CO_2 and H_2O entering, and sugar and O_2 leaving. The illustration seems to have something to do with photosynthesis, since CO_2 and H_2O are raw materials and sugar and O_2 are products.

• **Second, read the question.**

8. The diagram represents some events that take place in a plant cell. With which organelle would these events be most closely associated?

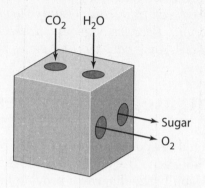

Before reading the choices provided, write what you think the answer should be on a separate piece of paper. Then compare your answer to the choices provided.

(F) mitochondrion

(G) chloroplast

(H) ribosome

(J) vacuole

EXPLANATION OF ANSWER Mitochondria are associated with cellular respiration, ribosomes with protein synthesis, and vacuoles with storage. Since this diagram illustrates photosynthesis, which occurs in chloroplasts in plant cells, the correct answer is choice (B) chloroplast.

Note: If you realized that the process was either photosynthesis or respiration but weren't sure which one, you could at least narrow your choices to (A) and (B) and improve your chances of guessing the right one.

A.5: Strategies for Questions Based on Data Tables

Most data tables contain information that summarizes a topic. A table uses rows and columns to condense information and to present it in an organized way. Rows are the horizontal divisions going from left to right across the table, while columns are vertical divisions going from top to bottom. Column headings name the type of information included in a table. Sometimes different categories of information are listed down the left-hand column of the table.

Examine the sample data table. It provides information collected during an old study of the death rates of policyholders of a large life insurance company.

Deaths as a Result of Disease

Cause of Death	Deaths per 100,000 People	
	1911	1957
Tuberculosis	224.6	6.7
Other communicable disease	58.9	0.1
Cancer	69.3	136.2
Heart disease	156.4	256.2

Before attempting to answer any questions based on the data, go through the following steps.

1. Find the title of the table. It is usually located across the top. What is the title of the sample table? Answer: *Deaths as a Result of Disease*

2. Determine the number of columns in the table and their purpose. There are three columns in the sample table. They show the causes of death and deaths per 100,000 people during the years of 1911 and 1957.

3. Determine the number of rows and their purpose. There are four rows in the sample table. The rows provide you with the number of deaths due to tuberculosis, other communicable diseases, cancer, and heart disease.

4. Read across the rows and down the columns to determine what the relationships are. Notice how the numbers of deaths changed for each disease between 1911 and 1957 in the sample table. Some have decreased and some have increased.

Now you are ready to read the question with the sample data table and answer it.

9. The study most clearly indicated that during the time period examined

(A) cancer of the lungs was increasing

(B) people were living longer

(C) children were safer from communicable diseases

(D) better housing reduced deaths from tuberculosis

EXPLANATION OF ANSWER Choice (F) doesn't work because even though cancer death rates increased from 69.3 to 136.2 per 100,000, there is no way to tell what type or types of cancer caused the difference.

Choice (G) is not correct because you have no information about how long old people were living in either 1911 or 1957.

Choice (J) is not correct because no information is provided about what caused the decrease in deaths due to tuberculosis. You only know that the death rate decreased from 224.6 in 1911 to 6.7 per 100,000 in 1957.

The correct answer is choice (H), children were safer from communicable diseases. The number of deaths decreased from 58.9 per 100,000 in 1911 to 0.1 per 100,000 in 1957.

Practice Questions

Base your answers to questions 10 and 11 on the following information:

A dog was placed in a special room free of unrelated stimuli. On repeated trials, a tone was sounded for 5 seconds; approximately 2 seconds later, the dog was given food. Trials 1, 10, 20, 30, 40, and 50 were test trials; that is, the tone was sounded for 30 seconds and no food was given. The following data were collected.

Dog Salivation Data

Test Trial Number	Drops of Saliva Secreted	Number of Seconds Between Onset of the Tone and Salivation
1	0	——
10	6	18
20	20	9
30	60	2
40	62	1
50	59	2

10. The greatest increase in the number of drops of saliva secreted occurred between test trials

(F) 1 and 10

(G) 10 and 20

(H) 20 and 30

(J) 30 and 40

EXPLANATION OF ANSWER The increase for choice (A) amounted to 6 drops, since it increased from 0 drops to 6 drops between Test Trial Numbers 1 to 10.

Choice (B) resulted in an increase of 14 drops, since test trial number 10 resulted in 6 drops, while test trial number 20 resulted in 20 drops. The difference is 14 drops.

Choice (D) only resulted in an increase of 2 drops.

The correct answer is choice (C) 20 to 30. The number of drops of saliva secreted increased from 20 in test trial 20 to 60 in test trial 30, for an increase of 40 drops of saliva.

11. At test trial 60, the number of drops of saliva secreted would probably be closest to

(A) 75

(B) 55

(C) 35

(D) 25

EXPLANATION OF ANSWER Choice (F) is wrong, since it shows a large increase.

Choices (H) and (J) are both incorrect. This is because the decrease in number of drops is very large. These numbers do not fit the trend shown in the data table.

The correct answer is choice (G) because the number of drops of saliva secreted between trials 30 and 50 has been changing slowly and at trial 50 has started to go down.

A.6: Strategies for Questions Based on Graphs

Graphs represent relationships in a visual form that is easy to read. Three different types of graphs commonly used on science examinations are line graphs, bar graphs, and circle graphs. Line graphs are the most common. They show the relationship between two changing quantities, or variables. When a question is based on any of the three types of graphs, the information you need to correctly answer the question can usually be found on the graph.

When answering a question that includes a graph, first ask yourself these questions.

• What information does the graph provide?

• What are the variables?

• What seems to happen to one variable as the other changes?

After a careful analysis of the graph, use these strategies along with the other strategies you have learned.

• Read the question.

• Read each of the possible answers and consider which is the correct choice by referring to the graph.

Practice Questions

Use the following graph to answer question 12.

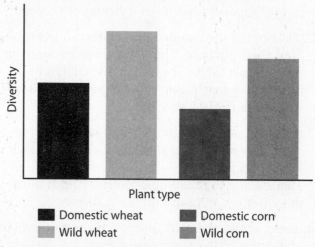

Genetic Diversity in Corn and Wheat Varieties

(y-axis: Diversity; x-axis: Plant type)

Legend: Domestic wheat, Wild wheat, Domestic corn, Wild corn

12. Which types of plants represented on the graph have the greatest diversity?

(F) wild wheat and wild corn

(G) wild wheat and domestic corn

(H) domestic wheat and wild corn

(J) domestic wheat and domestic corn

EXPLANATION OF ANSWER Choices (G), (H), and (J) do not work because they each contain one or more of the domestic plant types that do not extend as high on the diversity scale.

The correct choice is (F) wild wheat and wild corn. The bars for wild wheat and corn extend higher on the diversity scale than the others.

13. Which statement best describes the relationship between enzyme action and temperature shown in the following graph?

Enzyme Action and Temperature

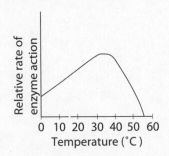

- **First, study the graph** to determine what it is about and what information it gives you about the variables.

- **Second, read the question** and analyze the choices by referring to the graph.

 (A) Enzyme synthesis begins at 30°C.

 (B) Enzyme activity constantly increases with increasing temperature.

 (C) The pH has a greater effect on this enzyme than temperature does.

 (D) Enzyme activity increases as the temperature increases from 32°C to 34°C.

EXPLANATION OF ANSWER Choice (A) is not correct because the graph tells you nothing about enzyme synthesis. The graph starts to show data at 30°C, but shows nothing about synthesis.

Choice (B) is wrong because enzyme activity does not continue to increase. It starts to decrease rapidly at about 37°C.

Choice (C) is incorrect since there is no mention of pH anywhere on the graph.

The correct answer is choice (D). If you follow the graph line, it does show an increase in relative rate of enzyme activity as the temperature increases from 32°C to 34°C.

Appendix B: Strategies for Reading Science

B.1: Identifying Main Ideas

Identifying the main idea helps you understand what you are reading. Sometimes the main idea is easy to find. For example, suppose that you are reading just one paragraph. Very often you will find the main idea in the first sentence, the topic sentence. The other sentences in the paragraph provide details or other ideas that support the topic sentence.

Sometimes, however, the first sentence is not the topic sentence. Sometimes you may have to look further. In those cases, it might help to read the paragraph and summarize what you have read. Your summary can give you the main idea.

A textbook has many paragraphs, each one with its own main idea. However, just as a paragraph has a main idea and supporting details, so does the text under each heading. Sometimes the main idea is the heading itself. Other times it is more difficult to find. You may have to infer a main idea by combining information from several paragraphs.

To practice this skill, you can use a graphic organizer that looks like this one.

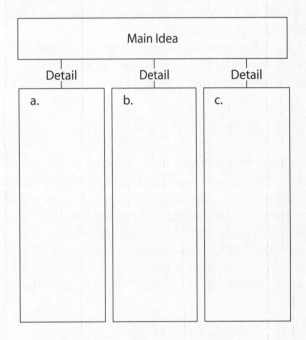

B.2: Comparing and Contrasting

You can use comparing and contrasting skills to better understand the similarities and differences between two or more concepts. Look for clue words as you read. When concepts or topics are similar, you will probably see words such as *also, just as, like, likewise,* or *in the same way.* When concepts or topics are different, you will see *but, however, although, whereas, on the other hand,* or *unlike.*

To use this skill, it sometimes helps to make a Venn diagram. In this type of graphic organizer, the similarities are in the middle, where the two circles overlap.

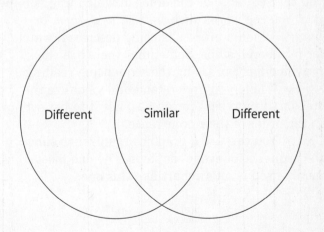

B.3: Relating Cause and Effect

Identifying causes and effects can help you understand the relationships among events. A cause is what makes something happen. An effect is what happens. In science, many actions cause other actions to occur.

Sometimes you have to look hard to see a cause-and-effect relationship in reading. You can watch for clue words to help you identify causes and effects. Look for *because, so, since, therefore, results, cause,* or *lead to.*

Sometimes a cause-and-effect relationship occurs in a chain. For example, an effect can have more than one cause, or a cause can have several effects. Seeing and understanding the relationships helps you understand science processes. You can use a graphic organizer like this one.

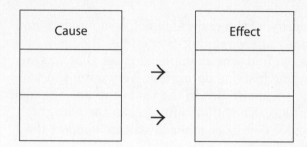

B.4: Asking Questions

This book is organized using headings and subheadings. You can read the material under those headings by turning each heading into a question. For example, you might change the heading "Understanding the Biosphere" to "What is the biosphere?" Asking questions in this way will help you look for answers while reading. You can use a graphic organizer like this one to ask questions.

Question	Answer

B.5: Sequencing

Sequencing is the order in which a series of events occurs. As you read, look for clue words that tell you the sequence or the order in which things happen. You see words such as *first, next, then,* or *finally.* When a process is being described, watch for numbered steps. Sometimes there are clues provided for you. Using the sequencing reading skill will help you understand and visualize the steps in a process. You can also use it to list events in the order of their occurrence.

You can use a graphic organizer to show the sequence of events or steps. The one most commonly used is a flowchart like this one.

Sometimes, though, a cycle diagram works better.

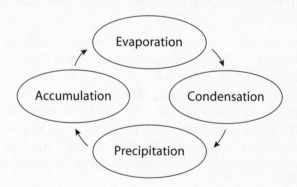

B.6: Previewing Visuals

Looking at visuals before you read can help you better understand a topic. Preview the visuals by reading labels and captions. For example, if you preview the visuals in a section about photosynthesis, you will see more than just diagrams of chloroplasts. You will see illustrations of plant cells and plants. There likely will be tables and cycle diagrams that clarify the series of events taking place during photosynthesis. These might tell you where and when photosynthesis takes place. A chemical equation might be used to tell you what raw materials the plant must take in and what the products of photosynthesis are. Previewing visuals helps you understand and enjoy what you read.

One way to apply this strategy is to choose a few photographs, diagrams, or other visuals to preview. Then write questions about what you see. Answer the questions as you read.

B.7: Identifying Supporting Evidence

In science, you will read about hypotheses. A hypothesis is a possible explanation for scientific observations or an answer to a scientific question. A hypothesis is tested over and over again. The tests may produce evidence that supports the hypothesis. When enough supporting evidence is collected, a hypothesis may become a theory.

Identifying supporting evidence in your reading can help you understand a hypothesis or theory. Evidence is made up of facts. Facts are information that can be confirmed by testing or observation.

When you are identifying supporting evidence, a graphic organizer like this one can be helpful.

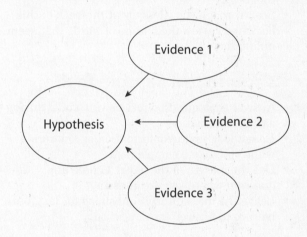

B.8: Building Vocabulary

To understand what someone is saying, you have to know the language that person is speaking. To understand science, you need to know what the words mean.

There are many ways to build your science vocabulary. You can look up the meaning of a new word in the glossary or dictionary. Then you can write its definition in your own words. You can use the new word in a sentence. To figure out the meaning of a new word, you can use clues or surrounding words. Look for prefixes or suffixes in the new word to help you break it down. Building your science vocabulary will get easier as you practice.

Maryland High School Assessment Samples

The following Biology Public Release documents were prepared by the Maryland State Education Department to give you examples of the question format and content used on the Maryland Biology High School Assessment (HSA) examination.

Before You Test Yourself

- Take a sample test only after you have reviewed the entire course content.
- Review the test-taking tips in the Appendix of this book.
- Scan through the Glossary at the back of this book and review definitions of words that seem unfamiliar.

As You Take a Sample Test

- Answer each question just as you would during a real examination.
- Do not look up any information or answers while you take a sample test.
- Use the margin of the paper to note any question where you are guessing.
- Leave the more difficult questions for last, but be sure to answer each question.

After You Test Yourself

- When you finish taking a sample test, have your teacher score your examination.
- Note which questions you answered incorrectly and which ones you marked as "guesses" in the sample test's margin. Use this information and your teacher's suggestions to determine the areas where further study will be most helpful.
- Re-read the topics in this book that gave you the most difficulty on the sample test.

Session 1

Sample A

Which of these instruments should a student use to measure the length of a housefly?

A   microscope

B   metric ruler

C   funnel

D   graduated cylinder

Sample B

Which of these systems <u>directly</u> provides support for the human body?

F   skeletal

G   excretory

H   endocrine

J   reproductive

STOP

irections

Use the information below to answer Numbers 1 and 2.

Aphids are insects that feed on fluids from the stems of plants. After the aphids ingest the plant fluids, they excrete a liquid called honeydew.

1 Ladybugs eat aphids, which are a source of protein for the ladybugs. Which of these terms best describes the relationship between the ladybugs and the aphids?

A   mutualism

B   parasite–host

C   predator–prey

D   commensalism

2 Some species of ants protect aphids from predators. The ants benefit by feeding on the honeydew produced by the aphids. Which of these terms best describes the relationship between the aphids and the ants?

F   mutualism

G   parasite–host

H   predator–prey

J   commensalism

3 The graph below shows the relationship between annual rainfall and plant tissue growth rates in an ecosystem.

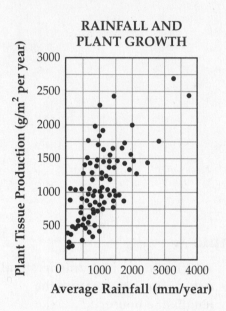

RAINFALL AND PLANT GROWTH

Which of these statements describes the trend shown by the data in the graph?

A   As rainfall increased, the amount of plant material decreased.

B   The amount of rainfall decreased as the amount of plant material increased.

C   As rainfall increased, the amount of plant material increased.

D   Rainfall had no effect on the amount of plant material.

4 How many nucleotides are needed to code for one amino acid?

F 1

G 3

H 4

J 6

5 Cyanide is a poison that prevents mitochondria from using oxygen. As a result, the mitochondria <u>cannot</u> produce

A lipids

B sugar

C minerals

D energy

6
BCR A team of scientists conducted a study of a wetland. Using samples collected from the wetland, the scientists estimated the total biomass at each trophic level. Their data are shown below.

BIOMASS SAMPLE FROM A WETLAND

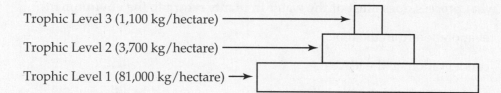

Trophic Level 3 (1,100 kg/hectare)

Trophic Level 2 (3,700 kg/hectare)

Trophic Level 1 (81,000 kg/hectare)

Explain the relationship between trophic levels and biomass. In your response, be sure to include

• the roles of the organisms found at the different trophic levels

• how each trophic level obtains energy

• why the available energy changes at each level

• why the amount of mass differs at each of the trophic levels

Write your answer in your Answer Book.

7 A scientist is trying to discover a new treatment to stop cancer cells from dividing. In the cancer cells, which of these processes will stop if the treatment is successful?

A mitosis

B chemosynthesis

C binary fission

D genetic recombination

8 The presence or absence of freckles is determined by one gene. The allele for freckles (F) is dominant and the allele for the absence of freckles (f) is recessive.

A couple has several children. All of the children have freckles because their parents' genotypes can only produce children with freckles.

Which of these are <u>most likely</u> the genotypes of the two parents?

F Ff and ff

G FF and ff

H Ff and Ff

J ff and ff

9 On Earth, water cycles through the atmosphere, oceans, land, and organisms. By what process does <u>most</u> of the water in plants return to the environment?

A evaporation from the roots

B condensation on the leaves

C evaporation from the leaves

D diffusion from the roots

Directions

Use the information below to answer Numbers 10 and 11.

The largest flower in the world, called a rafflesia, is three feet wide and weighs up to 36 pounds. The rafflesia has no roots, stems, or leaves. It lives on and takes nourishment from a vine called tetrastigma. The rafflesia harms the vine.

The seeds of the rafflesia are dispersed in an unusual way. Plantain squirrels and tree shrews eat parts of the rafflesia plant. Scientists observe that when the animals chew the rafflesia, seeds get caught in their teeth. The animals will then chew on tetrastigma vines, leaving the seeds where they can germinate.

10 Specialized cells in the rafflesia flowers undergo a process that produces gametes. What is this process called?

F   binary fission

G   meiosis

H   fertilization

J   enzyme regulation

11 Rafflesia flowers produce the smell of rotting flesh. This smell attracts flies. When the flies land on the flowers, the pollen attaches to them. The flies then transport the pollen to other flowers.

Producing a smell to attract flies is an example of

A   parasitism

B   adaptation

C   replication

D   predation

M-6

Directions

Use the technical passage and the table below to answer Numbers 12 and 13.

ELEPHANTS DON'T NEED EMAIL

Researchers have observed that elephants seem to know where other elephants are and where they are going, even when they are separated by miles of dense forest. Elephant families will suddenly stop grazing, turn their heads in the same direction, and walk into the forest. The elephants act as if they are communicating with each other.

It is believed that these elephants are responding to low frequency sounds, called infrasound. Human ears cannot hear most elephant rumbles, but sometimes humans can feel the vibrations. Infrasound vibrations are below 20 cycles per second. The frequencies of sounds normally heard by elephants and humans are shown in the table below.

RANGE OF NORMAL HEARING

Animal	Hearing Range	
	Minimum Frequency (cycles per second)	Maximum Frequency (cycles per second)
Elephant	14	16,000
Human	20	20,000

Katherine Payne, a researcher from Cornell University, felt vibrations in the air while she was watching the elephants at the Metro Washington Park Zoo in Portland, Oregon. She believed the elephants might be communicating using infrasound.

Payne and other researchers conducted a study on wild elephants living in southwest Africa. The researchers placed microphones and speakers in areas where elephants live. They recorded the elephants' rumbles and observed their behavior. They found that elephants "talk" to each other in frequencies ranging from 14 cycles per second to 16,000 cycles per second.

To learn how far the rumbles could be heard, they played recordings of low frequency elephant rumbles and watched the reactions of distant elephants. The researchers found that elephants hear low frequency sounds that are produced as far as two and one half miles away. The researchers did not test beyond two and one half miles. The sounds that elephants produce and hear may travel even farther.

GO ON

12 Elephants travel long distances in search of food. Using infrasound, family members traveling separately can communicate with each other.

The ability of the elephants to communicate over long distances probably developed

F   slowly over millions of years

G   over a ten year period

H   as a strategy to decrease reproduction

J   as a way to communicate with other species

13
BCR The researchers found that the elephants could communicate with each other using infrasound over a distance of two and one half miles. The sounds that elephants hear may travel even farther.

Design an experiment that would determine the maximum distance from which elephants can hear infrasound.

Be sure to include

• a hypothesis

• a materials list

• the specific steps to follow in the experiment

• the method of collecting data

Write your answer in your Answer Book.

14 Loggerhead turtles in the Atlantic Ocean return to lay their eggs on the same beaches where they hatched. Scientists have observed that the turtles have a "compass sense." This sense allows them to use Earth's magnetic field to find their way back to the beaches where they were hatched.

Which of these terms best describes the turtle's ability to use Earth's magnetic field?

F   diversity

G   habitat

H   succession

J   adaptation

GO ON

M-8

Directions

Use the information and the food web below to answer Numbers 15 and 16.

A marine environment provides a habitat for a variety of plants and animals. A small part of a marine food web is shown below.

MARINE FOOD WEB

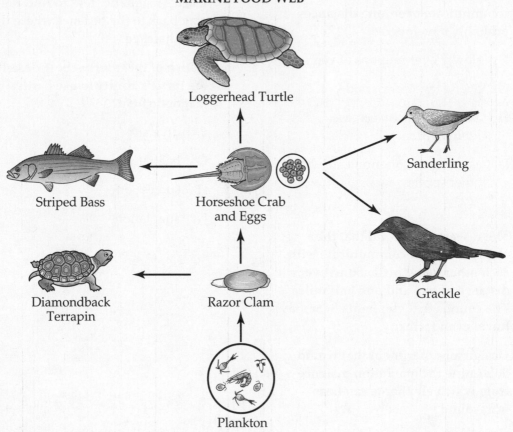

15 Which of these describes the role of the sanderling in the marine food web?

  A   producer

  B   herbivore

  C   carnivore

  D   omnivore

16 Horseshoe crabs are used by fisherman for bait. If the horseshoe crab population were reduced by overfishing, which of these groups of organisms would most likely decrease in number?

F plankton, razor clams, and loggerhead turtles

G sanderlings, loggerhead turtles, and striped bass

H grackles, plankton, and diamondback terrapin

J striped bass, sanderlings, and razor clams

17
BCR The diagram below shows the early embryos of a fish, a reptile, and a bird. The embryos of these organisms are similar in structure and appearance.

EARLY EMBRYOS

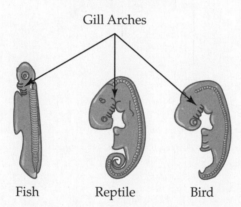

• What other evidence do you see that could be used to determine relatedness?

• Explain what would provide the most reliable evidence that two organisms are related.

• What evidence in adult fish, reptiles, and birds would show relatedness?

Write your answer in your Answer Book.

Public Release, Fall 2004 © 2004 Maryland State Department of Education

M-10

18 Students are conducting an experiment to determine if sugars are present in foods. They heat a test tube containing a sugar solution in a beaker of water.

Which of these is an unsafe laboratory practice in this experiment?

F   heating the sugar solution in a closed test tube

G   rinsing hands with water after handling the materials

H   using a test tube clamp to hold the test tube

J   wearing safety goggles while heating the sugar solution

M-11

Directions

Use the information and the table below to answer Numbers 19 and 20.

Mammals, birds, modern reptiles, and theropod dinosaurs are vertebrates. The table below shows some of the differences and similarities among these groups of vertebrates.

CHARACTERISTICS OF VERTEBRATE GROUPS

	Mammals	Birds	Modern Reptiles	Theropod Dinosaurs
Number of ear bones	3	1	1	1
Legs directly under body	yes	yes	no	yes
Produce milk	yes	no	no	no
Constant body temperature	yes	yes	no	yes
Live birth	yes	no	some	no
Skin covering	hair	feathers/scales	scales	feathers/scales

19 According to the table, which of these vertebrates are most closely related?

A   mammals and modern reptiles

B   theropod dinosaurs and modern reptiles

C   mammals and theropod dinosaurs

D   birds and theropod dinosaurs

20 Birds, mammals, and theropod dinosaurs can maintain a constant body temperature. The ability to maintain a constant body temperature is an example of

F   respiration

G   homeostasis

H   a reptilian trait

J   an acquired trait

M-12

21
BCR All organisms must be able to exchange chemical substances between their cells and their environment. Some organisms are unicellular and others are multicellular. These organisms have different strategies to obtain and use these chemical substances.

- What chemical substances must be exchanged between each organism and its environment?

- Describe the processes that cause these chemical substances to move into and out of cells.

- Describe the role of the cell membrane in the exchange of materials in both types of organisms.

- Describe the role of body systems in the exchange of materials in a multicellular organism.

Write your answer in your Answer Book.

Directions

Use the information and the table below to answer Numbers 22 and 23.

The breathing rate of a goldfish can be measured by the number of times the goldfish opens its mouth. In an experiment, students placed a goldfish in a container of water at 26°C and counted the number of times the fish opened its mouth. They gradually lowered the water temperature and counted the number of times the fish opened its mouth at 20°C, 14°C, 8°C, and 2°C. The results are shown in the table below.

BREATHING RATES OF GOLDFISH

Trial	Water Temperature				
	26°C	20°C	14°C	8°C	2°C
1	101	80	54	30	2
2	98	75	52	27	3
3	102	81	53	29	2
4	103	78	55	28	4

22 Which of these descriptions best explains the decrease in the breathing rate of the goldfish?

F The demand for oxygen increased.

G The rate of metabolic activity decreased.

H The demand for carbon dioxide decreased.

J The fish's activity levels increased.

23 Which of these procedures would be a good control for this experiment?

A Use a different kind of fish for each water temperature.

B Determine the breathing rate of a goldfish kept at a constant 26°C.

C Put the goldfish in 2°C water and then increase the temperature.

D Repeat the experiment using a different species of goldfish.

M-14

24 Maryland white oak trees make their own food. Their cells contain structures that capture energy from the sun. What are these structures?

F   chloroplasts

G   nuclei

H   mitochondria

J   ribosomes

Directions

Use the diagram of the two different organisms and the information below to answer Numbers 25 and 26.

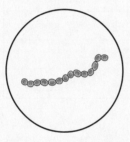

Streptococcus (1000×)   Frog

Streptococcus is a type of bacteria that causes strep throat in humans. A frog is a multicellular organism that lives in aquatic environments.

25 Which of these is the type of reproduction used by *Streptococcus*?

A   binary fission

B   meiosis

C   crossing-over

D   budding

26 Which system in the frog produces chemicals that regulate functions in different parts of its body?

F   respiratory system

G   excretory system

H   endocrine system

J   circulatory system

M-15

Directions

Use the information and the figure below to answer Numbers 27 and 28.

The diagram below shows a colony of prokaryotes and a single-celled eukaryote. The eukaryote contains organelles that resemble the three types of bacteria found in the colony of prokaryotes. More than a billion years ago, bacteria like these may have joined other prokaryotes to form colonies of cells. Researchers think that these once free-living prokaryotes became the organelles of modern-day eukaryotes.

COLONY OF PROKARYOTES

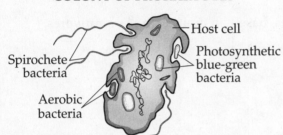

EUKARYOTE

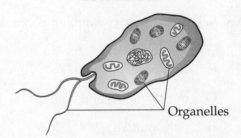

27 In the eukaryote, which of these organelles are used to make sugars?

A   flagella

B   ribosomes

C   mitochondria

D   chloroplasts

28 One of the organelles in the eukaryote releases energy from sugars. What is this process called?

F   respiration

G   transpiration

H   photosynthesis

J   chemosynthesis

M-16

29 Which of these results when one nitrogen base replaces another in a segment of genetic material?

A   an enzyme substrate

B   a mutation

C   a feedback loop

D   an adaptation

30 Scientists classify humans as omnivores, based on their teeth. As omnivores, humans eat

F   only fungi

G   mostly plants and animals

H   only animals

J   mostly bacteria and fungi

31 Which statement describes the major role of lipids within a cell?

A   They cause DNA to replicate.

B   They move RNA in the cytoplasm.

C   They catalyze chemical reactions in the cell cytoplasm.

D   They are the main structural components of membranes.

Session 2

M-18

32 After an egg cell containing 16 chromosomes is fertilized, how many chromosomes will be present in the zygote?

F   8

G 16

H 32

J 64

Public Release, Fall 2004 © 2004 Maryland State Department of Education

M-19

33 The pesticide DDT was used to kill mosquitoes for many years. DDT entered bodies of water, moved up the food chain, and built up in the tissues of fish. When female bald eagles ate these fish, they produced eggs with very thin shells. The eggs broke when the eagles sat on their nests. The U.S. government banned the use of DDT in 1972.

Which of these graphs <u>most likely</u> shows how the ban of DDT affected the bald eagle population?

A

C

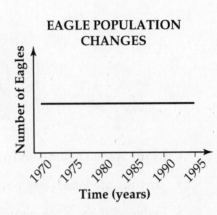

B

D

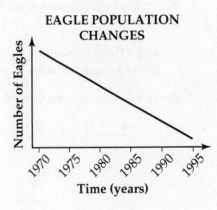

Public Release, Fall 2004 © 2004 Maryland State Department of Education

34

BCR Rafael was given an assignment to determine how the appearance of frog blood cells change when they are placed in distilled water. He is using an incorrect setup to perform his investigation. His laboratory setup is shown in the figure below.

Critique Rafael's setup shown in the figure. In your response, be sure to include

- any unsafe laboratory equipment and procedures shown in the figure

- a description of the materials and safe setup for the correct investigation

- an explanation of why it is important to follow the correct procedures in the laboratory

- any safety precautions you have used during an investigation in biology; provide specific details and the reasons for taking the precautions

Write your answer in your Answer Book.

Public Release, Fall 2004 © 2004 Maryland State Department of Education

35 What molecules control the reaction rate of photosynthesis?

    A   sugars

    B   enzymes

    C   fatty acids

    D   nucleic acids

36 In horses, the allele for straight hair (B) is dominant to the allele for curly hair (b). Which of these sets of parents can produce offspring with curly hair?

    F   a heterozygous male with straight hair and a homozygous female with straight hair

    G   a homozygous male with curly hair and a homozygous female with straight hair

    H   a heterozygous male with straight hair and a heterozygous female with straight hair

    J   a homozygous male with straight hair and a homozygous female with straight hair

37 Which of these is <u>not</u> a use for DNA fingerprinting?

    A   to determine how individuals are related

    B   to make messenger RNA

    C   to determine a genetic sequence

    D   to study inherited diseases

Public Release, Fall 2004 © 2004 Maryland State Department of Education

38
BCR Hemoglobin, a protein found in red blood cells, carries oxygen. Abnormal hemoglobin cannot carry as much oxygen as normal hemoglobin. The sequences below show sections of the DNA sequence that produce both the normal and abnormal types of hemoglobin.

SECTION OF GENE FOR HEMOGLOBIN

Normal DNA sequences: GGA   CTC   CTC

Abnormal DNA sequences: GGA   CAC   CTC

MESSENGER RNA CODON TABLE

Codon	Amino Acid
GUG	Valine
CAC	Histidine
CUC	Leucine
ACU	Threonine
CCU	Proline
GAG	Glutamic acid

- Write the messenger RNA sequences that would be produced from the normal and abnormal DNA sequences shown above.

- Using the codon table, write the amino acid sequences produced from the DNA for normal and abnormal hemoglobin.

- Beginning with DNA, describe the process that forms proteins such as hemoglobin.

Write your answer in your Answer Book.

40 In a recent experiment, scientists studied the effects of increased carbon dioxide levels on the growth of pine trees. The scientists observed that increased levels of carbon dioxide resulted in an increase in the average circumference of the tree trunks. The change in circumference is a result of the process of

F   osmosis

G   adaptation

H   transpiration

J   photosynthesis

41 A student performed an experiment to determine the relationship between air temperature and growth in plants. She divided 36 seedlings into six groups and grew each group at a different temperature. She recorded the average height of the plants in each group after a four-week period. Her results are shown below.

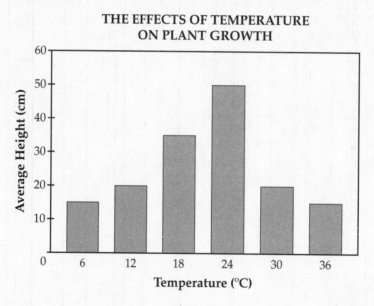

THE EFFECTS OF TEMPERATURE
ON PLANT GROWTH

Which of these statements <u>best</u> describes the results shown in the graph?

A   As temperature increases, the average height of the plants continually increases.

B   Temperature only affects average height between 18°C and 24°C.

C   As temperature increases, the average height of the plants first increases and then decreases.

D   Average height levels off at a temperature of 18°C.

Directions

Use the description of the experiment below to answer Numbers 42 and 43.

A student washes her hands with antibacterial soap and water. Then she touches the agar in a petri dish with her thumb. The agar contains nutrients that support the growth of bacteria. Other students repeat the procedure after washing their hands with three different kinds of antibacterial soap. The petri dishes are kept warm overnight to allow bacteria to grow. The next day the students count the number of bacterial colonies in each dish.

42 Which of these questions are the students <u>most likely</u> trying to answer?

F How long does it take soap to kill bacteria?

G Which soap is most effective in killing bacteria?

H Which nutrients are necessary to grow bacteria?

J How many bacteria are on the average thumb?

43 What should be the effect of the soap in this experiment?

A It should be toxic to the bacteria.

B It should help the bacteria to grow.

C It should change the pH of the agar.

D It should destroy the nutrients in the agar.

Public Release, Fall 2004 © 2004 Maryland State Department of Education

Directions

The energy pyramid below shows the flow of energy through the organisms in a kelp forest ecosystem in the Pacific Ocean. Use the energy pyramid to answer Numbers 44 and 45.

FLOW OF ENERGY IN A KELP FOREST ECOSYSTEM

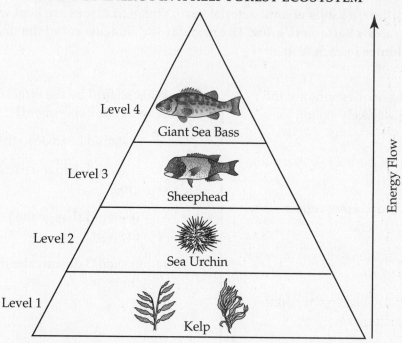

44 How would the populations of other organisms in the energy pyramid be affected if the population of sea urchins suddenly decreased?

   F Both the kelp and the sheephead populations would increase.

   G Both the kelp and the sheephead populations would decrease.

   H The kelp population would decrease, and the sheephead population would increase.

   J The kelp population would increase, and the sheephead population would decrease.

45 What is the <u>lowest</u> level of the energy pyramid that contains carnivores?

   A Level 1

   B Level 2

   C Level 3

   D Level 4

46 Which RNA sequence is produced using the DNA sequence AGC-TAC-ACT?

F   UCG-AUG-UGA

G   UCG-UAC-ACU

H   TCG-ATG-TGA

J   AGC-UAC-ACU

47 A dog gets many nutrients from its food including amino acids. Which of these can be built directly using the amino acids?

A   proteins

B   carbohydrates

C   lipids

D   minerals

Directions

Use the information and the table below to answer Numbers 48 and 49.

Elodea, a freshwater plant, releases gas bubbles when it is placed in direct light. In an investigation, a student placed a lamp at different distances from an aquarium containing *Elodea*. The student counted the number of bubbles produced by the *Elodea* plant. His data are shown in the table below.

GAS BUBBLE PRODUCTION BY *ELODEA*

Distance of Plant From Light (cm)	Production of Gas Bubbles/Minute
10	40
20	20
30	10
40	5

48 What energy source is used by *Elodea*?

F   heat

G   light

H   oxygen

J   carbon dioxide

49 The bubbles released by *Elodea* contain mostly

A   oxygen

B   carbon dioxide

C   nitrogen

D   water vapor

Public Release, Fall 2004 © 2004 Maryland State Department of Education

50
BCR Cardinals are birds that spend the winter in Maryland. Many people feed them sunflower seeds during the winter months. Some of the carbohydrates in the cardinal's diet come from these seeds. Describe

- the building blocks of carbohydrates

- how the sunflowers produce carbohydrates

- how carbohydrates are used by living organisms

Write your answer in your Answer Book.

51 A rare disorder is caused by changes in a gene. Parents of individuals with the disorder have only normal copies of this gene. Which of these <u>most likely</u> causes this disorder?

A   mitosis

B   gene splicing

C   mutation

D   natural selection

52 Four important scientific discoveries are listed below.

1. Some animals can regrow their limbs.

2. All plant and animal tissues are made up of cells.

3. Dominant and recessive traits are passed from parents to offspring.

4. Chromosomes replicate during cell division.

Which two discoveries required the use of a microscope?

F 1 and 2

G 2 and 4

H 1 and 3

J 3 and 4

53 A student used a microscope to observe several protists. The student sketched the protists and recorded their magnifications. The drawings and measurements are shown below.

  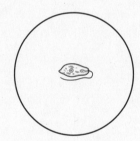 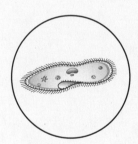

Difflugia (4×)   *Stentor* (4×)   *Euglena* (10×)   *Paramecium* (10×)

Which of these protists is the largest?

A *Difflugia*

B *Stentor*

C *Euglena*

D *Paramecium*

Session 1

Sample A

Which of these instruments should a student use to measure the length of a housefly?

A microscope

B metric ruler

C funnel

D graduated cylinder

Sample B

Which of these systems <u>directly</u> provides support for the human body?

F skeletal

G excretory

H endocrine

J reproductive

1 Students will conduct a laboratory experiment using the following materials: a Bunsen burner, a beaker of water, glass tubing, four test tubes containing different chemicals, and rubber stoppers. Which of these steps is <u>most</u> critical for students to follow when using these materials in the lab?

A wearing eye protection at all times

B writing the lab procedure in a notebook

C washing hands before starting the experiment

D placing a stopper on all test tubes before heating them

2 Which of these are the repeating units that form a DNA molecule?

F fatty acids

G nucleotides

H amino acids

J chromosomes

M-33

3 The table below shows the number of species of different types of simple land plants.

NUMBER OF SIMPLE PLANT SPECIES

Simple Plants	Number of Species
Bryophytes	20,000
Club mosses, spike mosses, and horsetails	1,000
Ferns	12,000
Total	33,000

According to the table, approximately what proportion of all simple plant species are bryophytes?

A $\frac{1}{3}$

B $\frac{1}{2}$

C $\frac{2}{3}$

D $\frac{3}{4}$

4 A protein called p53 can keep cells from dividing. To prevent cell division, this protein <u>most likely</u> stops

F osmosis

G mitosis

H respiration

J mutation

GO ON

5
BCR A student reads an advertisement from a fertilizer company. The advertisement claims their fertilizer increases the growth of tomato plants by 25 percent. The student decides to perform an experiment to test this claim. She performs the following procedure.

1. Choose three similar-sized tomato plants.

2. Plant each tomato plant in a small pot.

3. Place all three small pots into one container and place on a window sill.

4. Add fertilizer mixed with water to Plants 1 and 2.

5. Add only water to Plant 3.

6. Record the heights of the three plants after four weeks.

The student's results are shown in the table below.

THE EFFECT OF FERTILIZER ON TOMATO PLANTS

Plant	Height (centimeters)
1	23
2	20
3	20

Analyze the student's experiment to determine if it supports the claims made in the fertilizer company's advertisement. In your response, be sure to include

- a description of the data needed to support the company's claim

- an explanation of the results of the student's experiment

- an evaluation of the student's experiment

- a description of any changes you would make to the experiment; explain your answer

Write your answer in your Answer Book.

M-35

Directions

Use the information and the diagram below to answer Numbers 6 and 7.

Starch turns blue-black in the presence of iodine solution. A selectively permeable dialysis sac containing a starch solution is placed into a beaker of iodine solution.

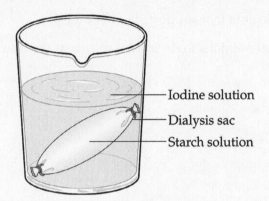

Iodine solution

Dialysis sac

Starch solution

6 If the dialysis sac is permeable <u>only</u> to water and iodine, what will the solutions in the beaker and the sac look like after two hours?

F   The iodine solution in the beaker will turn blue-black; the starch solution will not change.

G   The starch solution in the dialysis sac will turn blue-black; the iodine solution will not change.

H   Neither solution will turn blue-black.

J   Both solutions will turn blue-black.

7 Which of these processes is demonstrated by the experiment shown in the diagram?

A   cellular respiration

B   active transport

C   endocytosis

D   diffusion

8 A scientist is performing an investigation funded by a company. Which of these would be <u>least likely</u> to produce biased data?

F making the results please the company paying for the research

G being open minded and honest throughout the research project

H using only the data that supports the hypothesis

J using personal opinions to decide the results of the research

Page 6

M-37

9 The energy required for photosynthesis is provided by

A   proteins

B   sunlight

C   chlorophyll

D   carbohydrates

M-38

Directions

Use the technical passage below to answer Numbers 10 and 11.

SHORTAGE OF HONEYBEES

Honeybees are very important to agriculture. They produce honey and they pollinate many plants, making seed and fruit development possible. In recent years, severe weather and attacks by newly introduced insects have seriously affected both wild and domestic honeybee populations.

Two species of mites entered North America around 1980. These mites weaken and kill honeybees by consuming their bodily fluids, blocking their respiratory passages, and spreading germs. European and South American honeybees developed an immunity to the effects of these mites. However, North American honeybees did not develop this immunity. By 1995, infestation with mites reached epidemic levels. In addition, the harsh winter of 1995 to 1996 killed honeybee colonies in many states.

Scientists have observed a significant decline in both wild and domestic honeybee populations. This loss affects beekeepers and farmers. Fifteen percent of all agricultural crops require bee pollination. Farmers have had to look for other species to pollinate their crops.

Honeybees are not the only pollinators that have decreased in numbers. Many other insect and vertebrate pollinators throughout the world have been killed by the overuse of pesticides and habitat destruction. Many wild plants, including a number of endangered species, depend entirely on one animal species for pollination. The solutions to this "pollination crisis" are complex. It is clear that efforts to save threatened pollinators cannot be separate from efforts to preserve threatened plants and habitats.

M-39

10 According to the passage, which of these is <u>most</u> responsible for the decline of honeybee populations?

F   an increase in pollution

G   the use of bees to harvest honey

H   the introduction of foreign species

J   the use of bees to pollinate crops

11 South American honeybees are resistant to the mites. Scientists believe that the North American honeybees may also become resistant to the mites in another ten years.

Which of these processes will cause the honeybee population to become resistant to the mites?

A   natural selection

B   chemosynthesis

C   aerobic respiration

D   succession

12 A sperm cell of a moth has 112 chromosomes. How many chromosomes are in the moth's wing cells?

F   66

G   112

H   224

J   448

13
BCR
There are approximately 14 species of bay grasses in Chesapeake Bay. Bay grasses provide a habitat for birds, fish, and shellfish. Most bay grasses grow attached to the bottom substrate in shallow water.

Scientists estimate that the area covered by bay grasses once exceeded 600,000 acres. In 1978, scientists learned that bay grasses only covered 41,000 acres.

Scientists began working to improve environmental conditions in the bay. They replanted bay grasses in some areas. They set a goal of having 110,000 acres of bay grasses by the year 2000. The data collected from yearly surveys of bay grasses is shown in the graph below.

BAY GRASS COVERAGE IN CHESAPEAKE BAY
(1984–2000)

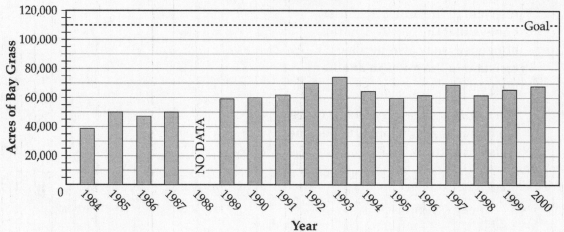

Evaluate the success of this project. In your response, be sure to

• predict the most likely value for the missing data in 1988; explain your answer

• describe the trend in the area covered by bay grasses in Chesapeake Bay from 1984 to 2000; use specific information from the graph to support your answer

• suggest possible reasons for the changes in the graph between 1993 and 1995

• describe ways that individuals can help in the restoration of bay grasses

Write your answer in your Answer Book.

M-41

Directions

Use the information and the graph below to answer Numbers 14 and 15.

A group of students studied the effect of light intensity on the rate of a cell process in Elodea plants. The students exposed Elodea plants to different light intensities. A gas was produced by the cell process. The amount of this gas was measured. The rate of the cell process was determined by the amount of gas produced. A graph of the students' measurements is shown below.

**THE EFFECT OF LIGHT INTENSITY
ON A CELL PROCESS IN ELODEA PLANTS**

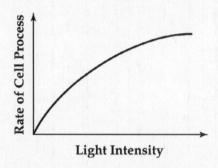

14 Which of these is the independent variable in this experiment?

F rate of cell process

G volume of gas

H size of Elodea plant

J intensity of light

15 Which of these parts of the Elodea plant cell produces the gas measured in the experiment?

A mitochondrion

B chloroplast

C ribosome

D nucleus

M-42

16 Which of these combinations results in the expression of a recessive trait?

    F   two dominant alleles

    G   a dominant sex-linked allele and a Y chromosome

    H   two recessive alleles

    J   a dominant allele and a recessive allele

M-43

17

BCR

Scientists are studying how four species of deer are related. The scientists believe that Species 1 is the common ancestor. The four species have some traits in common. They also have traits that are unique to their species.

Scientists used the process of gel electrophoresis to study the relatedness of the four deer species. The results of their gel electrophoresis study are shown below.

**ELECTROPHORESIS GEL
OF DEER SPECIES**

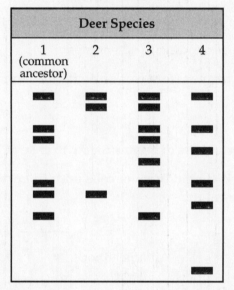

Describe how three species of deer evolved from the common ancestor. In your response, be sure to

- identify which species is most closely related to the common ancestor; explain your answer using the results of their gel electrophoresis

- identify and describe the process that leads to the development of different species

- explain what factors affect this process in the deer species

Write your answer in your Answer Book.

M-44

18 Certain plant crops are genetically engineered to grow faster and resist disease. These genetically engineered plant crops cannot reproduce because they have a "terminator" gene that keeps their seeds from sprouting. However, once the genetically engineered plant crops are planted outside, they may cross-pollinate with unaltered plant crops.

The use of terminator genes is <u>least likely</u> to result in

F   increased costs for seeds

G   decreased varieties of food

H   terminator genes spreading to other crops

J   scientists being harmed from working with the terminator genes

Directions

Use the information and the diagrams below to answer Numbers 19 and 20.

A student observed different types of cells under a microscope. Four of the cells he observed are shown below.

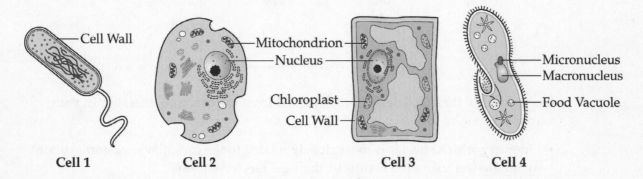

Cell 1   Cell 2   Cell 3   Cell 4

19 Which of these structures in Cell 3 releases energy for use in cell processes?

A   nucleus

B   cell wall

C   chloroplast

D   mitochondrion

20 Cell 4 has many hair-like structures that it uses for movement. What are these structures called?

F   cilia

G   flagella

H   vacuoles

J   pseudopodia

M-45

21 Which of these organ systems is responsible for the removal of metabolic wastes from the blood?

   A   endocrine

   B   nervous

   C   respiratory

   D   excretory

M-46

22
BCR A population of sea urchins in a kelp forest ecosystem is being overfished. A team of students believe that a decline in the number of sea urchins will affect the organisms in the kelp forest ecosystem. The kelp forest food web below shows the relationships among the organisms in the kelp forest ecosystem.

KELP FOREST FOOD WEB

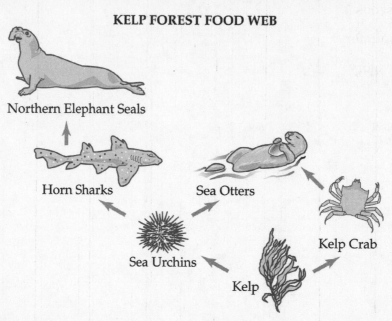

The students believe that the kelp crab population will decrease if the sea urchin population decreases. Use the kelp forest food web to support or refute the students' conclusion. In your response, be sure to

- describe the roles of the kelp crab, sea otter, and sea urchin in the food web

- describe the relationships between the kelp crab, sea otter, and sea urchin

- explain how each organism in the food web would be affected by a change in the sea urchin population

Write your answer in your Answer Book.

Directions

Use the information and the food chain below to answer Numbers 23 and 24.

Cholera bacteria live inside copepods, tiny marine organisms. This type of microscopic bacteria harms the copepods by feeding off their internal tissues.

Both of these organisms are found in oceans throughout the world. Unfavorable temperatures or salt levels may cause cholera bacteria to become inactive. When inactive, they do not feed or reproduce. When conditions become favorable, they become active once again.

A cholera population may depend on the population of copepods in the surrounding water. A simple food chain showing this relationship is shown below.

MARINE FOOD CHAIN

Cholera bacteria

Copepods

Microscopic algae

23 Cholera bacteria perform binary fission to

A   reproduce asexually

B   digest food rapidly

C   regulate temperature

D   increase body size

24 Which of these describes the relationship between cholera bacteria and copepods?

F   mutualism

G   parasite–host

H   commensalism

J   producer–consumer

M-48

25 Scientists are developing a microscopic submarine to deliver medicine to sites within the body. A biomotor that uses bacteria would move the submarine. The scientists are experimenting with several species of bacteria to find which one works best in the biomotor.

Which of these is the dependent variable in the scientists' experiment?

A the species of bacteria

B the movement of the submarine

C the size of the submarine

D the sites within the body

26 A scientist cloned a goat. Which of these is a true statement about the cloned goat?

F It has new genes and traits.

G It lacks the genes for reproduction.

H It has genes that are identical to the original goat.

J It looks the same as the original goat but has different genes.

M-49

27 Hemoglobin is an important protein in red blood cells. The DNA code for hemoglobin contains the following segment:

TGC-GGA-CTC-CTC

Which of these is the messenger RNA code for this segment of DNA?

A ACG-CCT-GAA-GAA

B TCC-GGT-CTC-CTC

C ACG-CCU-GAG-GAG

D UGC-GGA-CUC-CUC

28 Reproductive cells are produced during

F mitosis

G meiosis

H fertilization

J budding

M-50

No test material on this page

Session **2**

M-52

Directions

Use the information below to answer Numbers 29 and 30.

A team of marine scientists is studying biotic and abiotic factors that affect the stability of a deep-sea ecosystem.

29 The scientists discovered a species of fish that eats other fish and decaying matter. Which of these does <u>not</u> describe the newly discovered fish?

A   consumer

B   predator

C   scavenger

D   producer

30 The deep-sea ecosystem is a stable ecosystem. Which of these is a characteristic of <u>most</u> stable ecosystems?

F   They contain a wide variety of organisms.

G   They contain very few organisms.

H   Organic nutrients are in short supply.

J   Sunlight is not used to make food.

31
BCR How is carbon related to the flow of energy between the environment and organisms?

• Name the carbon compound that is exchanged between plants and their environment.

• Describe how plants use carbon from the atmosphere to create more complex molecules.

• Describe how animals that eat plants change these molecules and return carbon to the atmosphere.

Write your answer in your Answer Book.

32 Which of these will <u>most likely</u> result in variation within a species?

F   mutation

G   succession

H   diffusion

J   competition

33 Cells in the stomach produce pepsin, an enzyme, to help digest food. Pepsin works best at a pH of 2. Which of these graphs <u>most likely</u> shows what will happen to the activity of pepsin as the pH of the stomach is increased?

A

EFFECT OF pH ON PEPSIN ACTIVITY

C

EFFECT OF pH ON PEPSIN ACTIVITY

B

EFFECT OF pH ON PEPSIN ACTIVITY

D

EFFECT OF pH ON PEPSIN ACTIVITY

M-54

Directions

Use the information and the figure below to answer Numbers 34 through 36.

Scientists have recently discovered hydrothermal vent communities on the ocean floor. A diagram of a hydrothermal vent community is shown in the figure below.

HYDROTHERMAL VENT COMMUNITY

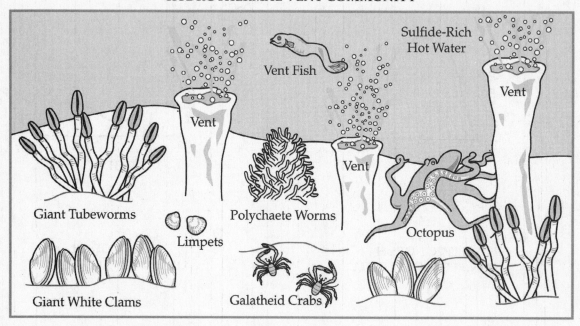

The organisms in this community live near heated vents. Inorganic compounds such as sulfides mix with extremely hot water when they are released from the vents. Bacteria use the sulfides to make food for themselves and other animals. Many of these bacteria live in the bodies of the giant tubeworms and the giant white clams that live in this community.

34 Hydrothermal vent communities are often destroyed by lava erupting from the ocean floor. After the lava has cooled, different organisms begin to inhabit the area. Over a period of a few years, organisms inhabit the area in the following order:

sulfur bacteria → crabs → giant tubeworms → clams and mussels

Which of these <u>best</u> identifies this sequence of events?

F   evolution

G   mutation

H   succession

J   translation

35 The bacteria that live in the bodies of the giant tubeworms and the giant white clams are classified as

A   eukaryotes

B   prokaryotes

C   plants

D   fungi

36 Which of these is an abiotic factor that influences this ecosystem?

F   food

G   bacteria

H   water temperature

J   giant tubeworms

GO ON

M-56

37 Amylase is an enzyme that allows the human body to digest starch. Which of these diagrams <u>best</u> represents part of the structure of amylase?

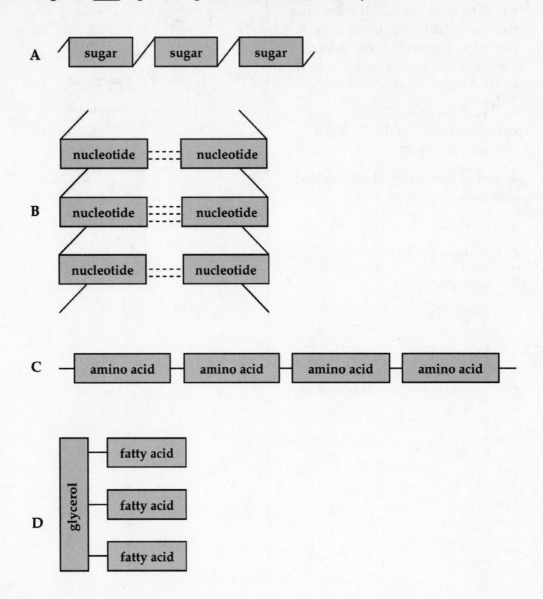

A   sugar   sugar   sugar

B   nucleotide - - - - nucleotide   nucleotide - - - - nucleotide   nucleotide - - - - - nucleotide

C   amino acid   amino acid   amino acid   amino acid

D   glycerol — fatty acid   fatty acid   fatty acid

M-57

38
BCR Galactosemia is an inherited disorder in humans. A person with the disorder cannot digest the sugars in milk. The allele for normal digestion (G) is dominant; the allele for galactosemia (g) is recessive.

A female who is heterozygous for the galactosemia trait and a male who has galactosemia have a child.

Describe how this disorder could have been passed on in the family. In your response, be sure to

- identify the genotype of the father

- complete a Punnett square to show the possible genotypes and phenotypes of the child

- describe the probability that the child will inherit galactosemia

- describe all the possible genotypes and phenotypes of the father's parents; explain your answer

Write your answer in your Answer Book.

39 Nitrogen compounds are a part of all organisms. What happens to the nitrogen in an organism after it dies?

A   It is destroyed by decomposition.

B   It is recycled and used by other organisms.

C   It remains trapped in the organism's tissues.

D   It is all used up by the time the organism dies.

40 The global water cycle consists of water circulating among the land, the atmosphere, the oceans, and organisms. Trees get <u>most</u> of their water directly from

    F   lakes

    G   air

    H   streams

    J   soil

M-59

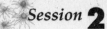

41 **Which of these is produced as a result of fertilization?**

    A   a zygote with twice the number of chromosomes as a gamete

    B   an egg with half the number of chromosomes as a zygote

    C   a gamete with twice the number of chromosomes as a zygote

    D   a zygote with half the number of chromosomes as a gamete

M-60

Directions

Use the information and the food web below to answer Numbers 42 and 43.

Part of the food web in Yellowstone National Park is shown below.

YELLOWSTONE NATIONAL PARK FOOD WEB

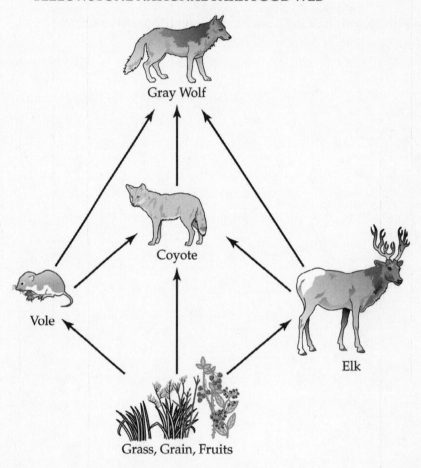

Gray Wolf

Coyote

Vole

Elk

Grass, Grain, Fruits

Gray wolves were reintroduced into Yellowstone National Park in 1995. Two years later, the population of coyotes had decreased by 50%. Coyotes were found in all habitats of the park before the gray wolves were reintroduced. Now, coyotes are most often found in the hills and mountains.

42 Coyotes and gray wolves have a high degree of relatedness. Which of these <u>best</u> describes why the two species are closely related?

F   They have similar behaviors.

G   They have a common ancestor.

H   They feed on the same types of food.

J   They are found in the same habitat.

43 Which of these describes the role of the vole in the Yellowstone ecosystem?

A   decomposer

B   producer

C   herbivore

D   carnivore

44 Scientists estimate that 200 non-native organisms have been introduced into Chesapeake Bay. Which of these statements is <u>not</u> true about non-native organisms?

F   They often form mutualistic relationships with native organisms.

G   They can deplete the food sources of native organisms.

H   They are often aggressive at acquiring and maintaining territory.

J   They can prey on native organisms causing them to go extinct.

Directions

The diagram below shows the key steps for making proteins. Use the diagram to answer Numbers 45 through 47.

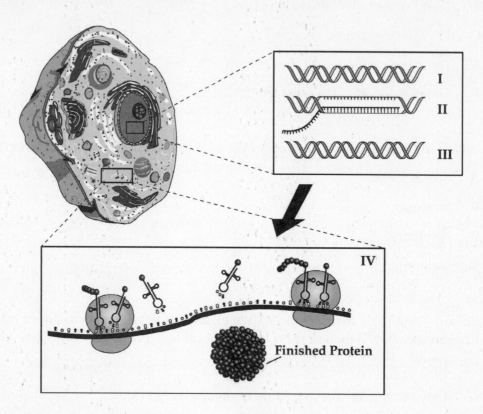

45 According to the diagram, in which step is messenger RNA being constructed?

A I

B II

C III

D IV

46 Which step involves transfer RNA?

F I

G II

H III

J IV

47 Which step involves ribosomes?

A I

B II

C III

D IV

M-63

48
BCR Mammals are exposed to a variety of outside temperatures. However, they are able to maintain a constant internal body temperature.

Describe ways that mammals warm and cool themselves in response to their environment.

Include in your response

- an example of a mammal and its environment

- both body structures and activities they use

- specific examples of both warming and cooling

Write your answer in your Answer Book.

49 Which of these body systems transports glucose and other substances in the blood to the cells of the body?

A   digestive system

B   endocrine system

C   circulatory system

D   reproductive system

M-64

50 Reef-building coral are marine animals with single-celled algae living in their tissues. The coral provide protection for the algae and the algae provides food for the coral. Which of these statements <u>best</u> explains what would happen to the coral if the algae die?

 F The coral would grow well because it does not have a competitor.

 G The coral would die because it needs the food produced by the algae.

 H The coral would grow well because it does not have a parasite.

 J The coral would die because it cannot produce food for the algae.

Directions

Use the information and food chain below to answer Numbers 51 and 52.

A summer camp was built near a lake in the mountains. The campers used the lake for swimming, fishing, and boating. The relationships between three organisms found in the lake are shown below.

LAKE FOOD CHAIN

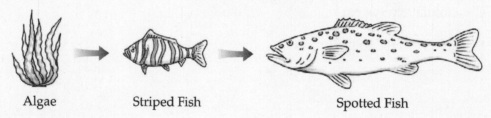

  Algae   Striped Fish   Spotted Fish

51 Which of these fish cell structures would be <u>most directly</u> affected by a change in the oxygen level of the lake?

 A mitochondrion

 B chloroplast

 C golgi apparatus

 D endoplasmic reticulum

52 Striped fish are affected by biotic and abiotic factors in their environment. Which of these factors is biotic?

 F water temperature

 G mineral nutrients

 H freshwater algae

 J inorganic sediments

M-65

53 A researcher recently discovered a species of bacteria. DNA sequences were obtained from it and from several other species of bacteria. The DNA sequences came from the same part of the bacterial chromosome of each species.

	DNA Sequence		
Unknown Species	ACT	GCA	GCC
Species I	ACA	GCG	CCG
Species II	ACT	GCT	GGC
Species III	ACA	GCC	GGG
Species IV	ACT	GCA	GCG

According to the data above, the unknown bacteria are most closely related to which species?

A   Species I

B   Species II

C   Species III

D   Species IV

M-66

Glossary

abiotic nonliving parts of the environment

acid a compound that releases hydrogen ions when dissolved in water; a substance, such as vinegar, with a sour taste

acid rain rain that is more acidic than normal

active transport the process by which cells use energy to transport molecules through the cell membrane from areas of low concentration to areas of high concentration

adaptive value any trait that helps an organism survive and reproduce under a given set of environmental conditions

aerobic respiration respiration carried on in the presence of free oxygen, in which glucose is completely oxidized to carbon dioxide and water

agarose a gel-like substance used in bacterial cultures

AIDS (acquired immunodeficiency syndrome) the disease that results when the HIV virus attacks the human immune system

alleles one or two or more forms of the gene for a specific trait

allergy a condition in which a person's immune system is overly sensitive to environmental substances that are normally harmless

amino acid any one of several building blocks of protein

anaerobic respiration respiration in the absence of free oxygen, in which glucose is partially oxidized

angiosperms flowering plant; forms seeds within a layer of tissue that protects the seeds

animal a complex, multicellular organism with specialized tissues and organs, but no cell walls; a heterotroph that obtains energy by consuming other organisms

antibody a protein, produced by the immune system that either attacks invading pathogens or marks them for killing

antigen a molecule found on the outer surfaces of cells that the immune system recognizes as either part of the body or an outside invader

antihistamine a substance that reduces the effects of histamines and the symptoms they cause

artificial selection the process of breeding two organisms with desirable characteristics to produce offspring that have the advantages of both parents

asexual reproduction a method of reproduction in which all the genes passed on to the offspring come from a single individual or parent

assumption something accepted as true that may or may not actually be true

atoms the smallest particle of an element that has the properties of that element; the unit of which elements are made

ATP (adenine triphosphate) a compound that stores energy in cells

autosomes a chromosome other than a sex chromosome

autotroph an organism that produces its own food; the source of energy for all other living things on Earth

authotrophic nutrition a type of nutrition in which the organism does not require performed inorganic substances from its environment

bacterium any one of many single-celled organisms without a distinct nucleus

balance a tool that measures mass by comparing the unknown mass of an object with an object of known mass

base a compound that produces hydroxide ions when dissolved in water

bias a tendency to favor something; prejudice

binary fission the simplest form of asexual reproduction, in which the parent organism divides into two approximately equal parts

biochemical process a chemical process that occurs in a living thing

biodiversity the variety of species in an area

biomass total amount of living tissue within a specified trophic level. Usually expressed in terms of organic matter per unit of area

biomass pyramid representation of the amount of potential food available for each trophic level in an ecosystem

biome large groups of ecosystems with similar climates and organisms; examples include the tundra, taiga, temperate forest, chaparral, tropical rain forest, desert, temperate grassland, tropical savanna grassland, and polar and high-mountain ice

biosphere all of Earth's ecosystems, collectively; the biologically inhabited portions of Earth, including all of the water, land, and air in which organisms survive

biotechnology the combination of technology and biological sciences

biotic the living parts of the environment

bond the chemical link between atoms that hold molecules together

budding a type of asexual reproduction in which the parent organism divides into two unequal parts

calibrate to adjust the scale of a measurement tool

cancer disorder in which some of the body's cells lose the ability to control growth. Cancer cell undergo rapid mitotic divisions

carbohydrates a compound of carbon, hydrogen, and oxygen in which the ratio of hydrogen to oxygen is 2 : 1

carnivore an organism that survives by eating animals

carrier term used to describe a female who has a defective allele on one X chromosome and the normal allele on the other X chromosome. The female is not affected by the defective recessive allele

carrying capacity the largest population of any single species that an area can support

catalyst a substance that can speed up the rate of a chemical reaction without being changed or used up during the reaction

cell the basic unit of structure and function that makes up all organisms

cell membrane the thin boundary between the cell and its environment

cellular respiration the process in which nutrients are broken apart, releasing the chemical energy stored in them

cellulose a complex carbohydrate found in plant cell walls. It serves as dietary fiber in the human diet

Celsius a temperature scale based on 100 equal units, with 0 as the freezing point of water and 100 as the boiling point of water

chemosynthesis a form of autotrophic nutrition in which energy for synthesizing organic compounds is obtained from inorganic compounds rather than light

chloroplast the green organelle that contains chlorophyll; where photosynthesis takes place

chromatography a laboratory technique used to separate mixtures of molecules

chromosome a thick, threadlike structure that contains genetic information in the form of DNA

chromosome mutation a change in chromosome structure, resulting in new gene combinations

cilia (singular, cillium) a hairlike organelle on the surface of a cell, with the capacity for movement

circulation the flow of materials within a cell as well as between parts of a multicellular organism

classification the grouping of organisms into defined categories based on specific characteristics

classify to group things based upon their similarities

climax community a relatively diverse and stable ecosystem that is the end result of succession

clone an organism that is genetically identical to the organism from which it was produced

cloning a technique used to make identical organisms

commensalism a type of symbiotic relationship in which one organism benefits from the association and the other is not affected

common ancestry a set of organisms in which all of them share a genetic relationship because they all have an ancestor in common

community a combination of all the different populations that live and interact in the same environment

competition the struggle between organisms for the same limited resources in a particular area

compound light microscope a tool that uses more than one lens and a light source to magnify an object

compounds a substance made of two or more kinds of atoms combined in definite proportions

conclusion the decision made about the outcome of an experiment; usually based on how well the actual result matches the predicted result

consumer an organism that obtains its energy from producers

control that group in an experiment in which everything—except the variable to be tested—is identical; the standard of comparison in an experiment

control group the group in a controlled experiment in which no change is made

controlled experiment an experiment in which all variables—except for the one being tested—are exactly the same

covalent bonding a chemical bond formed by the sharing of electrons

coverslip a thin slice of glass that covers the specimen on a slide

cross over the process in which pieces of homologous chromosomes are exchanged during synapsis in the first meiotic division

cytoplasm the jellylike substance that is between the cell membrane and the nucleus and that contains specialized structures

data the results of specific trials or tests completed during experiments

decomposer an organism, generally a bacterium or fungus, that consumes dead organisms and organic waste

decomposition the process whereby dead organisms, as well as the wastes produced by living organisms, are broken down into their raw materials and returned to the ecosystem

deforestation forest destruction that results from human activity

density the measure of mass per unit of volume

dependent variable the part of an experiment that is changed to test a hypothesis

depletion a serious decline or reduction

detrimental damaging; harmful

deviation a change from normal circumstances

dichotomous key a guide that compares pairs of observable traits to help the user identify an organism

dietary fiber bulky, indigestible material in food

differentiation the process that transforms developing cells into specialized cells with different structures and functions

diffusion the movement of molecules from areas of high concentration to areas of low concentration

digestion the process that breaks down large food molecules into simpler molecules that the organism can use

direct harvesting the destruction of an organism, or the removal of an organism from its habitat

disease a condition, other than injury, that prevents the body from working as it should

dissection the act of cutting apart a dead organism to examine its internal structure

DNA (deoxyribonucleic acid) the material found in all cells that contains genetic information about that organism

dominant trait the trait that appears in the offspring of a cross between two pure individuals showing contrasting forms of the trait

dynamic equilibrium the constant small corrections that normally occur to keep an organism's internal environment within the limits needed for survival

ecological niche the specific role played by an organism or a population of organisms in the ecosystem

ecological succession the process by which an existing community is replaced by another community

ecology the study of how living things interact with one another and with their environment

ecosystem all the living and nonliving things that interact in a specific area; a subdivision of the environment

egg a sex cell produced by a female

electronic balance a balance that measures mass automatically

electrophoresis a tool that allows scientists to separate mixtures of molecules according to size

element a substance consisting of only one kind of atom

embryo an organism in the early stages of development (prior to birth)

endocrine glands various hormone-producing glands that secrete substances directly into the blood or lymph

endoplasmic reticulum an organelle that transports proteins and other materials from one part of the cell to another

energy flow the movement of energy through an ecosystem

energy pyramid a diagram showing how food energy moves through the ecosystem

environment every living and nonliving thing that surrounds an organism

environmental impact statement a statement that includes an analysis of how a new project or technology might affect the environment

enzymes proteins that speed up the rate of chemical reactions in living things

equilibrium a state of balance and stability

estrogen a hormone (produced by the ovaries) that controls female sexual development and the reproductive process

eukaryotes all organisms whose cells contain nuclei

evidence support for the idea that something is true

evolution the process by which species have changed over time

excretion the removal of all the wastes produced by the cells of the body

experiment a series of trials or tests that are done to support or refute a hypothesis

experimental control in a controlled experiment, two identical experiments are set up. The setup in which no change is made serves as a reference and is called the control

expressed the way that an unseen gene is seen in an organism as an actual physical trait

extinction the disappearance of all members of a species from Earth

Fallopian tubes that part of the female reproductive system where the egg cell is fertilized by the sperm cell

feedback mechanism a cycle in which the output of a system either modifies or reinforces the first action taken by the system

fertilization the process that combines a sperm cell and an egg cell

fetus the unborn, developing young of an animal during the later stages of development

finite limited

flagella (singular, flagellum) a hairlike organelle at the surface of a cell, with the capacity for movement

flow of energy the movement of energy through an ecosystem

food chain a representation that identifies the specific feeding relationships among organisms

food web a representation of many interconnected food chains that shows the feeding relationships among producers, consumers, and decomposers

forceps a tool used mainly during dissection to lift out small parts, to move structures, and to pry parts open

fossil the preserved remains of ancient organisms

fossil fuel a fuel, such as coal and gas, that comes from the remains of organisms that lived millions of years ago

fossil record a collection of fossils used to represent Earth's history

fungus the kingdom of organisms that are mostly multicellular, have cell walls made of chitin, and are heterotrophic

gamete an egg or sperm cell; a sex cell

gas exchange the process of obtaining oxygen from the environment and releasing carbon dioxide

gene a segment of DNA (on a chromosome) that contains the code for a specific trait

gene expression see *expressed;* the result of activated genes

gene mutation a change in the sequence of the bases in a gene, that changes the structure of the polypeptide that the gene codes for

gene splicing the process of producing altered DNA, usually by breaking a DNA molecule and inserting new genes

genetic engineering a set of technologies that humans use to alter the genetic instructions of an organism by substituting DNA molecules

genetic recombination the formation of a new combination of genes during sexual reproduction

genetic variation the normal differences found among offspring

genotype the genetic makeup of an individual

geologic time Earth's history as revealed by layers of rock

global warming a increase in Earth's average surface temperature caused by an increase in greenhouse gases

glucose a sugar that is a major source of energy for cells

golgi apparatus an organelle of stacks of membranes forming flattened sacs in the cytoplasm, which serves as a storage center for proteins synthesized by a cell

graduated cylinder a tool used to measure the volume of a liquid

greenhouse effect the trapping of heat by gases in the atmosphere

greenhouse gas an atmospheric gas that traps heat

growth an increase in the size or number of cells

guard cells specialized cells that control the opening and closing of the pores on the surface of a leaf

habitat the place where an animal or plant lives

herbivore an organism that eats only plants

heredity the passing of traits from parent to offspring

heterotroph organism that cannot make its own food; a consumers

heterotrophic nutrition a type of nutrition in which the organism requires performed organic substances from its environment or its food

heterozygous having two different alleles for a trait

histamine a chemical that is released as the immune system's reaction to an allergy

homeostasis the ability of an organism to maintain a stable internal environment even when the external environment changes

homologous chromosomes a pair of chromosomes having the same size and shape and carrying alleles for the same traits

homologous structure structures found in different kinds of organisms that have the same basic arrangement of parts and a similar pattern of embryonic development

homozygous having two identical alleles for a trait

hormone a chemical produced in the endocrine glands

host the organism in a parasitic relationship that provides a home and/or food for the parasite

hot water bath in the science laboratory, usually a large beaker of water heated on a hot plate; used to heat test tubes that contain a flammable liquid, such as alcohol

humerus the long bone in the upper part of the arm

hybrid an individual that is a heterozygous for a trait

hypothesis a statement that predicts a relationship between cause and effect in a way that can be tested

immune system the body's primary defense against disease-causing pathogens

immunity the body's ability to destroy pathogens before they cause disease

independent assortment the principle of genetics stating that different traits are inherited independently of one another

independent variable a factor that might influence the dependent variable in an experiment

indicator a substance that changes color when it encounters certain chemical conditions

industrialization the process of converting an economy into one in which large-scale manufacturing is the primary economic base

inference a conclusion or deduction based on observations

infinite without limits or bounds

inorganic a type of molecule that does not contain both carbon and hydrogen but can contain any other combination of elements

insulin a hormone that prompts glucose to move from the blood into body cells, resulting in a lower glucose level in the blood

ionic bonding the force of attraction between two ions in a chemical bond

ions an atom or group of atoms with an electric charge

karyotype an illustration showing the genetic makeup of an individual

kingdom a group of related phyla; the largest category in systems of classification

law of dominance the principle of genetics stating that when organisms pure for contrasting traits are crossed, all their offspring will show the dominant trait

limiting factor any factor in the environment that limits the size of a population

lipid any one of a group of organic compounds that includes oils, fats, and waxes

locomotion self-generated movement from one place to another

magnification the ability of a microscope to make an object appear larger

mass a measure of the quantity of matter in an object

meiosis the process that results in the production of sex cells (sperm and egg)

meiotic cell division cell division that occurs only in sex cells and that produces monolipid cells; reduction division

meniscus the curved surface at the top of a column of liquid

messenger RNA the type of RNA strand that carries the code for a polypeptide from DNA in the nucleus to the ribosomes in the cytoplasm, where it is translated into amino acid sequences during protein synthesis

metabolism all the chemical reactions that occur within the cells of an organism

metric ruler a tool used to measure the length of an object

microbe any microscopic organism

micrometer a unit of length equal to one millionth of a meter

microscope a tool that uses a lens or a combination of lenses to magnify an object

mineral an inorganic substance found naturally in Earth's crust

mitochondria pod-shaped organelles that contain enzymes used to extract energy from nutrients

mitosis the process that divides the cell's nucleus into two, each with a complete set of genetic material from the parent cell

model a representation used to explain or demonstrate a process or structure; also used to predict what might occur in a new situation

molecule a particle in which two or more atoms combine to form a single unit; the smallest unit of a compound

monosaccharides the simplest type of carbohydrate, with the empirical formula CH_2O; a simple sugar

MSDS (material safety data sheet) a description that provides proper procedures for handling or working with a particular substance. MSDS's include information such as toxicity, health effects, first aid, reactivity, storage, disposal, protective equipment, and spill/leak procedures

muscular system a body system comprised of tissue that contracts when it is stimulated; the combination of muscles that enables the body to move

mutation any alteration in the sequence of DNA

mutualism a symbiotic relationship in which both organisms benefit from their association

natural selection the process by which the organisms that are best adapted to a specific environment survive and produce more offspring than organisms that are not as well adapted

negative feedback a type of feedback that tends to oppose an initial change and thus maintains the stability of the quantities involved

niche the specific role played by an organism in its ecosystem

nitrogen cycle the movement of nitrogen from the atmosphere to the soil and organisms and then back to the atmosphere

nitrogen fixation the process by which nitrogen forms compounds that can be used by living things

nonrenewable resource any resource, such as fossil fuels and minerals, that cannot be replaced

nuclear fuel an energy source that results from splitting atoms

nucleotide the basic unit of DNA, containing a sugar, a phosphate group, and one of the four nitrogenous bases

nucleus a large structure within a cell that controls the cell's metabolism and stores genetic information, including chromosomes and DNA

nucleic acids large, complex organic molecules that contain the instructions cells need to carry out their life processes

nutrient a substance that provides the body with the materials and energy needed to carry out the basic life of cells

nutrition the process by which materials are taken from the environment into an organism and changed into usable forms

objective one of the lenses of a microscope

observation any information that is collected with any of the senses

ocular the eyepiece lens of a microscope

opinion ideas people have that may or may not be based in fact

optimum the most favorable condition

organ a body structure made of different kinds of tissues combined to perform a specific function

organ system several organs that work together to perform a major function in the body

organelle a structure within the cell that carries out a specific function

organic term used to describe molecules that contain both hydrogen and carbon

organic compound a compound that contains both hydrogen and carbon

osmosis the diffusion of water across a semipermeable membrane from a region of high concentration to a region of low concentration of water

ovary the organ of the human female reproductive system that produces an egg cell; the female gamete

overproduction the potential for a species to increase its numbers beyond the area's carrying capacity

oviduct the part of the female reproductive system where the egg cell is fertilized by the sperm

oxygen-carbon dioxide cycle the movement of oxygen and carbon dioxide between living things and the environment

ozone layer atmospheric layer in which ozone gas is relatively concentrated

ozone shield the layer of ozone gas in the upper atmosphere that protects Earth from some of the sun's radiation

pancreas an endocrine organ that secretes insulin

parasite an organism that survives by living and feeding on other organisms

parasitic relationship an arrangement in which one organism lives in or on a host organism, deriving some or all of its nourishment from the host, to the host's detriment

parasitism a symbiotic relationship in which one organism benefits from the association and the other is harmed

pathogen an organism that invades the body, causing disease

pedigree chart that shows relationships within a family

peer review the process by which scientists carefully examine the work of other scientists to look for possible flaws in their experimental design or their interpretation of results

pH a measure of whether a substance is acidic, neutral, or basic

phenotype the physical trait that appears in an individual as a result of its genetic makeup

photosynthesis the process by which some organisms are able to capture light energy and use it to make food from carbon dioxide and water

pioneer organisms one of the first organisms to inhabit an area

pioneer species the first organisms to become established in a new habitat

pipette a laboratory tool that looks like a slender tube but works something like an eyedropper

placenta the organ that enables nutrients and oxygen to pass from the mother's blood to the fetus and waste products to pass from the fetus to the mother's blood

plant any complex, multicellular organism that obtains energy through photosynthesis and consists of cell walls and specialized tissues and organs

poaching illegally capturing or killing an organism

polarity the term is often used to describe the positive and negative ends of molecules such as water

pollution a harmful change in the chemical make-up of the soil, water, or air

population all the individuals of a single species that live in a specific area

positive feedback when a variable changes in a system, such as the human body or an ecosystem, the system responds. In positive feedback, the response is to change more in the same direction

predator an animal that hunts and kills other animals for food

predator-prey relationship the connection between predators and prey that limits the growth of both populations

prey an animal that is hunted and killed by predators

primary succession the first group of communities that moves into a previously lifeless habitat

producer an organism that makes its own food from light energy and inorganic materials

progesterone a hormone associated with sexual development and the reproductive system

prokaryotes unicellular organisms lacking a nucleus

proportion the relationship of one thing to another in terms of size, number, amount, or degree

protein a compound consisting of one or more chains of amino acids

protist a single-celled organism with both its genetic materials and its organelles enclosed in membranes

pseudopodia a temporary projection of the cell surface in amebas and similar cells

punnett square a diagram used in genetics to show the results of a cross

quarantine confined isolation

radius one of the two long bones of the lower forearm

receptor molecule certain protein molecules in the cell membrane that can receive chemical messages from other cells

recessive an allele whose phenotype is not expressed if the dominant allele is also present

recombination the additional mixing of genetic material from a sperm and egg which results in a unique combination of genes

refute to disprove

replicate to copy

renewable resource Earth's resources, such as our food supply and solar energy, which, given time, can be replaced

research plan the initial stage of an experiment that involves finding background information, developing a hypothesis, and devising an experimental method for testing the hypothesis

respiration the process by which the chemical bond energy stored in nutrients is released for use in cells

reproduction the process by which organisms produce new organisms of the same type

ribosome one of the tiny structures in the cell that is the site of protein production

rider one of the devices that is moved along the beam of a balance

RNA (ribonucleic acid) the nucleic acid that carries out instructions coded in DNA

scavenger a carnivore that feeds on the bodies of dead organisms

science a way of learning about the natural world and the knowledge gained through that process

scientific literacy a basic knowledge of the natural world combined with an understanding of the diverse ways that scientists gain knowledge

scientific notation a method for writing numbers frequently used by scientists to write large and small numbers. Numbers are written using powers of ten in the form $A \times 10^b$ or $A \times 10^{-b}$

scientific theory a concept, which has been tested and confirmed in many different ways, that explains a wide variety of observations

secondary succession a type of change that occurs when a disturbance empties an existing habitat without destroying the soil

segregation in genetics, the separation of alleles during meiosis; the presence of only one allele for a particular trait in each gamete

selective breeding the process of choosing a few organisms with desirable traits to serve as the parents of the next generation

semipermeable membrane a membrane that allows the passage of some materials but not others

sensor a structure that reacts to stimuli by sending a nerve impulse to the brain

sex cell an egg (female) or a sperm (male)

sex chromosomes the two unmatched chromosomes that determine the sex of an individual; represented as X and Y

sex-linked genes a trait that is controlled by a gene found on one of the sex chromosomes

sexual reproduction a method of reproduction that involves two parents to produce offspring that are genetically different from either parent

sibling a brother or sister

simple sugar the result of digested starches

skeletal system the body system that contains the bones, provides shape and support, and protects internal organs

smog a kind of air pollution that results when certain pollutants react with sunlight

solute a substance that is dissolved in a solvent to make a solution

solvent substance in which a solute is dissolved to make a solution

species a group of organisms that share certain characteristics and can mate with one another, producing fertile offspring

sperm the male sex cell

splice to join two things together

stain a chemical used to make cell structures more visible when viewed under a microscope

steady state the condition in which something remains relatively constant in spite of minor fluctuations

stereoscope a microscope that uses two eyepieces; often used for dissections

stimulus any change in the environment that causes an organism to react

stomata a tiny pore found on the underside of most leaves

substrate the substance on which an enzyme acts

subunit the section of a DNA molecule that contains a sugar, a phosphate, and a base

symbiotic a kind of long-term association between members of different species in which at least one species benefits and neither species is harmed

symbiotic relationship a relationship in which two different types of organisms live in a close association that benefits at least one of them

synthesis a life process that involves combining simple substances into more complex substances

tare button a function on an electronic balance that returns the mass reading to zero

taxonomy the science of classifying organisms and assigning each organism a universally accepted name

technology all of the practical scientific knowledge that has been used to meet human needs

template the pattern for a new molecule

testes the male reproductive organ that produces sperm and the hormone testosterone

testosterone a hormone associated with male sexual development and reproduction

theory an explanation, supported by many observations and/or experiments, that can be used to accurately explain related occurrences

thermal pollution a kind of water pollution in which the temperature of the water increases

tissue a group of specialized cells that perform a specific function

toxic poisonous

toxicity the degree to which something is poisonous

trait a characteristic that is passed from parent to offspring through the genes

trade-off an exchange or agreement made to reach a compromise

transfer RNA the type of RNA that carries a particular amino acid to mRNA at the ribosome in protein synthesis

transpiration the process whereby plants absorb water through their roots and eliminate it through tiny pores on the undersides of their leaves

transport all the processes by which substances pass into or out of cells and circulate within the organism

triple-beam balance a tool, with a single pan and three bars calibrated in grams, used to measure mass

trophic level step in a food chain or food web

tumor a clump of cells that develops when cancerous cells divide uncontrollably

ulna one of the two long bones in the lower forearm

uterus the organ, in female animals, where the embryo develops into a fetus

vaccine a substance made of weakened, killed, or partial pathogens and designed to protect the body from future invasions of that pathogen

vacuole storage sacs within the cytoplasm of a cell that may contain either wastes or useful materials, such as water or food

vascular tissue the xylem and phloem of a plant; vascular tissue

vertebrate an animal with a backbone

vestigial a nonfunctional structure in a modern organism that is a remnant of a structure that was functional in some ancestral form

virus a nonliving particle of protein and genetic material that reproduces by invading the cell of a living organism

vitamin an organic nutrient needed in very small amounts for certain body functions

volume the space occupied by something

water cycle the process by which water continuously moves from Earth's surface to the atmosphere and back

zygote the cell that results from the joining of the egg and sperm

Index

Italicized *t* indicates table. Italicized *f* indicates figure.